£ꟷ 50

K Sea

TURKEY

SYRIA

JORDAN

Caspian Sea

ARMENIA SSR

TURKMEN SSR

Tehran

Baghdad

IRAQ

Abadan

Kuwait

IRAN

AFGHANISTAN

PAKISTAN

Dhahran

Riyadh

Strait of Hormuz

Mecca

SAUDI ARABIA

Muscat

Keren

Aden

Addis Ababa

ETHIOPIA

Indian Ocean

KENYA

NORTH AFRICA, THE NEAR AND MIDDLE EAST.

Antitank

AN AIRMECHANIZED RESPONSE
TO ARMORED THREATS IN THE 90s

RICHARD E. SIMPKIN

Antitank
AN AIRMECHANIZED RESPONSE
TO ARMORED THREATS IN THE 90s

BRASSEY'S PUBLISHERS LIMITED

a member of the Pergamon Group

OXFORD · NEW YORK · TORONTO · SYDNEY · PARIS · FRANKFURT

U.K.	BRASSEY'S PUBLISHERS LIMITED, a member of the Pergamon Group, Headington Hill Hall, Oxford OX3 0BW, England
U.S.A.	Pergamon Press Inc., Maxwell House, Fairview Park, Elmsford, New York 10523, U.S.A.
CANADA	Pergamon Press Canada Ltd., Suite 104, 150 Consumers Road, Willowdale, Ontario M2J 1P9, Canada
AUSTRALIA	Pergamon Press (Aust.) Pty. Ltd., P.O. Box 544, Potts Point, N.S.W. 2011, Australia
FRANCE	Pergamon Press SARL, 24 rue des Ecoles, 75240 Paris, Cedex 05, France
FEDERAL REPUBLIC OF GERMANY	Pergamon Press GmbH, 6242 Kronberg-Taunus, Hammersweg 6, Federal Republic of Germany

First edition 1982

British Library Cataloguing in Publication Data

Simpkin, Richard E.
Antitank
1. Tank warfare
I. Title
358'.18   UE159
ISBN 0–08–027036–0

Printed in Great Britain by A. Wheaton & Co., Ltd., Exeter

Contents

CONTENTS

Illustrations

TABLES (SEE ALSO APPENDIX)

Photo credits

British Ministry of Defence (Crown Copyright); US Department of Defense; Försvarets Materialverk Stockholm; Editor, *Armor Magazine*; The Tank Museum, Bovington Camp; British Aerospace (Dynamics Group); Patrick Barrington (in conjunction with *Tank* magazine); Brassey's Publishers Limited.

Acknowledgements

Let me again begin by thanking my wife for her help in research and checking, specially over the Russian material, and Anne Best for her invaluable combination of typing and editing skills. Any resemblance these acknowledgements bear to their predecessors is anything but coincidental, since I traded once again on the kindness of those who helped me before. The Directorate of Public Relations, Ministry of Defence, once more reacted most promptly and constructively. British Defence Staff, Washington, went to greater efforts even than before to get me updates and photos, while a new but equally firm friend was the Editor of *Armor Magazine*. On this side of the Atlantic the combined backup of Ministry of Defence/Royal United Services Institution, Staff College Camberley, Royal Military Academy Sandhurst and Royal Army Education Corps Centre Libraries has — as I hope the reader will remark — led to a more fully researched book. I am also most grateful to the Commanding Officer, Royal Air Force Lossiemouth, and the staff of the Jaguar Operational Conversional Unit for a most interesting and enlightening discussion.

Once again I have leaned heavily on the wisdom of Sven Berge, who is most kindly honoring this book with a Preface, General Dr. F.M. von Senger und Etterlin and General Israel Tal — though this should not be taken to mean that all or any of them would agree with everything I say. In this context I should also like to thank the Israeli and Swedish Defence Attachés for their help in smoothing and speeding communication. I mentioned the support I received from Professor John Erickson of Edinburgh and Joseph R. Backofen, Jr. of Battelle Columbus Laboratories in the Introduction. Additionally, as the Bibliography shows in part, Joe Backofen provided most useful technical and analytical inputs, including a stimulating exposé of some personal views.

Maybe though, the most encouraging new source of support has been the way I am kept in the swim by direct and published feedback on *Tank Warfare* and (just starting as I have been writing this book) on *Mechanized Infantry*. Support and criticism are just about equally valuable; once again I hope my new book does justice to these inputs.

FRONTISPIECE

This is a model of the articulated concept mentioned, of which a prototype is now being built. It mounts the German 120-mm smoothbore. It could be developed as a tank destroyer at around 25 t (12 t + 13 t) or as a MBT successor at some 45 t (22 t + 23 t)

Preface

This is a book of very wide scope. Immediately after writing *Tank Warfare* and *Mechanized Infantry*, Richard Simpkin has set about analyzing what kind of doctrine, major equipment and force structure the mechanized battle as a whole, on the ground and in the air space just above it, may call for in the closing decade of this century of technological revolutions.

With his wide experience, Richard Simpkin is, as readers of his previous books and many others know, eminently qualified to make an analysis of this kind. As always, he has gone to work forcefully and with spirit, putting his arguments and conclusions with a refreshing freedom from preconceived opinions. Because of this he may, of course, seem provocative to some. An example is that he has taken the courageous step (in a way a justification for the title of the book) of suggesting abandonment of the kind of 50-60-tonne (t) main battle tanks that increasingly dominate the armored equipment of the West. He favors, instead, a diversified family of lighter and more mobile armored vehicles.

To me, for more than four decades a most interested observer of the development of ways and means of mechanized warfare in all quarters and for most of that time active in the technological aspects of this development in my native country, neutral Sweden, both the theme and the message of this book appear at a very opportune moment. There are several reasons for this.

First, I have in mind the impact on the mechanized battle of those multifaceted but rather protracted developments of new countermeasures to armor-defeating weapons which have started to come to fruition. It is, in fact, not until quite recently, after decades of highly classified research and development effort, that the very existence and the general properties of these new means of protection have been released to the public, thus offering the first opportunities to make a balanced and complete unclassified analysis of the kind Richard Simpkin presents here. I see it as most gratifying to all concerned in governments, armed forces

and defense industries alike that he has made good use of these
opportunities so soon after they have arisen.

The new countermeasures differ very much in kind and
function. Most of them have in common the major feature of
increasing protection against weapons of the shaped-charge type.
The best known, the nature and effects of which are most often
referred to in this book, is compound armor, well exemplified
by the British Chobham armor. Others are the means of sup-
pressing lethal fires in the ammunition, fuel or hydraulic fluid
on board armored vehicles. Compound armor is by now widely
acknowledged to have created a most important change in the
conditions of the mechanized battle. Personally I wonder,
however, if not an even greater change will follow from the new
means of reducing the incidence of lethal fires. These means of
protection increase resistance to most kinds of attack but in
particular that of the shaped charge from *all* directions, whereas
the effect of compound armor (and also that of the very new
forms of dynamic armor) is limited to certain sectors, mostly the
frontal arc. Furthermore, there are reasons to expect that a
reduction of lethal fires will have a markedly positive impact on
the morale of units under the stress of battle. Other probable
gains are fewer crew fatalities and improved availability of
vehicles for battle (because fewer will be beyond reasonably quick
repair).

Still other new means of protection, passive and active, have
the effect of making.armored vehicles difficult for the opponent
to acquire and hit. In the long haul such means may well have the
greatest potential. A common feature of many of these, as also of
the majority of active means of directly neutralizing hostile
antiarmor weapons, is that they do not form part of the
individual vehicles they protect but are contained elsewhere in
the force structure, necessitating a far-reaching integration and
coordination of the characteristics of different pieces of
equipment. This in turn underscores the importance of following
a course of action in planning and procurement which I can fully
endorse and which Richard Simpkin touches upon in his
Introduction and returns to later as a key point in his discussions
of the optimum use of new technological options, not least of the
composition of a future family of antiarmor weapons. I would
describe it as a matter of avoiding the sub-optimal solutions
which inevitably result from premature statements of detailed
operational requirements for individual pieces of new equipment
— statements made, that is, at too early a stage in the development of new armed forces as a whole.

In order to arrive, for a given future timeframe, at the optimum total effect from available resources and to avoid premature obsolescence of major equipment, the course of action referred to calls for the state of the art and the technological potential to be examined in parallel with new approaches to doctrines, force structures and logistics. From my own observation the best results emerge from integrated studies and trials, where there is a series of recycling interactions between user and designer, all the way from analysis of the threat to the complete new concept of equipment, force structure and operations. In this kind of process operational requirements mainly take the form of a confirmation of what user and the designer have finally and jointly arrived at as the optimum for the given timeframe.

Just as much as this course of action goes for weapon effects and means of protection does it apply to all aspects of mobility, where I find further reasons to see this book as a very timely document. One reason concerns mobility in its broadest sense; another is confined to the specific problems that all participants may encounter in case of a major conflict in the potential new theaters of the Middle East.

Richard Simpkin makes his opinion very clear that the time has come for NATO to seek quite new avenues in the mobility of its mechanized forces. As indicated earlier, he wants to see the present 50-60-t MBTs replaced by lighter and more mobile vehicles. He suggests splitting up the tasks of these MBTs over a family of vehicles in the 30-40-t class. This would mean a gain in mobility, in particular operational mobility, to an extent that was pointed out in a most explicit way by the present Commander-in-Chief of the Allied Forces in Central Europe, General Dr. F.M. von Senger und Etterlin, in his Introduction to *Tank Warfare* 2 years back. It would essentially put an end to the prevailing disparity between NATO's operational mobility and that of the Warsaw Pact.

To the initiated I think it is obvious that the latest MBTs of the West, with a gross weight close to the 60-t mark, represent the end point of that technological approach. NATO and many others too are becoming increasingly aware of the urgent need to find new approaches for the future; it is all to the good that Richard Simpkin has taken the initiative at this moment and analyzed current mobility problems in detail. His suggested family of lighter vehicles will certainly stimulate the thinking of many decision-makers, study groups and other bodies active in this field all over the world.

The new technology needed to realize this particular family of vehicles looks to me to be well within reach in the near future. My appraisal is based on the results from studies and tests and (as regards the S Tank) operational use of similar vehicle concepts under our special Swedish conditions which, as regards mobility, are more severe than, for instance, those of the NATO center.

These special conditions have long had a marked influence on the design of Swedish military vehicles. The large proportion of them which are amphibious and exert a low ground pressure demonstrates this. Among the unarmored light models there are many tracked vehicles of the articulated type. The latest development project, released to the mass media early in 1981, concerns use of the articulated principle for heavier, armored vehicles too (see Frontispiece). The feasibility of this principle will be extensively tested for vehicles of 15 t and upwards. If the results of these tests prove satisfactory, a host of new options will be available not only in tactical and operational mobility, but also in survivability and logistics. This will make the armored vehicle mobility targets set by Richard Simpkin easier to attain.

The articulated tracked vehicle is by no means a novelty in the armored vehicle context. The first related patent is a British one from 1909. One of the first tank designs laid before the Landships Committee, founded in 1915 at the instigation of the then First Sea Lord Winston Churchill, was just such a vehicle. It was rejected by the Committee and I can very well imagine why. There were at that time and for long after no means available to make the sharp turns needed in confined spaces with this sort of vehicle. In fact it was not until about 5 years ago that a viable solution to this problem appeared. It came as a spin-off from the development of the new generation of Swedish soft-skinned articulated vehicles.

If, as I personally am inclined to believe, the articulated tracked vehicle proves to offer a technological breakthrough in armored vehicle mobility, it will still far from satisfy all the new mobility requirements which Richard Simpkin strongly advocates in this book. His analysis winds up by outlining a future air-mechanized division, where helicopters and artillery have taken over and, as regards helicopter missions, greatly expanded some functions nowadays assigned to direct-fire ground elements. The prospects he depicts of what such a division will offer in speed, agility and instantaneous firepower are, to say the least, spectacular.

The full success of such an airmechanized division requires, as the analysis indicates, that acceptable solutions are found to some crucial technological problems. The dominating problem is unquestionably how to cope with the weapons of electronic warfare. While waiting for more sophisticated and effective countermeasures to come forth one should in this context not disregard the use of old proven expedients. I think many readers, perhaps especially the younger ones, will greatly appreciate the reminders in this book about the value of such old tricks as, for instance, the use of flares.

Turning back to ground mobility, I find this book very timely, as I hinted at above, because of the information it gives about the characteristics of infrastructure, terrain and weather in the Middle East oil countries. Considering the acute need felt by many countries to prepare for defense of their interests in that area, access to the informed broad-brush picture Richard Simpkin paints in Chapter 1 about the related physical conditions, or rather the constraints imposed on movement of mechanized forces, ought to be most welcome to many decision-makers, vehicle designers and others.

Apart from UN missions with strictly limited roles, Sweden does not prepare forces for operations outside her frontiers. The specific needs for operations in the Middle East are therefore, as such, of minor interest to this country. It strikes me, however, that the obstacle-crossing requirements for vehicles intended to operate in the Middle East, as outlined in Chapter 1, coincide very closely with those for the dedicated vehicles of the brigades in North Sweden. I know just how hard the Swedish requirements for crossing soft ground (swamps or snow), wadi-like rivers and narrow defiles have proved to reconcile with the requisite payload of armament and other essentials. So this book has in its turn made me aware that there are good reasons for Sweden and other countries with similar topography to monitor attentively what comes onto the world market in the way of vehicles designed to be effective in the Middle East.

Finally, I am aware that it is high time to give the reader a chance to see what Richard Simpkin himself has to say. I am confident that this book will be of great interest and benefit to a vast number of people engaged in the development of armed forces all over the world.

Stockholm, Sweden   Sven Berge

Introduction

Just 2 years back, when I put together the introduction to *Tank Warfare,* I was able to rough in a scenario that had held, give or take the odd fluctuation of temperature and sway of military fashion, for almost a quarter of a century. Likewise I had — or so I hope — no problem in justifying my use of combat manpower as a base parameter for effectiveness. In summer 1979, moving into *Mechanized Infantry,* I must admit to some relief that my manpower arguments were already, as the gunners say, "on the way". But the scenario was still in fine shape. Then the departing seventies went supersonic with a double bang, leaving the eighties in their turbulent wake.

Already my manpower arguments have been stood on their heads. Despite an aging population, the West is once again feeling that combination of demographic and economic pressures that seem to have been the tinder for World War I and maybe, when the chips are down, for World War II as well. My guess is that the oil-induced recession will force Western governments to limit unemployment by expanding their armed forces. Some of them are already raising the geopolitical temperature to make this move acceptable to their electorates.

The NATO center still offers a credible scenario but has become at best *primus inter pares.* Two years back I predicated that future wars, wherever and with whatever lineups they might be fought, would be fought with hardware designed for the NATO center. Now this is true only for hardware already committed to production.

So, in an endeavor to stay one jump ahead of the trend, I have had to replace a cozy peep back into history with a whirl of a rather large-diameter crystal ball — and this at a time when even the highest-priced crystal balls are getting hit out of the ground on strike one. But before opening the book proper with this rather specious exercise, I want to address some broad questions which bear on my theme and have arisen from the very welcome published and direct feedback from *Tank Warfare.*

Looking with standoff and a measure of hindsight at an arena in which I spent many years milling around has, I guess, taught me two general lessons. One is that, while military *action* of every kind should be rigorously constrained by political will, military *thinking* must not be. Soldiers like everybody else need to make public noises about defense being exclusively defensive, but military decision-makers need to draw an absolute distinction between political aggression and *off*ensive military action in support of a *def*ensive political goal. I touched on this distinction in *Tank Warfare,* but the scenarios we will examine in Chapter 1 call for it to be loudly, clearly and frequently restated.

I am not thinking so much of preemptive action, though. In the NATO center most of the forces and all of the backup and infrastructure are already there. Since nobody envisions a march on Moscow, offensive action would be confined to the tactical and operational levels. By contrast other possible future theaters require the West to go on the strategic offensive — in other words to establish a military presence where they had none before — just to get into business. The saga of the United States hostages in Iran demonstrated that, even on a small scale, this is no easy matter.

The second lesson I think I have learned, and the second reason for repeating myself like I just did, is the need to see mechanized warfare *as a single whole.* A long cool look at operational concepts, specially Soviet ones which are oriented towards the offense, suggests that the components of a mechanized force we are apt to associate with the defensive, like men on their feet and antitank weapon systems, are in fact even more essential in gaining and sustaining the momentum of offensive action. To clear a paradox before somebody else does it for me, I affirmed in *Tank Warfare* that an offensive scenario offers significant advantages in tank design. This is true; but the main battle tank as we know it looks like coming most into its own in defense. In a word, a balanced force is a balanced force whatever its posture.

Fact is, as one moves towards a broader and more balanced view of mechanized warfare, he comes to wonder whether the MBT concept is valid over the full depth in time and the full scope of the mechanized warfare era; or whether this concept relates only to a relatively narrow band of progress in the state of the art. This question in its broadest sense would be one way of expressing the *leitmotiv* of this book.

The difficulties that face serving officers and officials in taking a broad, integrated and balanced view when they are in the melée of decision-making are highlighted in a recent book on the British Army[1] by Henry Stanhope, defense correspondent of *The Times*. He shows how an army is shaped less by geopolitical and strategic reason than by a complex of intractable social, political and human forces which have rather little to do with the business of war. To this I would add a more extreme personal view, drawn both from my own experience and from sociological and economic studies of large organizations: whatever the theme and whatever the arguments marshalled, the actual determinant in peacetime decisions is sectional rivalry over control of manpower. The decision-maker finds himself girdled in a three-way stretch — the complex of political constraints, often not so much foreign policy as budget limits and economic chauvinism; sectional loyalty; and the need, if not to please, at least to come up with solutions which stand a chance of acceptance.

In both my previous books I have come at the problem the other way, treating force structure as something derived from, and thus subordinate to, operational concepts and the state of the art. While I was careful to stress that my suggestions on force structure were largely artifacts aimed at concretizing operational concepts and requirements, these exercises have reinforced a long-held view that arms of the service are a luxury modern armies can no longer afford. Traditional names of regiments, corps and the like have a key role as focuses for recruitment and loyalty, and as a means of integrating the armed forces with society as a whole or linking units to geographical locations. But it is hard to see why these important traditions need to be rigidly associated with specific roles in the framework of mechanized warfare.[2]

The French and Swedish Armies — neither of them exactly short on tradition — have learned to live with composite battalions providing organic integration of armor and infantry down to company level. I cannot see why other armies could not do the same; or why the composite platoon I suggested in *Mechanized Infantry* should not be just as feasible.

The third thing I have learned, not so much a lesson as a fact, stemmed from a comment made by Joe Backofen of the Battelle Columbus Laboratories when reviewing *Tank Warfare* in *Armor Magazine*. This concerns the existence and availability of first-rate Soviet published material on every aspect of mechanized

1 *See* Bibliography.
2 See also *Tank Warfare*, pages 198, 199.

warfare. My first reaction was one of shame and self-reproach because, over the years I was concerned with equipment policy and with teaching armored vehicle technology and the like, I had remained totally unaware of this material. Reflection and a few carefully placed probes then convinced me that indignation, and vocal indignation at that, would be a more constructive response.

It so happens that I spent a good deal of time in close contact with the nerve centers of combat development and equipment policy not only of the British Army but also of the US Army and the Bundeswehr, not to mention the central NATO organization, on projects where the information I speak of would have been invaluable. It also so happens that, from experience earlier in my career, I have high intelligence awareness. I used to importune G2 with requests for this kind of information and devote much time to studying proceedings and reports of national and international technical intelligence conferences. So I think I can fairly suggest that those in certain quarters might do well to ask themselves why, then and seemingly now, military policy and decision-makers in NATO countries have to rely for inputs of this kind on nonofficial bodies like the Battelle Institute or the Institute of Strategic Studies and on a sprinkling of individual academics.[3]

The value of information like this goes well beyond the scope of army-wide and fairly elementary "know your enemy" programs. For instance, a major, maybe definitive work, *Tank*,[4] published in 1954 has *separate* chapters on mobility and agility and states a set of parameters for each. Simple awareness of this fact would have thrown much light on the lively Anglo-American discussions of that decade which led, as I recall, to the coining of the buzzword "mobiquity". This Soviet analysis could well have made a contribution to the development and trials of Chieftain, M60, Leopard 1 and the S Tank. Likewise knowledge of it would have given the teams working on MBT70/KPz2 (US/FRG) and MBT80/KPz3 (UK/FRG) help both in drafting requirements and in improving their feeling for the Soviet beyond. Yet again a 1978 Soviet book, *Tracked Transporters and Tractors*,[4] contains depth analyses on track dynamics and the like which would

---

3 For my part, I now am lucky enough to have the support of Professor John Erickson, Professor of Defence Studies in the Department of Politics at the University of Edinburgh, in my study of the threat—though not unfortunately in time for this book to reflect anything approaching the full scope of his expertise. I have listed in a separate section of the Bibliography Soviet material to which I have had access or of which I have, at least, gained knowledge. *See* my note at the head of that section.

4 *See* Bibliography (Antonov).

provide — and one hopes have in fact provided — significant inputs to American and German work on ultrahigh mobility vehicles.

More important still, depth study of material like this over a period would provide a real insight into the way the Soviets go about their major equipment programs and the reasons for their consistent success. I have not carried out such a study and I doubt that the material for it is available in the UK, but even a quick glimpse of some bare bones throws a useful amount of light on this topic. Since all this bears on the approach I use in this book, I want to rehearse some of the thoughts that have struck me about Soviet procurement.

Their centralized socialist constitution puts the government of the USSR in a position to exercise comprehensive and integrated control over their scientific and technological resources, human and material alike. Incentives of every kind draw the best talent into the physical sciences and engineering. Likewise, although the growth rate of technical awareness and skill among the population is limited, the organs of education offer a closed-loop system within which levels of attainment can be monitored and fed to policy-makers and designers. These people in their turn tune their designs to realistic levels of operator and technician skill; they also feed back into the educational system targets for the nature and levels of skill required for the future. Likewise central government establishes, develops and allocates material engineering resources to match specific military and economic goals — in that order, one suspects. This is a grossly simplistic outline of a massive and complex phenomenon, but I believe it will suffice to indicate why the Soviets manage the man/machine interface in various fields so much better than free societies can.

Historically the Russians have always steered a judicious middle course between the chauvinism of Western engineers and the slavish copying that was — and if one looks beneath the skin often still is — the hallmark of Japanese industrial development. Like the czarist régime before them, the Soviets are expert in the creation of elaborate fictions to show how every good idea originated within their Empire. But they never allowed this to interfere with the thoroughly commonsensical way they adopt, adapt and evolve the technology they need. The historical part of a recent Battelle presentation *Soviet Kinetic Energy Penetrators*[5] provides an excellent model of the Russian approach, lacking only the normally inevitable claim of origination. In the past this

5 *See* Bibliography (Backofen).

attitude has allowed the USSR to get quickly and effectively into the fields she needed, even in rather high technology areas. Now it allows her to concentrate her engineering talent not just on the fields she needs but on the subfields where imported technology does not match Soviet requirements; and of course on narrow and deep thrusts forward.

Another factor in Soviet success with armored vehicles stems I think partly from geographical accident and partly from a sensible approach to the control of information. Outside earth-moving plant, which has quite different parameters than high-performance tracked vehicles, the West has virtually no civilian counterpart to, or spinoff from armored vehicle technology. This fact combines with commercial confidentiality, a liberal dose of chauvinism and a largely justified fear of Soviet information-gathering capabilities to make armored vehicle technology a kind of folklore, a mumbo jumbo shared only among initiates and passed on by word of mouth.

Terrain, climate and a vast hinterland still lacking most of the rudiments of a communications system combine to make the technology of medium- and high-performance tracked vehicles a key one for the Soviets. As a result, there is a substantial and respectable body of knowledge in this field, which is not just published and openly discussed, but is widely disseminated as a matter of policy. Although Russians are secretive and bureau-cratic by nature, the Soviets only classify the information they really need to protect and are confident they can protect. For instance, the extent and timing of their disclosures on the T72's gun-ammunition system were surprising even by today's American and German standards and astonishing when compared to British practice.

Ever since I have known it, equipment procurement in the West has been based on a marketing approach — in other words user-oriented. With force structure imposed as a constraint, we proceed from a scenario to a concept of operations and thence to operational requirements. Government agencies and/or industry come up with solutions and the cycle we all know so well is set in train. Up to that moment the state of the art is a secondary input. Trouble is, the "market" is an artifact. Even when the basic scenario is stable, new personalities in key political or user positions can change the concept of operations however they wish. Likewise technical promise rather seldom seems to be matched by performance. Engineers paint a rosy picture to get the project in general and their solution in particular adopted;

policy-makers then set "state-of-the-art plus" goals to make sure the successor equipment offers an advance that is and is seen to be cost-effective.

So the goals set are two jumps ahead of the true state of the art. We are apt to land up with projects based on notional requirements and wildly optimistic technical inputs. Once the hardware starts taking shape this gap shows. Schedules slip, shortfalls arise and costs escalate. Then the arguments start — those circular arguments which waste years or even decades of time and millions of dollars. We suddenly find the Soviets with an achieved goal, like Hind D or F for instance, while the West is still dancing up and down waving its arms on or behind square one. If this happens twice running in one field — as it has in some cases in both the United States and Britain — the result is a virtually unbridgeable gap.

I guess the grass isn't emerald green all over in Soviet pro-curement circles either, but the West's incessant problems do suggest a further reason for Soviet success. The Soviets move with the state of the art and make quantum jumps only from firmly anchored, powerful springboards. I suspect they have a recycling technique which allows the definitive operational concept to be based on balanced, genuinely optimized technical solutions as opposed to pipedreams. As much evidence suggests, they get new toys that work and then set about learning how to play with them. Their Achilles heel, like that of all other armies, appears to be rigidity of force structure; the great BMP controversy[6] suggests that internecine strife between arms is a favorite military sport in the Soviet Union too.

Yet whatever the realities of Soviet procedure and the relative merits of concept-oriented and hardware-oriented approaches, the West's procedure can only work when the scenarios on which it is based hold from the start of development to the midpoint of service life, say 15 years at least. As I remarked above, this was largely true of NATO from 1955 to 1980. But the dynamic of which Iran and Afghanistan are the most conspicuous recent symptoms has only just started to roll as I write. No way is it going to wait for the West's procurement procedures to catch up with it.

So this is a moment to do what I hinted at in *Tank Warfare* and use scenarios not as primary inputs but as broad constraints. In tackling the antiarmor problem I shall try both to lead with the technical arguments and the state of the art, and to look at the

---

6 See *Mechanized Infantry*, pages 34-37 and 73-77.

principles and trends of weapon systems rather than their historical origins. One key input which I cannot represent in a book is grassroots user opinion. This is needed first in consultation during development and then, to debug the product and make it fightable and maintainable, in trials on pilots and preproduction models. Oddly enough the technologist is, I suspect, more likely to come up with a usable product first time if he has freedom of movement within an envelope of constraints than if he is pinned down by the kind of detailed stipulations which characterize an operational requirement.

Likewise, at least within the constraints of a book, this approach tends to drive into the background the human aspects of mechanized warfare and broader considerations like the imperative of local air superiority. The engineer who is given a freer hand for real needs to return the compliment by a far greater readiness to seek out and hoist in the views of the tactician and the user than he has usually shown in the past.

Elgin   *Richard Simpkin*

Antitank 90

1
Which war?

In this introductory chapter I want to establish common even if debatable ground with the reader; to create a set of parameters for my subsequent approach to the antiarmor problem; and to demonstrate the kind of pattern of constraints and guidelines within which I believe the designer of military hardware should be left free to operate. Since I do not wish to get avoidably entangled in the thickets of geopolitical and economic analysis, my purpose is simply to propose what I hope is a reasonable set of assumptions. My only deliberate venture into unreality will once again be a refusal to accept existing force structures as a constraint. By contrast I shall not spell out here the kind of basic technological and biotechnological design constraints I covered in *Tank Warfare*.

The last 25 years have, one is told, seen more shooting wars between organized forces than any other quarter century in history, to say nothing of the emergence of other forms of conflict — revolutionary warfare in all its manifestations, and the overt use of economic weapons. Nonetheless the *leitmotiv* of the period has been a rather simple one of two superpowers, each with full supporting cast, manipulating what is aptly if sensationally termed the balance of terror.

Since 1975, however, new forces have begun to make their presence felt. Within the geographical belt of the Rich North, China has emerged from the normal postrevolutionary phase of grizzly introspection at home and subversion abroad to set about taking her place as a great power. She looks like staying nonaligned in name, while deeply suspicious of the USSR but ready to develop the economic relations she desperately needs with the West and maybe a closer relationship still with her old enemy Japan. Japan meanwhile remains an economic giant and a military dwarf but is beginning to make political noises that match her economic rather than her military status.

Meanwhile, thanks to, or more probably despite the EEC with

11

its mind-blowing history of checks and imbalances, the liberal democracies of Western Europe show signs of evolving a concerted foreign policy. Those who are not French or German, along maybe with many who are, may have rather deep reservations about the Bonn-Paris axis; but the mass surrounding this axis is beginning to exert a marked gravitational pull. It is premature but no longer meaningless to talk of Western Europe, probably including Britain, as "a great power".

Unfortunately a rift exists between this concert of European opinion and United States policy. The USA is very properly concerned *at any cost* to prevent her southern flank being turned and to safeguard her supplies of Middle East oil. The cost currently includes tolerance, clandestine support and even open encouragement of extremely oppressive right wing régimes in South America and the Middle East, coupled with mounting hawkishness towards the USSR. At the time of writing it looks like Europe will go along with the USA over Middle East oil — a vital interest for her too — but may increasingly oppose the United States attitude to Latin America.[1] Evidently Europe means to continue to talk *détente* with the USSR and her satellites, with the aim or at least in the hope of reuniting Germany and demolishing the Iron Curtain in the long haul.

While their goals may be similar, Britain, France and the FRG hold widely differing views over the degree of risk to West European security entailed by divergence from United States policies. The FRG is in a special position here. BAOR's readiness and effectiveness has been dragged down from its early sixties peak by undermanning, financial stringency and the ongoing Ulster overstretch. The combat value of the minor forces in the NATO center remains questionable. So Bonn desperately needs US 7 Army as well as the nuclear shield. By contrast, ever since de Gaulle effectively took her out of NATO, France has shown that she feels free to act as she pleases. One suspects this attitude stems less from *folie de grandeur* inspired by the *force de frappe* than from a hypothesis which is cynical but probably correct — whatever Western Europe does or does not do about her own security or about alignment with United States policies, the USA could not tolerate the shift in the balance of power that would result from Warsaw Pact occupation of Western Europe.

Hard on the heels of this potential rift within NATO have come the first signs of a tradeoff to close it. In grossly over-

---

1 At the time of writing, there is growing evidence that the British Tory Government is an exception.

simplified terms, Western Europe seems ready to buy freedom to negotiate with the Warsaw Pact about Europe by accepting an extension into the Near and Middle East, and by implication North Africa, of NATO's sphere of interest. As well as suiting both Western Europe's and the USA's book in the short haul, this shift looks completely in tune with emergent longer-term trends.

Quite apart from the presumably transient perturbation of the American hostages, the Iranian revolution has laid the whole Middle East oilfields wide open to Soviet-sponsored régimes in Syria and Iraq, and to the USSR herself — so much so that in this context the provocation offered by the Soviet invasion of Afghanistan looks as superfluous as it was extreme. Possibly the Soviets saw the confusion in Iran and the quarrel between Iran and the USA as a smokescreen behind which it could make an opportunist move with quite different and much longer-term goals.

In any event by the time this book is published the Warsaw Pact as a whole and the USSR herself are likely to have become net importers of oil. She thus stands to gain doubly from incursions into the Middle East oil region. Luckily the USA made her position absolutely clear and backed it by establishing a naval presence; for the moment this has produced a measure of restabilization. Nonetheless the Middle East proper must now be seen as a potential theater of a major limited war in which some European members of NATO and Warsaw Pact satellites might well become involved.

Meanwhile the Near East remains a cauldron which looks like switching once again from simmer back to boil. To Israel's south and east there is as I write *relative* stability. But there is no progress here; the Israeli-Egyptian peace talks remain deadlocked over seemingly intractable problems, and Jordan refuses to join in them. More importantly maybe King Hussein does not get any younger; his death or incapacitation is highly likely to lead to a Palestinian rising and a revolution with or without extensive civil war. Jordan would then inevitably join Syria and Iraq under the Soviet aegis. In Egypt too the durability of Sadat had long given reason for surprise rather than confidence. Again there is a singular lack of evidence that, even after his overthrow, he would be succeeded by a moderate pro-Western régime. One step along, Libya continues to pose a major threat to both her neighbors and to be a thorn in the flesh of just about everyone else.

Nearer home and critical for NATO's southern flank is the Turkish problem. Until the situation in Cyprus is resolved, the

West has little choice but to cold shoulder Turkey. The entry of
Greece into the EEC, exploited by a rapidly growing scale of
Soviet-backed subversive activity, must surely exacerbate this
breach to the point where Turkey will finally cease to be an
effective member of NATO even if she remains a nominal one. In
sum, the mounting instability of the Middle East compounds with
continuing turbulence in the Near East to make the probability of
direct United States-Soviet or NATO-Warpac conflict there far
higher in the eighties than it has been in the past two decades.

Along with this destabilization of the East-West situation comes
a threat which first caught the public eye in 1973 in the shape of
OPEC. The African and Asian members of OPEC need to sell
their oil almost as much as Japan and the West — and now the
whole of the Rich North — need to buy it. By the same token this
part of the Third World still depends on the North's technology
for exploitation of its oil revenue. So genuine mutual interest
exists and argues at the economic level for a degree of moderation
in use of the oil weapon. But a scan of the northern half of Africa
(down to about 10°N) and of Southeast Asia from Morocco and
northern Nigeria through to Pakistan suggests that this economic
threat is only the tip of the iceberg.

Whether in the form of military dictatorships, absolute
monarchies or socialized republics, Islam is patently on the
march. It will take a while yet for some of these countries to
reorganize themselves and start looking outwards. It will take a
while longer for some of them to acquire or regain military
strength; and maybe a shade longer still for fanaticism to override
self-interest. But by the early or mid-nineties, when defense
hardware which goes into design now will be in service, the whole
of the Rich North, NATO and Warsaw Pact alike may find itself
threatened by an economic and military jihad.

At least two or three Islamic countries[2] probably have nuclear
weapons already. In 15 years' time this capability could be widespread and massive. Even the most cursory glance at history and
Islamic belief leaves little doubt that Islamic governments would
be much readier to use nuclear weapons than would any segment
of the Rich North. In the meantime, as part of the price of oil,
these Islamic countries will surely continue to insist that their
respective sponsors not only help develop their infrastructures but
supply them with advanced military hardware and train their
men to use it. So the conventional threat, while not in the same

---

2 Pakistan, Libya, Iraq.

ballpark as that which NATO and the Warsaw Pact see in each
other, would be far from negligible.

Having moved far out, let me reemphasize that I am
attempting only to present the reader with one possible set of
assumptions. If he sees these as coherent and credible, my
purpose is achieved. For the point I seek to make is that we can no
longer afford to look only or even mainly at the NATO center.
We need to consider other scenarios for high intensity
mechanized operations. But before I return to firmer ground and
examine the effects of these on equipment policy, I would ask the
reader to reflect for a moment on the likelihood of a strategic
nuclear exchange.

With the fingers of weak, aging or sick men on the trigger —
not to mention computers afflicted with *Schadenfreude* — there
is always the risk of an exchange being initiated either
accidentally or in some way largely irrelevant to the mainstream
of geopolitical events. This is the price we all have to pay for
living under the shelter of the nuclear umbrella. By contrast this
umbrella has proved remarkably effective in the 30 years or so
that Washington and Moscow have been holding it up. Over this
period advances in site monitoring and early detection, along
with improved hot-line communications and more experience in
using them, have largely invalidated the threat of the "trigger
strike" — the possibility that a minor nuclear power might launch
a strike against the USA or the USSR, or both, with the aim of
unleashing the superpower exchange.

Whether or not SALT II finally succeeds, the "metropolitan
theory" seems as valid as it ever was. The relatively recent coining
of the buzzword "theater weapons" (meaning intermediate range
weapons which cannot straddle the Atlantic) confirms this. As
long as the USA and the USSR have a second strike capability
with overkill — the condition so aptly known as MAD (mutually
assured destruction) — it remains most improbable that they will
launch a strike against each other's *metropolitan* territory. This
theory does not rule out the employment of tactical or theater
weapons by either superpower against the territory of its allies or
satellites. This "metropolitan theory" is in fact the main strategic
rationale behind the British deterrent and the *force de frappe*. A
credible capability of striking the opposing superpower's metropolitan territory is the only protection.

Despite this theory the risk of a strategic exchange evidently
becomes much increased if either superpower uses force to bring

about a major shift in the balance of power; more still if their
armed forces are in direct conflict; most of all if the nuclear
threshold is crossed in any way by either side or both. Luckily we
need to draw only three conclusions from this immensely complex
topic. Under the nuclear umbrella major limited war involving
direct hostilities between the two superpowers remains a
meaningful instrument of policy. Such a war would probably be
nonnuclear; but the risk of its going nuclear mounts with
remoteness from the metropolitan territories of the superpowers
themselves and/or of allies with a nuclear capability — and of
course with local imbalances of conventional strength. The
probability of nuclear weapons being used *ab initio* without
restriction is highest by far in a jihad-based scenario; but one
would scarcely expect the Islamic world to achieve MAD, let
alone nuclear parity, against the combined strength of NATO,
the Warsaw Pact and maybe China.

The NATO Center

This is a well-worn track and just needs some updates. One thing
unchanged but confirmed by a growing weight of opinion is my
earlier assumption that the Warsaw Pact will go chemical from
the start unless or until NATO acquires a substantial offensive
chemical capability.[3] Even then the opposition might with some
justice feel that their high standard of training, dedicated units
and high-capacity delivery systems would give them the edge in
chemical warfare.

There are indications that Soviet doctrine on tactical nuclear
weapons draws a sharper distinction than before between nuclear
and nonnuclear land operations. Either way the Soviets lay
increasing emphasis on speed — on launching an offensive
without buildup, that is with zero warning period, and paralyzing
political centers like Bonn or Brussels before NATO can react. As
I see it, this is a strategic concept in its own right, not directly
related to the rates of advance laid down in Soviet operational
and tactical doctrines. It means, as they hope, driving straight
out of barracks or maneuver positions on, say, a line Magdeburg-
Halle-Erfurt one misty evening and occupying Bonn, or at least
facing up to it across the Rhine ready for an airborne assault,

---

3 Some experts argue that the Soviets no longer think in terms of "going chemical" —
that CW munitions are simply another nature that they will use if and when commanders
and their artillery advisers think it would pay off. Myself, I do not find such political
naivety entirely credible.

before last light the following day. This represents about 10% of autobahn cruising speed for a truck; and rather over double the latest figure I know for the standard rate of advance of Warpac mechanized formations, which puts them on the Rhine 48 hours after crossing the frontier. If the Soviets feel they need nuclear weapons to achieve this ultrahigh speed, they are likely to use them massively on tactical and short-term interdiction targets from the start. Failing this the Warsaw Pact seems unlikely to go nuclear unless NATO does — or presumably unless the course of conventional operations turns seriously against them.

These chemical and nuclear options are two aspects of a more general point. At the same time as NATO is looking askance at growing Warsaw Pact superiority, the Warsaw Pact seems to be developing an increasingly healthy respect for the NATO antiarmor defense. The Soviets are absolutely unwavering about the importance of getting tank formations through the defense and loose as soon as possible. But — always on available information — their doctrine for the break-in battle is a far cry from the *fête champêtre* of the BMP and the headiness of "swift incisive slashes". One senses that the Soviet concept of operations may be shifting away both from the familiar steamroller and from the maneuver battle to the distinguishing characteristic of the Wehrmacht's blitzkrieg doctrine — the avoidance of battle in favor of operational and if possible strategic surprise.

At tactical level the acquisition of excellent self-propelled artillery has swung the emphasis to, or more precisely back to artillery fire. Soviet SOPs, it seems, provide for a platoon of artillery per attacking battalion combat team to be moved up to fire direct from overwatching positions 5000-6000 m deep. Given the changed dimensions of the battlefield, this reminds one of the old infantry guns and of course the SU family of assault guns.

Recently published literature strengthens the impression that the attacking Soviets and the defending Americans are about equally resolved to cover themselves, each other and indeed the whole battlefield with smoke. As a number of senior American officers have been quick to point out, this is a double-edged tactic at best, specially in the unpredictable conditions which West European climate and terrain often conspire to produce.

Some commentators suggest that, because Soviet doctrine is largely formulated on the steppes and most of their training is conducted on featureless terrain, Soviet officers cannot appreciate European ground and the way it confers strength on the defense. This I frankly find incredible. The Soviet Army has

almost every kind of climate and terrain at its disposal and is
hardly likely to think twice about dispatching officers, tank and
IFV commanders, and for that matter complete units, to train
over broken ground. A more accurate comment might be that
overly stereotyped SOPs make it difficult for Warsaw Pact armies
to operate on heavily featured terrain. But even this criticism may
be wide of the mark in the light of the vast stress the Soviets lay on
standards of training.

In my previous book I expressed the false view that the
ZSU23/4 self-propelled air defense weapon system was obsolescent. With a greatly improved version of the B76 on-mounting
radar (GUNDISH), ZSU23/4 in fact forms the key forward link
in a coherent tactical air defense network stretching from army
and front level (SA4) to company level with the hand-held SA7.
Regiments now have an organic mixed AD battery of ZSU23/4s
and SA9s (on BTR40PB, GASKIN) plus their associated control
vehicles. It is the conjunction of ZSU23/4, SA9 and SA7 that
constitutes such a formidable threat to attack helicopters.

Turning to helicopters, one finds both the Warsaw Pact and
NATO increasingly regarding them as a normal part of the
combat team. But the two sides' thinking on them looks
diametrically opposed. We shall be probing this point in depth
later, but one can say briefly here that Hind (pls. 27, 28) comes
near to being not just a flying tank but a complete flying
armor/infantry combat element. It would take not just a highly
skilled pilot but a magician operating in Brobdignagian terrain to
apply Western doctrine to this massive machine. The Soviets
seemingly envision its roles as flying "cabrank"-type close support
for advancing armor, and in the initial and fire support waves of
a heliborne assault.

I hope all these rather scrappy pieces of information don't add
up to an impression that the Soviet Army has all the answers. It
hasn't, and seems to be becoming increasingly aware that it
hasn't. We need to remind ourselves that, apart from counter-
insurgency operations in Hungary and Czechoslovakia and the
obscure goings on across the Soviet-Chinese frontier, the Soviet
Army remained untested until it invaded Afghanistan. Reports,
specially film and videotape, coming out of that country suggest
that the Soviets are learning in the hardest possible way a whole
lot of lessons that the United States, French and British Armies
have known for quite a while. The Afghanistan experience may
shake Soviet confidence in their mechanized warfare concepts
too. Inputs like this tend to reinforce the way they already look

like thinking — on the one hand towards the use of extreme speed and surprise to avoid battle; and on the other towards more traditional and deliberate tactics once battle is joined. Maybe an interesting question to close this section on is whether this trend also means that Soviet thoughts on handling armored spearheads which have broken loose will continue to favor randomness, speed and depth or turn, once again blitzkrieglike, towards a more controlled pattern of classical maneuver.

Oil and Islam[4]

Since Britain finally lost military interest in her former Empire, NATO's European armored vehicle producers, along with France and Sweden, have very sensibly concentrated on the bottom part of the temperature range, regarding the top end as a matter for lip service or button-on kits. One has the impression that, since extricating herself from Vietnam, the United States has done much the same — and the choice of power plant for the XM1 tank is striking confirmation of this supposition. So it may just be worth reminding ourselves of the prevailing conditions in the Islamic oil belt of North Africa and the Near and Middle East.

All these countries now have at least one major city, often amounting to a conurbation. Then there are significant industrial zones and increasing areas of intensive agriculture and man-made forest. These developed areas mostly have a reasonable if skeletal communications system. But it is far from being what the inevitable divided highway from airport to seat of government might suggest; few bridges for instance are likely to exceed MLC40. Both within these developed areas and outside them, the often excellent road systems of colonial days are literally crumbling at the edges; and cost-cutting in the vicious competition for contracts makes the military capacity of even the brash new highways of oil wealth suspect. Off this skeleton of main routes, one is quickly down to narrow unmetaled trails or even unprepared surfaces. Even in a small, busy territory like the Island of Bahrain, the peninsula of Qatar or Kuwait, the developed zones and strips represent a surprisingly small proportion of the whole. Elsewhere they are no more than pinpricks or threads. With limited exceptions the rest of the

---

4 This was written before the Iraq-Iran War, but at the latest possible moment of revision I see no need to change it.

terrain is desert or mountain — or both. Escarpments are steep and broken; dry gaps are wide, deep and steep-sided; passes and defiles are narrow, often with a single-track road carved out of rock. On the flat there is much good going, specially near coasts; but there are vast stretches of soft sand and boulder-strewn terrain, sometimes with no way round them.

In many places and most seasons the temperature/humidity state is on the margin of human tolerance in the open. Unless precautions are taken (when they can be) armored vehicles act as a heat sink. Conditions inside them become intolerable, and their outer surface presents a risk of burns and even of spontaneous combustion of light flammable materials. Well-trained, acclimatized Caucasians of good morale can cope with these conditions provided they are given latitude over dress and have enough water. But I find it hard to see how either mounted or dismounted troops could exist for long in protective clothing without some kind of individual and collective support in the shape of personal air conditioning. This makes the chemical threat an even graver one than it is in temperate climates; likewise radioactive contamination from fallout or ground bursts would impose exceptional constraints.

For hardware too ambient temperature and, in mountain regions, air density pose problems. But these are simple and readily identifiable compared with those presented by the makeup of the atmosphere. Within this geographical area the worst environment for equipment which I have personally experienced is Aden (South Yemen). This is in a different ballpark than North Africa (even the Sahara); considerably more severe than most of the Gulf States; and significantly worse than the Sinai desert (which in fact provides a useful model for "bad" desert conditions).

For mechanical systems the greatest single hazard is dust. This is no ordinary dust, but hard, abrasive grains of sand with a wide spread of particle size. Some particles are large enough to cause individual damage; many are small enough to demand meticulous filtration. In the worst case these particles serve as carriers for sodium chloride and other corrosive mineral salts. Sandstorms apart, every vehicle that moves, even on trails, throws up a dust plume which hangs for substantial periods. There is often plenty of room for vehicles to disperse, but in trying to keep clear of dust they can easily lose visual touch. Then navigation becomes a problem.

Most seemingly flat desert terrain in fact contains a surprising number of hollows and folds that offer hull or even turret defilade. But the dust signature is apt to nullify the tactical advantage of these unless speed is restricted to (literally) a slow walking pace. Away from hardened or plastic-surfaced pads, dust causes problems in the takeoff and landing even of light helicopters. Quick refueling and servicing turnrounds become very difficult to achieve. In nap-of-the-earth flying, dust thrown up by the downwash limits visibility, invades the air intakes of machines which are hovering or making tight maneuvers — and of course provides a visual signature which largely devalues this tactic.

The second atmospheric hazard to all equipment (and of course to humans too) is moisture content. Many seemingly "hot dry" environments — in the everyday sense that the temperature is high and there's no water around — are in fact hot humid. Relative humidity can approach or even exceed saturation level on the littorals, which are likely to be the scenes of intense and sustained military and logistic activity, and surprisingly far inland. It is high humidity combined with a high content of corrosive salts and with abrasive dust that makes the worst desert environments so severe.

These conditions of terrain and climate have been fully written up, and their parameters are incorporated in many military and industrial standards and specifications. But I felt a resumé worthwhile because the number of officers and defense technologists within NATO who have experienced "Mideast" conditions is dwindling; and the constraints these impose on the design and employment of hardware are apt to increase with sophistication. On the one hand the microenvironment has to be made acceptable to humans, as well as to hardware systems like engines that are sensitive to it. On the other extreme design measures are needed to achieve acceptable reliability and serviceability rates. And special thought must be given to the exclusion of dust and corrosive salts during servicing and *in situ* scheduled and nonscheduled maintenance.

The two non European scenarios I have postulated differ in severity of threat; in the most likely areas of operations for NATO forces; and in the *balance* of light/airborne, mechanized and dismounted forces likely to be needed. But the hardware aspects have much in common; they can be examined in terms of the more immediate and definable situation — a Soviet threat to Western oil supplies. Here the Arabian Peninsula and the Gulf

Area constitute the most likely theater. For the West the military problems are extreme.

First, the USSR is operating on short central land lines from her main base (fig. 1 on facing page). She can concentrate forces and logistic backing behind her own frontier anywhere from the Turkmen Republic (or now in fact Afghanistan) to Armenia. Abadan at the head of the Gulf is only on average some 1000 km away; and she can converge on it from the whole of the northeast quadrant. In particular, quite apart from her naval presence in the Indian Ocean, the occupation of Afghanistan makes it easy for the Soviets to close the Strait of Hormuz by a swift (400 km) airborne or land operation.

Strategically the Persian Gulf itself is a trap for the West unless that alliance has previously established a massive forward base and an adequate holding force inside, along with secure, developed surface links to a port outside the Strait of Hormuz. Possibilities are Muscat (roughly 1200 km), the route of the Haifa-Dhahran pipeline (1700 km!) or the even longer Jiddah-Mecca-Riyadh-Dhahran road. With land lines of this length and difficulty, mostly at the end of long sea lines, the logistic problem is to say the least severe. Even given that fuel would be available on the spot, "fuellike" provision must be made for water. For this scenario we need to sidestep the uncomfortable option of sea-based nuclear interdiction and start by assuming an adequate presence centered on, say, Dhahran.

Maybe we should take the attack helicopter question first. For reasons we have just looked at the NATO "softly softly" nap-of-the-earth doctrine is out over dry, loose-surfaced ground — and that means most of the terrain passable to armored vehicles. Thus even the types of specialized attack helicopter envisioned within NATO, let alone adapted light communications machines, will be hopelessly vulnerable within 1500 m of the line of contact, let alone beyond it. There seem to be two clear-cut options here. One is to rely on fixed-wing aircraft for antiarmor and close support roles. The other is to go for a much bigger chopper like the Soviet Hind, capable of mounting a useful amount of armor and a full array of electronic countermeasures. We shall explore later whether the latter course makes sense in face of the Soviet air defense threat.

Next we might go to the other extreme and look at hand-held and manportable antitank weapons. These would seem to be affected in two ways only, both matters of degree. Opportunities for short-range engagements may be few, so rocket-launcher

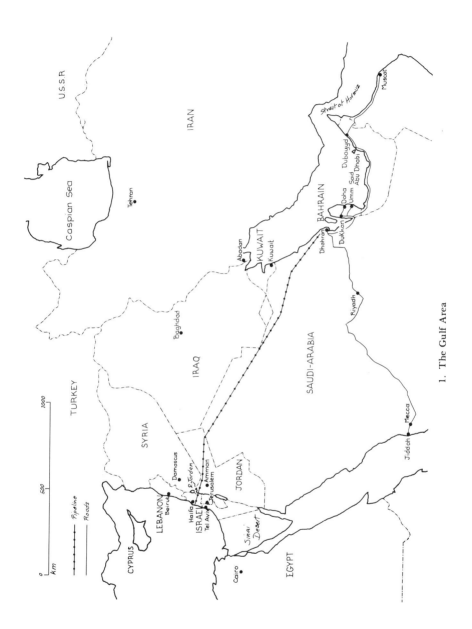

1. The Gulf Area

crews must be trained to a standard that gives them a useful hit chance at the far end of the system's range zone. The Soviets themselves showed this can be done with their RPG7; and the US Army, using captured equipment and Soviet training methods, have confirmed it.

The second point is that the more sophisticated surface-to-surface ATGMSs may hit problems to which first-generation wire command link systems are immune. Actual mirages are rare, but inversion and other factors are very apt to produce severe shimmer and refraction over wide areas. These conditions and/or dust may play tricks with the functioning of sophisticated markers and sensors. We shall be exploring signatures and sensors later. For the moment I just want to hang a large question mark over this whole area.

The US Army, along with some of its allies and the Soviet Army, seems increasingly to question the need for cavalry or other light forces in the European setting or at least to envision "economy of force" and other secondary roles for them. By contrast every aspect of the Mideast scenario screams out both for cavalry and for manpower-intensive light forces — in conventional terms nonmechanized infantry mounted in light APCs or heliborne.[5] Light forces spell logistic economy. Airportability gives them strategic mobility; and they have high operational mobility over difficult terrain.

Less obvious but no less important are the advantages high-performance light tracked vehicles offer in tactical mobility over extreme terrain — and in battlefield mobility where such terrain allows one to envision maneuver in detail. The greatest problem is narrowness of defiles in mountainous and other featured areas, and of wadis and similar passages in the escarpments of otherwise trafficable zones. Plate 1 makes the point better than words. The Matilda tanks shown were under 2.4 m wide — against M113A1's 2.69 m, BMP1's 3.15 m, Marder's 3.24 m or the 3.25-3.65 m of current main battle tanks. Route widening may often prove a somewhat deliberate and hazardous process.

At the other extreme come the fertile areas, specially where these are wet-cultivated like the paddy fields of the Far East. With the exceptions of the Cyrenaican *jebel* and several areas west of it and of the East Mediterranean littoral across to the Jordan and Jebel el Sharq (roughly Israel and Lebanon), most of these fertile areas are basins, deltas or the like with alluvial soil.

---

5 If this sounds Irish, see *Mechanized Infantry*, Chapter 9 and page 112.

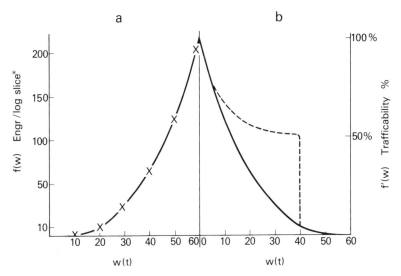

a   b

*(arbitrary units × 10³)

2. The weight problem
   (a) *Engineer/logistic effort.* Formerly logistic slice was taken to vary as the square of
       weight and engineer effort as something over the cube. Nowadays it seems
       reasonable to use the cube (*shown*) as a ballpark estimate for both.
   (b) *Trafficability.* Common sense and evidence from German studies suggest that the
       basic trafficability/weight curve is around the mirror image of the engineer/
       logistic effort *v* weight curve (*full line*). Development of the communications
       system for a specific purpose will distort this curve in something like the way shown
       (*broken line*, in this case with 40 t as a risk load for MLC40 routes).

In such terrain all-up weight rather than nominal ground
pressure is often the go/no go criterion. If a total load of more
than 20 t or so is applied to the kind of area represented by an
armored vehicle's track plan, the soil is apt to collapse *en masse*
over a rather larger area.

But if cavalry and other light forces are a must in this Mideast
scenario, it is wholly idle to suppose that they can hold off, let
alone drive back, the full weight of Soviet forces operating on
short central lines with comprehensive air support, much of it
home-based. To be remotely credible, let alone effective, any
Western intervention force must be based on first-rate armor.
Because intervisibility ranges are longer and attack helicopters
may be out of play, antiarmor fire-power requirements are even
more stringent than in Europe. Here we need to link back to my
earlier propositions[6] that logistic slice and engineer efforts vary

---

6 *Tank Warfare,* page 103; *Mechanized Infantry,* page 92, footnote 9.

roughly as the cube of battle weight and that this curve resembles
the mirror image of the trafficability curve for undeveloped areas
(fig. 2). Development puts a kink in this second curve in terms of
maximum weight and *to a limited extent* of width. The position
of the discontinuity will depend on the heaviest standard load
carriers and on specialized road traffic such as oilfield vehicles.
Semitrailers with desert running gear for ISO-containers and
pipeline sections, along with commercial low loaders, are likely to
be at least MLC40, making 40 t an acceptable risk load.[7] But
problems of narrow defiles and of weak embankments or
causeways in swampy areas will often remain in some degree.

Like the picture of the Dongolas Pass (pl. 1) these curves speak for
themselves. And when much of the logistic slice has to be carried
cross-country or airlifted, logistic self-consumption of fuel will
make the left-hand curve steeper still. We can now see the
trenchancy for this scenario of the argument *for* a light force of
around MLC10 with a matching width of around 2.2 m and
against "agile monsters" of 55 t. It is in fact around the 40-t mark
that the engineer/logistic curve really starts to run away and the
trafficability curve may well do so. In the NATO center, a top
weight of 40 t is a useful bonus — and one which the Soviets
enjoy. In this Mideast scenario it is an imperative. What is more it
is an imperative which Soviet tank design shows to be feasible at
the cost of fightability and habitability. Likewise the S Tank and
the United States HIMAG project strongly suggest it may be
attainable for the West by a rearrangement of roles — by "hive-
off" as opposed to tradeoff.

To sum up, the human factors of acclimatization and leadership are well known but demand exceptional attention to habitability of armored and other vehicles, specially in face of a
chemical threat. All equipment needs to be tropicalized with
particular attention to corrosion by mineral salts. Mechanical
equipment needs a two-pronged approach — design and
procedures to allow *in situ* repair without ingress of dust; and
large portable shelters to provide a controlled workshop
environment. But this is only the start of the logistic problem.
The fuel slice needs to be calculated on 75% or 100% of cross-
country consumption for supplier and supplied alike. Water has
mostly to be trundled or pipelined. Average speeds will be low;
hence overall turnround times will be high, as will wastage rate

---

7 A risk load because MLCs are based on short (US) tons; 40 (metric) tonnes = 44.2
(short) tons.

and down time — all of which adds up to more vehicles in the train and a higher proportion of reserves.

In many areas ground systems and fixed-wing aircraft will have to take back the attack helicopter's antiarmor and close-support roles — more of this later. Quite apart from the electronic warfare threat, all surface-oriented weapon systems using precise sophisticated guidance techniques, direct, autonomous and indirect alike, may be degraded by any of a variety of freak atmospheric conditions. Cavalry and lightly equipped infantry must have a full antiarmor capability, because there are many places where only light forces will reach in time — or indeed at all. Strategic, operational, tactical and battlefield mobility combine to place a very high premium indeed on reducing the weight and width of the main mechanized force's vehicles to something like those of the heaviest commercial loads — say MLC40 (40 short tons) as a target and 40 tonnes as a limit.

I am reminded of a story, doubtless apocryphal, told of an exchange between the notorious Earl of Sandwich and the equally notorious eighteenth-century politician, John Wilkes.

"Wilkes," said his Lordship, "you will either end on the gallows or die of the pox."

"That depends whether I embrace your Lordship's principles or his mistress."

Likewise agile monsters in the desert. They have three options though. They may die of thirst, sink in saltpans or wedge themselves in wadis.

PART 1

The Armored Vehicle Target

2

Target spectrum and damage criteria

The Soviets and Germans at least have long regarded the tank as the most important class of armored vehicle — indeed the most important single weapon system in the arsenal of the conventional land battle. Now that "heavy tanks" like the KV-JS-M10 series or Conqueror are, in name at least, a thing of the past, the MBT's frontal arc represents the toughest armored target. And "antitank" is a tidier concept to hoist in than "antiarmor". By one of those logical ellipses which seem to bug thinking on the mechanized battle, the main battle tank (MBT) widely came to be seen as the priority target among armored vehicles.

Yet back in 1944 or so, German commanders on the Eastern Front were achieving notable, if shortlived, defensive successes by separating Soviet tanks from their infantry and then destroying the tanks in detail. Some of these generals even opined that they would rather lose a tank than an APC. Since then, the increasing fighting power[1] of other armored vehicles has, I suggest, pushed the MBT down the priority list certainly for NATO's "antitank" battle and maybe for her potential opponents too.

As well as their inherent fighting power, the rarity value of some classes of vehicle enhances the effect on the battle of knocking just one of them out. This lesson was learned, mostly the hard way, by both sides in World War II. Commanders' and artillery forward observers' vehicles had to be indistinguishable in appearance from the general run if they were not to be picked off the moment they appeared.

---

1 By this I mean the degree to which a vehicle's combination of firepower, survivability and battlefield mobility can influence the mechanized battle. I believe we need some broader concepts like this, maybe not too well defined, to keep clear of "tramline" and circular thinking. "Operational effectiveness" I see as something broader again, applied to an organization, grouping or concept rather than a piece of hardware.

As I stressed in *Tank Warfare,* the tactical air situation in terms of fixed-wing aircraft — along maybe with electronic warfare — will normally be the greatest single factor in determining the run of the land battle. Then there is the direct intervention of scout and attack helicopters in armored operations. So pride of place among targets must surely go to all kinds of *air defense vehicles* (ADV) operating in the direct-fire zone. These are apt to be lightly armored and highly vulnerable to external damage, so they require a quite different type of attack than tanks. On Soviet concepts, the *attack helicopter* itself is well on the way to becoming a target for antiarmor as well as conventional air defense weapon systems — a rather speculative point to be noted in passing here and addressed later under the heads of "active protection" and the possible emergence of a heliborne maneuver force.

In *Mechanized Infantry* I put forward the hypothesis that tanks needed more in-house infantry[2] more acutely in the attack than in the defense. Certainly, as I remarked above, one of the very few aspects of mechanized warfare on which most experts agree is the defense's need to separate attacking tanks from their infantry. So it could well be that second priority must go to *infantry fighting vehicles* (IFVs). Here one is concerned not so much with severely damaging the vehicle as with immobilizing and disabling the men in it; and current IFVs, notably BMP1 and 2, are lightly armored. Once again this calls for a different type of attack than the MBT target.

The Soviets at least seem to be in little doubt that tanks need the support of *tank destroyers* too, even more in the attack — the break-in battle that is — than in the defense. And we may suppose that, to earn their place in the team, missile- and gun-based tank destroyers alike must either have some kind of technical edge on the MBT in its antitank role or complement it in some tactically important way. So we can probably allocate third place to tank destroyers. Unlike the first two categories of target, gun-based tank destroyers are apt to be tanklike targets in terms of toughness, behavior and damage criteria. Armored missile launchers lie somewhere between the ADV and IFV targets.

But it will be little use picking off the support weapon systems if we cannot deal with the tank itself whenever we can see it. If the MBT loses out on priority as a target because it is versatile rather than specialized, its numbers do much to restore the balance.

---

2 *Hausinfanterie.*

What is more, as with the infantry of World War I, it is what
happens to the tanks that will decide the outcome of the
encounter. The tank may no longer be queen of the battlefield,
but it remains the key piece — a potent mix of rook, knight and
pawn. We must be sure we can remove it from the board.

Just now this argument about hard target priorities is a
fashionable one in both Eastern and Western camps. Like most
fashions it may have gone too far. But in doing so it has brought
out one key point and signed the way to three major conclusions.
The key point is that to knock the steam out of an attack you must
take out the support weapon systems as well as, if not in
preference to, the tanks themselves. For reasons hinted at above
and to be explored later, this calls for *two modes of attacking
armor, one penetrative, the other disruptive.* I believe this is now a
distinction at least as important as the classical split between
kinetic energy (KE) and chemical energy (CE), the more so as it
ties in with possible novel approaches to the defeat of compound
armor.[3]

The second conclusion is that — and here I must parody the
arguments of an old and revered friend — probably the
conventional IFV like BMP, Marder or M2, and certainly an IFV
with antitank capability,[4] puts paid to any kind of neat pairing
off for battle — tank *v* tank, mechanized infantry *v* mechanized
infantry, air *v* air defense and so on. The Soviets have long
favored multipurpose armored vehicles, and I have long believed
them right. The fact that a given BMP1 is unlikely to use its
Sagger (ATGMS) and its 73-mm rocket launcher from the same
position at the same time is *not* an argument for putting the 73
mm on a squad BMP and Sagger on a dedicated tank destroyer
— though these too may be needed. I know multiple armament
makes it hard to train turret crewmen; but separately mounted
weapon systems often add up to capabilities lost because they
have somehow gotten into the wrong place. Like Shakespeare
preached and the Soviets evidently practice, I would put my
money on instructors and crewmen rather than commanders and
staffs.

Then again, this broadening of the hard target spectrum is not
just qualitative. In the Soviet lineup, one might ballpark the

3 I shall use this term throughout to cover: United States special armor, British
Chobham armor, *Schottpanzerung, blindage composite* and *kombinirovannaya bronya*
(combined armor). *See also* Chapter 4.

4 See *Mechanized Infantry,* Chapter 8, and my article in *Armor Magazine,* Nov./Dec.
1980.

increase in *numbers* of targets at 50-75%, and in the NATO
pattern at 100% or more. This means the defense has to think
even harder about exchange rates. I reckoned I had done well in
Tank Warfare to emphasize the need to consider *two* exchange
rates — enemy tanks *v* own tanks, and enemy tanks *v* depth of
ground ceded. This holds if you consider only one rate of
advance. I unconsciously fell into the trap of thinking in terms of
rates of advance based on historically achieved figures and the
pre-T72 Soviet doctrine — the 100 ± 25-km/24-hr ballpark.

Recent United States trials (page 36 below), Soviet claims for
tank speeds[5] and trends in Soviet doctrine (page 17) combine to
suggest that we should think about doubling this figure. If we
envision the dynamic effects of the movement of masses[5] in
mechanistic terms as a mix of momentum and energy, doubling
the rate of advance bumps the shock effect up by a factor between
2 and 4. In the light of this and of the broadened hard target
spectrum, I guess the defender needs to take account of a third
parameter — *the exchange rate of enemy tanks for time.* So we
can sum up these broad fundamental requirements for the
antiarmor defense:

> two modes of attack, penetrative and disruptive, optimized
> on a three-way stretch of exchange rates —
>
> > for own losses,
> > for ground,
> > for time.[6]

So it's back to that other eternal triangle I call the marketing
man's triangle[5] — except that I don't have a good enough
understanding of these parameters to use it on them. They could
even be just another way of saying "firepower, mobility,
protection"; but I don't think so.

The tanks *v* time exchange rate needs to be reckoned over a
period of the order of hours. Now let's switch to the order of
seconds with *engagement time,* defined as acquisition time plus
killing time. Traditionally the critical aspect of tank exposure has
been *firing exposure time* — once the passive counter-part of
killing time. Now two things have happened. Modern fire-control

---

5 *Tank Warfare,* Chapters 17, 2 and 6 respectively.

6 The buzzword for this type of analysis is "target servicing", in the sense, I suppose, of
ensuring that all targets are provided for. I have to admit I find this term confusing and
awkward to handle. Additionally, in considering the spectrum of antiarmor defense I
need to consider the three elements (own losses, space and time) separately.

systems allow the tank to maintain turret defilade until truly
ready to fire; along with this, standing-start initial accelerations
like those of Leopard 2 and XM1 reduce the time needed to move
from turret to hull defilade and back. More strikingly still one
Swedish concept (pl. 2) reduces the "hull down" target size to, say,
500 mm wide × 250 mm high, the width being dictated by the
gun trunnions. Apart from the muzzle itself, the parts exposed
could easily be replaced by on-board spares like the traditional
sight and periscope heads.

While killing time can be computed to fairly narrow limits, I
never saw any statistically valid data on tank v tank acquisition
time. This is not due to lack of figures, just that, even back in the
old 0-2000-m days, the variance bore an unhealthy resemblance to
the overall spread. I do, however, recall from those days an
average working figure around 15 seconds. On this basis,
doubling the range and sharing this enlarged surveillance area
between commander and gunner give a net factor of 2; so we
might guestimate 30 seconds. If this figure is (literally) of the
right order, it tells us two things. Properly handled, a firing tank
as such is no longer a target, though it may become one for any
number of reasons. By contrast the firing exposure time and size
of an attack helicopter armed with a direct-fire nonautonomous
missile makes it a potential target for fast antiarmor systems —
unless of course the chopper too can engage by exposing only a
sensor head.

We need to look then at *movement exposure time,* the time an
armored vehicle needs to cross a stretch of ground that is open or
provides only partial cover. There is a fair amount of evidence on
the lengths of such stretches in various types of terrain; despite a
very wide scatter, one might figure on averages ranging from 300 m
for cultivated European terrain to 800 m or so for steppes or
desert. However, two other variables play a part. One is the need
to think in terms of area-to-area, not crest-to-area intervisibility
(fig. 3). Another is the ability of the target to evade by jinking
and/or varying speed where the ground is open enough for
exposure to be protracted.

The German trials and analyses of the sixties on ultrahigh
mobility vehicles[7] may have proved abortive not so much because
they were ahead of the state of the art as because the Germans
were asking the wrong questions. They were looking at the
possibility of making a quantum jump in shock effect several
times greater than the doubling of rate of advance I mentioned

---

7 *Tank Warfare,* Chapter 15.

above — at fighting on the move at speeds up to 90 kph in a kind of naval warfare on land. Being thus little interested in fire and maneuver, they seem not to have hoisted in the payoff in reduced exposure times. Sure, this goal is reflected in Leopard 2 and XM1 in terms of power-weight ratio and the spacing and span of transmission ratios. But it took the United States HIMAG trials of 1979-80 to block in some figures.

In dynamic ride trials at speeds up to 95 kph, the HIMAG test vehicle (pl. 10), based on proven subsystems, covered a 15-km "mobility traverse" in 22 minutes against the 59 minutes of the M60 baseline vehicle. From this factor of 3 and a typical cross-country speed of 25 kph for a tank like M60, we get a speed of 75 kph or around 20 m/sec on average to good going. Applying this to my ballpark figures on length of open stretches, and assuming no evasive action, we get movement exposure times of 15-40 seconds, say 10-50 seconds. In a word, the HIMAG level of battlefield mobility *reduces typical movement exposure times of armored vehicles to the same order as the real engagement time of even the faster antiarmor weapon systems.* This is due to acquisition time, rather than killing time, becoming a function of the weapon system only with the slower ATGMSs.

I mentioned above the "nontarget" presented by the Swedish Marder/105-mm test vehicle in a fire position. Novel configurations like this excepted, we can reckon on any tank or gun-based tank destroyer presenting a target with a vertically projected area of at least 1 m^2 in a fire position — much more of course when the turret side is exposed or the vehicle is hull up. Within reasonable limits of shape, this target size is enough to give most modern antiarmor weapon systems an acceptably high chance of a hit at all ranges they are designed to cover.

Damage criteria and lethality

We will come again at the art of not getting hit, known as "indirect protection", in the next chapter. Meanwhile we need to take a rather deeper look at damage criteria. In his excellent paper "Armor/Armor penetration"[8] Backofen brings out just how far thinking on both naval and vehicle armor, and on the attack of it, has been dominated by the elementary notion of

---

8 *See* Bibliography.

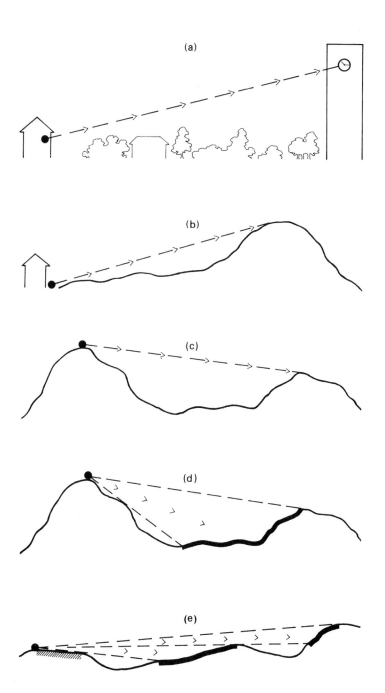

3. Types of intervisibility: (a) point-to-point, (b) point-to-crest, (c) crest-to-crest, (d) crest-to-area, (e) area-to-area

protecting, or conversely of disabling the individual or crew inside the armor — what we now call a P kill.[9]

Sure, the definitions of M, F and K kills[9] for tanks have been with us for a few decades. But the degree in which the attack of armor has focused on penetration of it shows up well in the astonishment evoked by the trials of the multibarrel, high-cyclic-rate Vulcan gun against a tank turret front.[10] There was no penetration, but superficial damage combined with the level and rate of energy transfer to achieve some rather conclusive F kills. Understanding of this effect was so slight at the time that the results were used, in my view elliptically and subjectively, to justify the choice of an automatic cannon as the armament for IFVs.[11]

Once again we are concerned with three related parameters:

type of damage required;

duration of effect;

level and mode of attack.

If we follow the convention of accepting that a K kill, total permanent disablement of the whole weapon system, is a bonus, the goal has to be an F or P kill. In antiarmor terms *lethality* is simply the chance that a hit will achieve an F or P kill. But the exact definition of these kills and thus the specific target subsystems involved vary. With tanks and tank destroyers it is the gun, ammunition and fire-control system; and a high power of penetrative attack is likely to be needed. In the case of ADVs, whether they mount weapons, sensors or control facilities, external damage from a fairly low level of disruptive attack will usually suffice. The same goes for attack helicopters. For a P kill on IFVs, classical reconnaissance vehicles and scout or troop-carrying helicopters, the problem is in fact the classical one of what damage needs to be done to the machine in order to disable the men inside it.

Neutralization by machinegun or artillery fires is con-ventionally taken to last as long as the fires last, but this concept is not too relevant to mechanized warfare, specially where attack helicopters are involved. Nor is the 30-minute duration of disablement conventionally stipulated for an M kill. At one extreme neutralization can be momentary — something that

---

9 i.e. personnel kill; mobility, firepower and total kills.
10 I think an M60 pilot, but maybe an M48.
11 *Mechanized Infantry,* page 51.

spoils a single engagement by a single enemy weapon system. At the other, notably in the case of an M kill from scatterable minelets, its initiation may be delayed and its effect quite long lasting. This broader definition of neutralization gives rise to two interesting thoughts. The first is that an M kill is most often a form of neutralization. Unless and until operations reach a protracted and relatively static phase where attrition becomes a major factor and repair falls into a meaningful timeframe, power train damage and some types of running gear damage amount to a K kill.

The second notion, of interest for different reasons to attacker and defender alike, I shall call *extended neutralization*. It may be an alternative, a forerunner or a complement to lethal attack. By "extended neutralization" I mean something that lasts longer by an order of magnitude or two than the fires which produce it and a shorter time than the repair of minimal significant damage — say the replacement of a single track link cut by a minelet. So I guess I am thinking of 5 to 20 minutes from a single neutralizing round or salvo. This could just be the conventional 30 minutes minimum of the M or F kill compressed into nineties tempo. But acceptance of extended neutralization as a concept in its own right opens up a whole new range of possibilities in the way of area attack on armored vehicles; likewise it makes sense of some existing modes of attack.

If you can stop the armor facing you from moving and firing, maybe silhouette and isolate it with some fashionable smoke too, you have a kind of shooting-gallery situation for your lethal antiarmor systems. If you can force the enemy to unbutton, artillery with conventional HE gets into the act too. The attacker who has not lost momentum may well find 10 minutes of extended neutralization of enemy armor, combined with normal covering fire, enough for him to bounce an objective. Certainly this combination will help him bypass opposition without the delay and distraction of deploying a flank screen.

For the defender extended neutralization operates at two levels. First, by freezing the attacker temporarily it gives the defender's lethal weapon systems a finite period of free play, thus in effect reducing the initial odds against him. Second, this improvement in all three exchange rates (*see above*), combined with the direct effect of reducing momentum, may be enough to make the attack bog down. This, the mechanized equivalent of an infantry attack being pinned down, is a complex phenomenon not too susceptible to analysis. In my view it takes place mainly in the attacking commanders' minds at combat team and company level, maybe lower. Probably it is in some measure related to actual casualty rates, rather along the lines of the rules of thumb about a unit ceasing to function at its normal tactical level.[12] Be all that as it may, nobody who has battle experience or has even glanced at any sector of military history will question the validity and importance of this phenomenon. Battles turn on it.

The third parameter, *level and mode of attack,* is derived from the first two and from the state of the art. I hope I have managed to achieve common understanding, if not common ground, with the reader on these first two. For the third and less debatable I shall take as points of departure: APDSFS,[13] shaped charge, self-forming fragments (SFF) and delayed effect munitions; and on the other side of the coin compound armor on the horizontal frontal arc[14] of the main armored vehicles, and vision and fire control systems mainly based on optics or optronics — systems, that is, which operate in or around the visible light spectrum. In these terms I believe we can provisionally define two levels and two modes of attack:

lethal attack (F or P kill) by —
penetration and residual internal effects;

disruption, causing external damage and sometimes broaching the main armored envelope;

neutralizing attack, ranging from momentary to a minimal M kill.

These will at least serve as planks on which to build an examination of target response and weapon effects. For paradoxical as it may sound, the importance of secondary effects arising within the target makes it logical to address the problem in this sequence. Along with them we need to note that a firing tank will not always present a feasible target; that with this exception target size is not critical; and that state-of-the-art movement exposure times are becoming critical *vis-à-vis* engagement times.

---

12 Like 30-40% casualties across the board, or the loss of a complete subunit.
13 Armor piercing discarding sabot fin-stabilized.
14 With the advent of compound armor and the established and growing part air-to-surface antiarmor weapon systems play, I think the traditional frontal arc must now be defined in three planes (*see* Chapter 4).

3

Indirect protection and signatures

Direct protection, armor and the like that is, reduces lethality — the chance that an actual or potential hit will kill. Looking at the beyond, one needs to say "actual or potential" because trends in both antitank weapon systems and armor suggest that "active protection", the spoiling of an attack that is about to hit, could be just around the corner. Following a logical and chronological sequence we need first to look at *indirect protection* — reduction of the chance of being hit. This concept breaks down again into *reduction of the chance of being acquired* and *reduction of the chance of being hit once acquired.* The signatures of a tank provide a link between these because acquisition, laying and guidance sensors may respond to the same signature.

From the World War II vintage of tanks up to the introduction of Leopard 2 and Abrams, progress in the armored world has been firepower-dominated. Both high-pressure guns and ATGMs now offer a useful first-round kill chance on a turret target out to a range some 4 times the maximum of the early fifties and over twice that of the late sixties. This double quantum jump has been matched only by a marginal increase in mobility. Sure, Leopard 1 is a halfway house; but against this one must set the British mobility regression after Comet. Even the claimed figures for T72 scarcely amount to a quantum jump; and that tank's probable performance is no more than an evolutionary advance. Led by the British, picked up by the Soviets and pursued rather more deliberately by the Americans and Germans, this dominance of firepower must in principle favor the defense. Likewise, as we shall see in the next chapter, compound armor represents a step advance in protection.

Acquisition time

So even in the absence of specific evidence, the development pattern of complex systems suggests that the closing decades of the century will see mobility on the move. As outlined in the previous chapter, HIMAG and other projects show this to be the case. Once the spreads of *movement exposure times* and *acquisition times* start to overlap, the chance of a moving tank being acquired falls off sharply. Given a few sweeping but reasonable statistical assumptions we can say that, if mean exposure time is twice mean acquisition time, there is a 50% chance of acquisition; if these mean values are the same, the chance of acquisition is halved to 25%. For visual acquisition, HIMAG mobility and "average" terrain (whatever that may be) the chance of an available target being acquired is around 30%.

If we think in terms of the proportion of available targets killed, which we must do to satisfy the three exchange-rate parameters (page 34), we are down in the $20 \pm \%$ ballpark even on optimistic assumptions of hit chance and lethality. As I hinted at in *Tank Warfare* (page 98), it looks like one key to a successful antiarmor defense lies in *reducing by an order of magnitude the acquisition time for a moving-tank target.*

Audio signature

In addressing the question of signatures, we should maybe first look at the one which is an aid to detection and sometimes identification but not, directly at least, to engagement. In first gear with engines ticking over, the German PzkwIII and PzkwIV tanks of World War II could creep about unheard within 200-300 m of the listener. By contrast British armored vehicles of the fifties and sixties had an audio signature that could be heard and identified over many kilometers. Centurion even had two — the squeak of its unshod dry-pin tracks, and ignition in the hot mufflers when the driver allowed the engine to go onto its governors. The wheeled Saladin and Saracen, even the Ferret scout car had loud and distinctive fan whines.

An audio signature which permits identification is a gift to the antiarmor defense, and not just at night. It will remain so even when armored vehicles have automatic two-way IFF[1] systems. As we shall see in the next chapter, any active electronic challenge

---

1 Identification friend or foe.

will at least alert the crew and may have more drastic direct consequences.

Visual signature

As long as the detection and sighting/tracking systems of armored vehicles and helicopters continue to make use of frequencies at or on the fringes of the visible light spectrum, an armored vehicle's visual signature will be the key one in spotting, identifying and laying alike. For nonspecialized observers it will always be the primary aid. So we need to consider visual signatures at three levels, which I shall call "indirect", "direct" and "crew dependent".

An *indirect visual signature* is one caused by the vehicle but not forming part of it. The most conspicuous (in every sense) are muzzle effects; these we shall return to later. A second signature which good crew training, specially discipline, can do much to suppress is movement dust. There are a lot of arguments for going fast, but often a whole lot more for going slow. Then again there are design-related signatures like Chieftain's notorious exhaust plume, often good enough for identification, or the afterglow of an unshuttered white light or IR searchlight.

In this group I would also mention sun glint on optical or optronic heads. I call this "indirect" for three reasons. Even good design cannot always prevent it when the vehicle is canted or when a moving top mirror is elevated. The vehicle thus spotted may be in turret defilade at the time and thus not present a target. And, to a Britisher at least, it is fortuitous because it depends on the sun.

Finally under this head come track marks, a certain giveaway to the airman and his electronic surrogates. Covering these or digging them level is an essential security measure.

The *direct visual signature* is provided by the vehicle itself. One might mention in passing that a whip antenna and more often still the shadow of an open hatch have given away many a good fire position. But here again I want to take two bites at the cherry — *detection,* and *identification* (normally termed recognition).

The ease with which a tank can be spotted depends in large measure on the detailed configuration of the turret and upper hull. If these are contoured and shaped in the same kind of way as ground and natural and man-made features, the target may be very hard to see. Vertical slabs, square edges and intense shadows are conspicuous. One can see this best from examples. The Soviet mushroom-shaped turret (pl. 3) is hard to see apart from the excrescence of the air defense machinegun (ADMG) mounting. The Chieftain turret (pl. 4) is good in this respect as in many others, the mantletless construction minimizing shadow; but these merits are to some extent degraded by the uncontoured bulk of the searchlight housing. The "compact" turret of M60A2 (pl. 5) is disastrous from this point of view as from others. More generally, the tendency of United States designers to sweep turrets upwards fore and aft (pl. 6) results in both shadow and HE pockets.

I personally think visual recognition of armored vehicles under battle conditions so difficult that I doubt the designer need strive to make it tougher still. Fact is, the kind of configuration and style that is easy to spot is easier to recognize too. The Soviet ADMG, the Chieftain searchlight, the slab side of M60A2 and the normal M60's upswept bustle and basket illustrate this point well.

Here I must allow myself a digression on *"disruptive" painting*; for while many things I did in my military career were, I guess, disruptive, my long battle to have camouflage painting of armored vehicles accepted in BAOR was both disruptive and constructive at one and the same time. Seriously this issue merits a word. The disruptive painting of ships in the days when acquisition was mainly visual, notably World War I, was just what its name implies. Parts of the silhouette were lost against the background of sea and sky, leaving the contrasty areas as isolated, unrecognizable shapes. Fact is a tank is too small for this principle to work — hence the quotes round disruptive. Nonetheless, variegated painting does reduce contrast with most backgrounds, lighten and break up shadows and soften hard, bulky lines. It should not be standardized, but left to the individual crew's taste within certain ground rules. However, in the trials we did the critical factor was judged to be the psychological effect. Crews felt their mounts more battleworthy, and themselves less vulnerable and more at one both with their vehicles and with the terrain.

By contrast single or group *camouflage,* skillfully and painstakingly done, can be highly effective against the human eye and visual sensors. With ample space and excellent crew discipline thrown in, it can deceive the trained ground observer even at ranges of tens of meters. Lest the reader disbelieves this, I must permit myself another brief reminiscence. My tank company was privileged to be affiliated to the Gurkha battalion running the annual Gurkha platoon commanders' course, held that year in Hong Kong. The main demonstration stand was a small mound. On the third evening of the practical phase, by which time everybody knew the ground intimately, we camouflaged a tank about 30 m down the open front slope of the stand. The next day this considerable gathering spent the whole morning on the stand and tea and "tiffin" breaks wandering around it. Having reassembled them for the afternoon briefing and got them looking the right way, we unmasked the tank without warning and traversed the gun onto them. The effect was rather dramatic.

The mixture of skill and discipline camouflage required leads naturally into my third subhead, *crew dependent signatures.* I have already hinted at a number of relevant points like desilhouetting antennas, not leaving hatches open, depressing the gun to kill mantlet shadow and covering track marks. Now I want to tackle the question of maneuver. Tank and IFV crews who do not understand "mounted fieldcraft" will not live long; and the antiarmor defense will stand little chance against an attack by well-trained crews unless they too understand this art and set out to confound it.

We can skip over elementary problems, like avoiding or rushing a skyline, by registering a few general points. Tanks must never bunch, either laterally or fore and aft. They must use cover to the full, never underestimating the value of partial cover or of a short stretch of cover between two pieces of open ground. The commander should not move until he knows the vehicles covering him are actually in position and ready to engage. Likewise he should not move if he can help it until he has picked a piece of cover to make for; if he cannot see the end of his bound, he should pick his new position the moment he can see it. He should brief his crew thoroughly before moving, then move fast and decisively.

I apologize to the reader for this peremptory excursion into basic armor training. But it sketches in the backdrop we need to address the real problem, *taking up and adjusting observation and fire positions.* The Wehrmacht were very good at this. I guess it is worth retelling the story of the Borquebus ridge[2] — how a mixed platoon of tanks and jagdpanzers worked its way down the almost open forward slope of the ridge under the eyes of the British, took some seventy advancing Shermans in the flank and

---

2 Operation Goodwood, east of Caen, 18-21 July, 1944.

withdrew with loss of only one vehicle to fight again on the ridge itself. My impression is that this skill is one the Bundeswehr has not inherited, and I have frankly never seen an American or British tank unit that really got to first base in this ballgame. Equally frankly I failed to find any effective way of training my crews. The more one hears of Soviet training standards, the more he feels they may be rather more successful. Nonetheless the message for the antiarmor side of the house to hoist in is clear. *Tanks and supporting vehicles are often at their most vulnerable just when they think they have moved into safety.*

Conversely I am in no doubt that a device which enabled crews to take up a correct position first time every time, whether moving in initially or adjusting after firing, would make as great a contribution to indirect protection as the combination of fire-control system and stabilizer which allows everything bar pressing the trigger to be done before breaking turret defilade. Since the problem is common to most types of antiarmor weapon system, we might probe it deeper, first noting that hull and turret defilade are normally defined with respect to the horizontal plane (fig. 4a).

The first problem is that nobody likes sitting with too much dead ground in front of him. So the lower edge of the area to be observed, or the shorter-range targets in a fire position, are likely to have a pronounced negative angle of site (fig. 4b). This makes some degree of exposure to an enemy on the same level inevitable; the amount required depends on the angle of depression available on primary vision and sensor heads, or the gun (fig. 4b) or again the controlling sight or guidance head or antenna of an ATGMS. The tendency is for vehicle commanders to be drawn forward until they offer a considerable target; in a fire position this target may include part of the relatively soft lower hull front.

The second factor that tends to make commanders and drivers overshoot is, I believe, the shape of the crest. In good tank country crests are apt to be convex; the crest angle (α in fig. 4a) is small and diminishes as one approaches the crest. As a result the rate of increase of forward field of view falls off progressively from the moment the highest part of the field first becomes visible. This again draws commanders forward in an attempt to see more; in fact I have seen it draw crews right over the crest onto the forward slope!

I suspect — though I must shamefacedly admit to only having thought of this after I no longer had the means to prove it at my disposal — that the difference in height between commander and

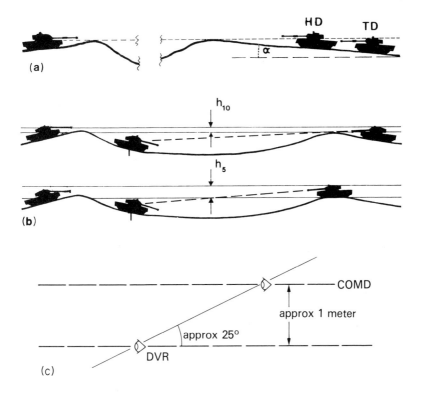

4. Hull and turret defilade
   (a) *Turret defilade* (TD, position of observation) and *hull defilade* (HD, fire position), *not* to scale. These are normally referred to a target on the same horizontal plane as the observing/firing tank. Note also the importance of the mean slope of the crest (α).
   (b) The *degree of exposure* to an opposing weapon system on the same horizontal plane depends on the negative angle of site of the target and the depression arc of the gun ($h_5 \equiv 5°$, $h_{10} \equiv 10°$). This schematic also shows how crews are apt to be drawn forward by dead ground in front of them.
   (c) The *difference in height between commander and driver* and the angle the line joining their vision heads makes with the horizontal prevent the driver from judging turret and hull defilade even closely enough to know when to expect the order to halt.

driver (fig. 4c), or more precisely the angle the line joining their vision heads makes with the hull horizontal, does not help commander and driver to establish a common view of the situation. The driver, who at the critical moment is still seeing the ground rising to the crest, is apt not to slow right down in time to respond to the commander's order to halt. This problem does not arise on the S Tank and other novel configurations now under trial, where commander and driver are either at the same level or share a common display. In conventional tanklike layouts, I believe that the driver should be provided with a commander-level display or else the commander with a driving override. Be that as it may, the crews of tanks and antiarmor weapon systems alike should be in no doubt of the importance of turret and hull defilade and the consequences of getting it wrong.

Thermal signatures

Before going on to examine the firing tank as a target, I want to look at the types of armored vehicle signature not perceptible to the unaided human senses. Let me stress that I am talking of natural and largely unavoidable emanations from the tank, *not* its response to various forms of electromagnetic insult. So far the most important of these signatures has proved to be the far infrared or thermal one.[3] Here we need to draw a distinction not entirely obvious at first glance. The thermal signature of a fully operative tank spreads right across the IR zone and spills over into the red end of the visible spectrum. When such things were around, an exposed gun tube or exhaust pipe could often be seen glowing on a dark night. The heat losses of the subsystems normally run in the standby condition like powered mounting and NBC protection, even electronic/optronic power packs, may sometimes be enough to produce a detectable signature spreading into the near IR band.

The true and unavoidable thermal signature comes from the basic physical nature of an armored vehicle — the fact that it is a large box made mostly of thick metal. In our Mideast scenario (page 20) we noted that when exposed to sustained full sunlight an armored vehicle absorbs large quantities of heat, making the inside intolerable and the outside sometimes dangerously hot. When the ambient temperature drops, this heat is released, not instantly but at a rate and over a period governed by the thermal characteristics of the vehicle. Likewise when the ambient temperature rises again, the vehicle takes a while — specially in

---

3 The infrared (IR) part of the electromagnetic spectrum is regarded as being divided into "near" (i.e. adjacent to the visible spectrum) and "far" bands. Active IR night vision systems use the near band. Near IR behaves rather like light, except that it is invisible to the human eye without a converter and has rather better penetration of mist and dust. Far IR has much greater penetration, *cf.* the "deep heat" or "diathermy" equipment used in therapy.

the absence of direct sunlight — to absorb enough heat to catch up.

This phenomenon, a form of hysteresis, is easiest to envision under hot conditions but occurs in temperate and cold climates too. Throughout the hours of evening and morning, sometimes right round the clock, there is a temperature differential between the surface of the vehicle and its environment. Additionally, because one is mainly metal and the other timber, vegetation, stone or whatever, their thermal radiation spectra are different. This second difference, much used in medicine, astronomy and satellite imaging techniques, is not too valuable in the antiarmor setting. But temperature differential is used by the successful technique known as *thermal imaging*.

This technique was initially developed for night fighting, first as a target detector and then, as the state of the art advanced, as a laying aid. Under many but not all conditions, the effect is usable at detection level in daylight too. Thermal imaging is, however, subject to two serious weaknesses. As already explained, it is not reliable round the clock in all conditions. More importantly far IR radiation is severely attenuated by the kind of dust that hangs around battlefields and any area where armored vehicles move cross country. So this signature earns a place in the chorus line but not as the solo turn it was thought to be a few years back.

Magnetic signature

As common sense suggests, an armored vehicle, specially a tank with heavy steel armor, does have a considerable magnetic signature. Degaussing techniques are well established for ships and certain other large metal bodies where magnetic effects are inconvenient. Ships of reasonable size can achieve this with on-board power at no real disadvantage. But in tanks the scaling effect is such that the power required represents a dispropor-tionate fraction of what is available. Despite this, two factors conspire to make magnetic signature of little value. It is short range, and it is easy to simulate. Studies made at a time when magnetic homing looked a probability for ATGMs showed that it would be very easy to confuse the sensor with dummy targets put out by hand, towed or even outrigged. This signature is used by influence fuses for antitank mines, specially shaped charge minelets; but once again outrigged devices may provide an easy means of clearance.

Transient signatures

I should maybe reemphasize that, although an armored vehicle responds to radio frequency irradiation, specially in the millimeter wave band, it does not normally emanate significant radiation at these frequencies. Nor does it emanate at laser frequencies, except to the extent that these coincide with its visual and thermal signatures. But the moment an armored vehicle emits a signal, this emission can be used against it. At the level of radio communications systems this fact is well known and thoroughly exploited by direction finding and intercept; but the dimensions of all that are several orders greater than those of the direct fire zone. Line-of-sight pulses emitted by a vehicle, whatever their frequency, provide a basis for detection and in some measure for active response.

The firing vehicle as a target

When an armored vehicle fires a high- or medium-pressure gun direct, what one might call its "muzzle signature" is virtually certain to be seen. Not much can be done about flash or the dust kicked up by blast on most terrains under most conditions — normally the better the fire position, the more the dust. As long as the breech is located within the crew compartment, the overriding need to extract smoke and fumes also makes it very difficult to avoid discharging a characteristic plume of smoke and condensates. This plume appears long enough after the muzzle effects proper to be pinpointed by those whose eyes have already been drawn to the spot. The launch signature of an ATGM is — or should be — much less prominent; but it is still not too hard to spot unless the system, like Swingfire and some others, can be fired "semiindirect" from behind the crest where its controller is located.

   Likewise the direction in which the weapon system is firing provides what might reasonably be called positive identification. So we start from the point where the target is firmly acquired.

   Missile launchers tend to be carefully sited in prepared positions in depth and/or defilade. Even direct-fire systems can as a rule fire without exposing more than a sight head, maybe plus a retractable launcher. So they will tend to stay in position until they have expended their ready missiles. Tanks and gun-based tank destroyers normally move after each round or at least each engagement. This is partly to avoid dust from their own muzzle blast but mainly because they must expose at least the part of the turret above the gun trunnions in order to fire. Future configurations of vehicle (e.g. pl. 2) may be able to engage without presenting a direct-fire target, but I guess they will still tend to move after firing. When no clear-cut direct-fire target exists or is instantly acquired, the opposing tanks and antitank guns often have the option of neutralizing the firer by putting down one or more rounds of explosive munitions or even medium-velocity smoke shell[4] in front of him. This gives the initial firer a short period of free play, but is apt to show a net payoff for an opponent who has tanks moving in the open, specially down a forward slope.

Let us for a moment exclude enfilade and overwatching by considering a face-to-face engagement between two tanks in turrets-down positions at the same level. Tank A spots a target other than tank B, prepares to engage, comes up and fires. If A is properly handled, it will not remain a target long enough to be engaged in its initial fire position. But B has now located A, can probably follow A's jockeying behind the ridge from dust or by watching A's antennas, and may even be able to track A with its main sight and gun. When B sees A coming up to fire again, maybe overshooting and exposing its hull, B has enough time to come up, engage and pull back.

It is when coming up to fire second and third rounds from alternative positions in the same area that A is most vulnerable. This fact and the sequence of events leading up to it needs to be taken account of in the design of antiarmor weapon systems, including attack helicopters. If tank B's fire-control system, powered mounting or launch arrangements and agility allow A, putatively the defender, to get away repeatedly with sequences like this, the defense is well on the way to achieving the exchange rates it needs.

Conclusions

I am not a great one for conclusions, having mostly found them to be hostages to fortune; but the discussion above highlighted some extremely important and none too self-evident points.

---

4 The smoke shell of most modern tank guns is a medium-velocity bursting round producing quick white phosphorus (WP) smoke and matching the primary explosive nature ballistically.

Everybody from designer to crewman needs to be clear about the three stages in an encounter between a tank and an opposing tank or other antiarmor weapon systems — *detection, identification* (together amounting to *acquisition*) and *engagement*.

The "sore thumb" requirement in antiarmor firepower is currently the *reduction of acquisition time by an order of magnitude,* with priority on acquisition of the moving tank target. This is likely to call for automatic detection, storage and monitoring of targets, and display of summary target data.

Next only to reducing the size of target offered by the weapon system in a fire position, designers need to concentrate on *eliminating or minimizing all elements of a vehicle's visual signature.*

By the same token first-rate *camouflage training and discipline* can on occasion offer a decisive edge, at tactical level mostly to the defender.

Far more important still, though, is the *correct taking up of turret and hull defilade positions.* This problem is so fundamental and so difficult in the conventional tank that designers should look at it in terms of basic configuration and of the provision of a dedicated subsystem to help the crew.

Modern armored vehicles have *no* permanent signature imperceptible to the unaided human senses which offers a reliable and universal means of detecting and acquiring targets.

The *basic thermal signature* (in the far IR band) can be a useful aid to detection round the clock and to acquisition by night; but it is not reliable in all conditions and is particularly susceptible to dust. Thermal imaging is probably more attractive for air-to-surface than for surface-to-surface acquisition systems.

By contrast any signal in the radio frequency zone or any laser frequency bands *emitted* by an antiarmor weapon system is always detectable in the target area and sometimes much more widely. It thus opens the way both to *protective action by the target* and to *offensive action by other weapons.*

Versatile weapon systems which can put down *local neutralizing fires* instantly and accurately have a considerable advantage over dedicated antiarmor systems. This advantage is likely to be greater to the attacker.

At least in the current and predictable state of the art and with existing NATO standards of crew training, fast antiarmor weapon systems should be optimized to engage a tank not necessarily the first time it fires (which may soon be impossible in the typical case), but the second or third time it fires from alternate positions in the same location.

Finally the possibility of tanks and gun-based antiarmor weapon systems which can fire without themselves offering a direct fire target calls for novel means of attack — a fact that we shall now see ties with the problems presented by modern direct protection.

4

Direct protection —
passive and active

At this point we need to recall that the name of the game is system survival. Indirect protection evidently confers this; but once I passed the stage of accepting conventional wisdom as taught, I parted ways with most British tankers and designers because I found it incredible that any system as small as a tank could accept the energy transfer involved in modern kinetic energy (KE) attack and remain battleworthy. Sure, I have counted forty-eight holes in one side of a Matilda tank (pl. 1) that was still·rolling and shooting as straight as anything shot in those days. But modern KE attack applies 60-100 times more energy than the heaviest of those strikes at almost twice the rate against a vehicle at the most 4 or 5 times heavier. The analogy of driving, say, an M60 tank flat out into an immovable object merits frequent retelling;[1] the comparison with the *stopping power* of a bullet is a useful one too.

After all, nobody questions that a normal high-explosive shell or warhead of a certain size bursting on a vehicle of a given weight class will disrupt the vehicle. An M113, say, will be ripped open by a 105-mm HE/HEP (the conventional HE effect being the critical one here). An MBT will take a direct hit with 155-mm HE in most places, but a heavy shell in the 200-mm ballpark may well take its turret off. Common sense suggests that an equivalent boundary exists for KE attack — *that there is a limit to the power of KE attack a vehicle of given weight and density can survive even if its armor system succeeds.* I suspect we may be at that limit if not past it. Unfortunately only "firing at" trials on a

---

1 Many authorities argue that it is the momentum (mv) not the kinetic energy ($mv^2/2$) of the strike that matters. I have to admit to finding this hard to accept, both because of the analogy of the braking of a vehicle and in view of the greatly increased penetrative powers of hypervelocity subcaliber projectiles. The truth probably lies somewhere between the two hypotheses.

statistical scale can prove or disprove the point; and these would have been prohibitively costly in the politico-economic climate of the sixties and seventies.

Here I feel bound to inflict on the reader one further point of personal philosophy. For vehicles in the APC/IFV category, the purpose of armor is the classical one of protecting men; this is evidenced by lethality being related to a P kill (page 38). Weapon platforms like tanks must I think give enough protection to their crews to maintain morale and encourage bold handling. But when these crews are fighting alongside exposed men, I do not think one can justify sacrificing other characteristics to protect them beyond the level of system survivability. Conversely he must try to guard crews against hazards like fires that arise from, or are aggravated by, their being in an armored box.

Finally before we move into the problem we should maybe define its limits. While resistance to direct hits with HE shell is, as noted above, limited by disruption, nobody disputes that armored vehicles should be given all-around protection against all other forms of attack from nonspecialized weapons. Presently this requirement can be just about met by the amount of steel needed for structural strength; there is little sign that this equivalence will change, the more so since it conforms to a classical phase in the evolution of armor systems.[2,3] Nor, while everybody is keen to hit upon configurations that minimize the volume of expensively protected air, would anybody argue for allocating more than around 22.5% of all-up weight to protection against specialized attack.[3] The questions we need to address are the distribution of this additional armor, its amount and the form it should take. In this way we can draw realistic conclusions about optimizing antiarmor weapon systems.

Armor distribution

The air threat to tanks has existed for a long time; but because it mainly took the form of shaped charge, nobody could do much about it. So consideration of armor distribution stayed geared to the classical concept of the horizontal frontal arc (fig. 5a). Now the advent of compound armor and the attack helicopter calls for a new look. So does the increasing likelihood, resulting from compound armor, of indirect fire attack by guided primary

2 Backofen, "Armor/armor penetration: land, sea, air and space": see Bibliography.
3 Tank Warfare, pages 134-136.

projectiles like Copperhead or by submunitions, and of down-
ward attack from crew served systems like STAFF. Here we
should note that the roof, sides and belly of a tank have areas
roughly twice those of the front and rear (fig. 5b).

Let us stay with the horizontal arc for the moment. I have seen
no figures for the azimuth distribution with respect to the tank's
front of helicopter attacks, although the US/German tank v
helicopter trials may well have produced some. Additionally
Soviet doctrine on attack helicopters may make frontal attack
more probable than we in the West might think. But my
guestimate is that the attack helicopter threat will give a butterfly
pattern on the conventional polar diagram (fig. 5c).

At this point we really need some assumptions about antiarmor
weapon mix. Since account has to be taken of the acquisition and
hit chances, lethality and rate of fire of each weapon system as
well as of its numbers, analysis of the contribution made by each
to the total threat is a task for a computer. Modern tactics which
envision a greater intermingling of opposing weapon systems are a
factor too. But all in all one can safely say that the composite
azimuth diagram will significantly broaden the arc of high risk
(fig. 5d).

The angles of arrival of air-to-ground, indirect and "overhead"
attacks require a three-dimensional armor distribution diagram.
But I never was much good at blowing bubblegum; and much
better analysis of the horizontal and vertical diagrams would be
needed before they could usefully be combined. A ballpark
vertical diagram will serve to make the point (fig. 5e). The full
level of protection needs to be maintained from at least -5 to
$+30°$ — and this is going to hurt design balance because it brings
in at least part of the large roof area.

With the squeeze on traditional frontal arc protection, we also
need to look rather more deeply than I did in *Tank Warfare* or I
have seen anyone else do at the distribution of attacks along the
height of the tank (fig. 5f). I reckon that, if tanks were driven cross
country without taking up positions or attempting to use cover,
the curve for the probability that a point at a given height will
be exposed whenever any part of the tank is exposed would
approximate to the curve shown as a broken line.[4] The upper part
of this curve is going to be modified by the taking up of hull and

---

4 In other words, to the Gaussian cumulative probability function, though I suspect
(on "feel") modified by a shaping constant of less than unity and by a scaling constant.
Someone somewhere must surely have done trials to establish these curves, probably in
conjunction with trials on exposure times.

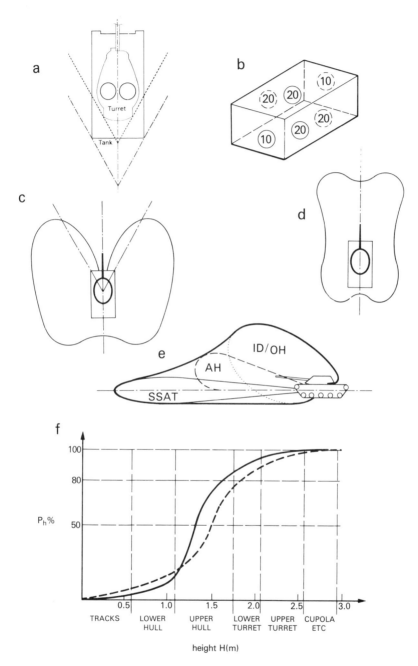

5. Frontal arc protection: (a) Classical frontal (azimuth) arc. (b) Relative areas of aspects (percent). (c) Azimuth arc — helicopter threat. (d) Possible future azimuth arc. (e) Vertical arc. (f) Height and exposure probability

turret defilade positions and by errors in so doing (page 45), and the lower part (in the opposite sense) by the deliberate use of partial cover. So I would place a certain amount of personal money on the curve shown by a full line being not too far from fact — the more so since, with the "lazy vic" configuration of the Chieftain hull front (on which the intercepts in the diagram are based) the junction of upper and lower slopes comes around the 45% probability level. This puts the join of modern hull fronts with the upper plate sloped at 75° or more[5] just about on the 50% mark.

Whether arrived at by instinct or by analysis, this 50% figure is, I guess, a significant one. Traditional frontal arc protection covered substantially lower risks than this. But the broadening and vertical extension of this arc is going to have rather dramatic effects. In future I would not be too optimistic about holding to the "even-money" criterion — specially since the whole or part of the vehicle top is likely to qualify for enhanced protection. Although the *major* KE attack will probably be limited to near horizontal, physical protection against shaped charge will need to be based on an angle of obliquity, of say, 30° instead of 60°. *Minor* KE attack in the form of self-forming fragments (SFF) will impact on both heavily sloped hull and turret fronts and on the roof at near-normal angles. This extension of the probable arc of attack is likely to outpace improvements in the "weight-bulk-effectiveness" of passive direct protection.

The message for the antiarmor side is loud and clear. *A threat pattern which imposes considerable extension of the frontal arc will force the armored vehicle designer to limit the level of frontal protection as well as trimming the frontal arc to a higher degree of risk.* By contrast the antiarmor side must never allow itself to be presented with a target it cannot defeat, or ignore the "stopping power" of massive KE attack. The need is for evolutionary development of the primary surface-to-surface attack with major effort on overhead attack — air-to-ground, indirect and short-range downward-facing systems alike.

F kill lethality

Up to the fifties most designers of armor-defeating ammunition, like bridegrooms in a nonpermissive society, were so concerned with achieving penetration that they paid little attention to what

---

5 On the Anglo-American convention which I shall use throughout. By the Continental convention this would read "15° or less"!

happened afterwards. For the British and Americans, the prow front of the Josef Stalin 3 tank (pl. 7) with its 120 mm of armor at a compound angle of 60° sustained this situation even while the techniques of systematic lethality studies were being developed. The evaluation of lethality requires computer techniques for three reasons. The basic procedure is rather simple, not unlike the occult practice of making an image of an enemy and sticking pins through it. But only a computer can provide an accurate external and internal model of a tank which tells in detail what the effects of the attack are without actually suffering them.

The postpenetrative effects have so many uncontrolled variables with wide scatter and in some instances knock-on effects that they can only be handled by Monte Carlo techniques; each attack path has to be rerun over and over. Then again, the possible combinations of compound angle of impact and point of strike, not to mention variations in residual velocity, are truly computerworthy in number. Fortunately once the model is set up and the software for attack inputs streamlined, lethality studies are relatively quick and cheap. Hitherto, as far as I know, this technique is confined to local effects directly related to a penetration. But with modern ADPS performances there seems no reason why general shock accelerations and disruptive effects should not be programmed in once enough is known about them.

Certainly the amount of work of various kinds done on lethality is enough to indicate the main parameters of postpenetrative effects —

residual energy;

area of penetration;

angle of spread of projectile material;

position/angle of strike;

primary effects (i.e. from projectile material);

secondary effects (i.e. from material of target);

tertiary or knock-on effects (beyond the subsystems damaged).

The first three of these are functions not of the tank as a whole but of the characteristics of the projectile and the armor system it is attacking. Perhaps the main point to note at this stage is that the achievement of penetration and the amount of residual energy are in direct conflict with area of penetration and angle of spread. Short of gross overmatch almost to the level of disruption, shaped charge, with its small hole and almost parallel jet, has always been low on lethality — to the point where penetrative performance has in the past been deliberately degraded in favor of enlarging and fanning out the jet. Likewise the amount of solid matter in the jet has been deliberately increased and various follow-up kill mechanisms have been tried.

By the same token the evolution of KE attack from full-bore solid shot to long rod penetrators — which, as we shall see, resemble shaped charge jets in many respects — has progressively degraded lethality. For the same residual energy, however, KE attack remains way ahead of shaped charge for two reasons. The mechanism of the attack is apt to generate immediate secondary effects in the shape of spalling at the inner surface of the armor. Additionally the projectile remnants tend to ricochet rather than penetrate anew, specially if the attack is marginal enough for the penetrator to deform or break up. We may as well note here one great difference between shaped charge and KE attack. With the first, lethality increases with overmatch through the level at which injurious or lethal overpressures occur to the point of disruption. With KE attack lethality will peak at a certain overmatch and then fall off rather rapidly to the point where the projectile goes in one side of the vehicle and out the other, leaving just two clean holes.

For any given combination of attack and armor system these primary effects are predictable within quite narrow limits and can be evaluated at fairly low cost by plating trials. Fact is though, primary effects are normally not too damaging. Lethality is really about secondary effects or *target response*. For given residual energy and area and spread of penetration, target response depends initially on the location and angle of strike — where the pin is stuck into the image. Given various additional sets of reasonably well-established parameters (like those discussed under armor distribution) and a powerful enough computer, the probabilities of a given path of attack are again calculable with considerable accuracy.

The joker in the deck is what happens inside. A fragment of the projectile or of, say, a light alloy instrument housing may miss a crewman, graze him, inflict a minor but disabling injury on him or kill him. If we look at this example we see at least five quite separate sets of variables —

energy of fragment;

path of fragment;

instantaneous position of crewman;

crewman's function(s);

behavior of a fragment of given weight and shape inside the human body.

Similar considerations apply to almost anything a fragment may strike. Each attack produces hundreds, maybe thousands of fragments. And the secondary effects may cause tertiary effects extending even beyond the target itself. An unpleasant but striking instance I recall was a burning tank with the crew trapped inside and the radio switched to send; for several days the morale of everybody on the net was, I think understandably enough, shaken to the point where it showed tactically.

Having come full circle, one is tempted to say good luck to the experts of earlier days whom I compared to Victorian bridegrooms. But I believe this brings out a general and fundamental point that needs to be stressed in any book of this kind because it is a frequent cause of misunderstanding and hence of mistrust between analyst and designer on the one hand and user on the other. Supposing all relevant conditions to be constant, the chance that a hit will penetrate is a reasonably consistent figure of equal value to designer and user; the latter can use it in various ways like laying down a maximum range of engagement. The lethality of a penetration is a statistically valid figure of great value to analysts and designers. But since the outcome of any given penetration may range from a K kill to insignificant damage, the lethality figure is meaningless to the user unless it is high enough to provide virtual certainty. Both this thought and the effect on morale of hitting targets without result suggest, to me at least, that *a very high F kill lethality is a key feature of an antiarmor weapon system.*

P kill lethality

"P kill" targets are of less immediate personal interest to the tanker than weapon platforms because they cannot so far shoot right back at him. But we saw above (page 32) that these are priority targets in the antiarmor scenario as a whole. Because of gross overmatch an antitank level of KE attack is unlikely to have acceptable lethality. Nor is the P kill lethality of matching KE attack such as that provided by the British 30-mm Rarden gun particularly high. The AP/HE round of 20-30-mm automatic cannon with its behind-armor kill mechanism is better. But quite apart from the questionable across-the-board tactical value of such weapons,[6] the use of IFVs to engage their like is subject to drawbacks, not least limited range.

By contrast tank gun explosive natures like 105-mm HEATFS or HE/HEP have in their different ways extremely high lethality, in fact at K kill level on vehicles of this category. They also have the range and hit chance associated with the weapon system's antitank capability. This is yet another argument for a Merkava-like combination of fire support tank and infantry fighting vehicle (FST/IFV).[6] Conversely, despite the evident dangers of carrying in-house infantry in a vehicle mounting a major direct fire weapon and objections to this concept from user and designer alike, it is extremely hard to see how a P kill might be inflicted on the rear compartment of an FST/IFV. The men in it may stand a rather higher chance of having to walk; but with this goes a much higher chance of being able to — a situation which does not entirely apply to a dedicated IFV, even if it has the same level of protection as a tank.

This brief discussion yields up three points of major importance to the antiarmor picture as a whole, and all of them tie to other points already made. The first and most important is *the ability of all antiarmor systems to be able to fire multipurpose explosive natures*; this links with the requirement to neutralize antiarmor weapon systems which can fire direct without presenting a target (page 51). The second and allied one is *the need for versatility* (page 33). The third is to be able to *reach right out to AD targets which threaten from depth and to IFVs* — thus achieving the key tactical goal of early separation of tank and infantry (page 30).

Armor arrays

Homogeneous rolled or cast steel armor was in vogue for almost half the life of the tank, say 1940-70; so it is hard to realize it was not always there. Fact is this single plate armor represents just a chapter in the story of modern vehicle armor and a brief paragraph in the history of armor as a whole. Initially tanks were

---

6 See *Mechanized Infantry*, page 51 and Chapter 8 respectively.

made of boiler plate or such and were of riveted construction. As specialized antiarmor weapons made their appearance, armor plate was bolted onto this shell to form what was known in Britain as the double skin or "D-skin" construction. More and more, specially in Britain which abandoned this construction only with Centurion (1946), an additional plate, the skirt plate, came to be fitted outside the suspension and running gear. Additionally special alloy steels derived *mutatis mutandis* from naval armor were adopted; these were subjected to complex treatments and extensive trials. I don't know what the Soviets were doing,[7] though welding of thick armor plate remained a problem in the USSR through to the sixties. But little else, or at least little different, was being done in the West.

It is worth glancing at these early plates, for although they were always very much harder than modern steel armor, they demonstrate in microcosm the encounter of projectile and armor. In moving away from boiler plate it seemed logical to enhance resistance per unit thickness by improving mechanical properties first by heat treatment, then by alloying and then by a combination of the two. This led to homogeneous hard plate. Systematic plating trials with solid steel projectiles led on the one hand to brittle failures of the plate and on the other to two forms of shot failure apart from simple nonpenetration. *Shot shatter* remained a limiting factor in velocity well into the APDS era and is still something to be reckoned with; it is, as its name implies, total compressive failure and is a function of striking velocity. *Shot breakup* (into large fragments) is mainly associated with oblique attack; it arises from nonuniform transverse compressive loads arising at and just behind the shoulder of the shot as the nose impacts. This phenomenon led to the adoption of a blunt punchlike nose in place of the traditional ogive and to the fitting of a windshield or "ballistic cap" — whence APBC. Later in response to the fitting of spaced armor (mainly skirt plates) a penetrative cap was interposed to keep the main shot intact for the main plate — whence APCBC (fig. 6a).

Although thicknesses were still absurdly low by modern standards and most heavier armor sections were cast, plate thicknesses were reaching a point where a hardness gradient was feasible and made sense. This led first to face hardening (of the outer face) and then to case hardening (of both sides). If we consider the basic armor array of a case-hardened armor plate

7 Though I hope shortly to set about finding out: *see* Introduction.

bolted to a mild steel structural plate (fig. 4b) we begin to see the emergence of the modern theory of the penetration/protection mechanism[8] —

hard — destabilize, i.e. stop, shatter, deflect;

tough — resist in hydrodynamic flow;

hard — destabilize, hopefully stop;

soft — absorb.

A skirt or other spaced plate, in early days normally of homogeneous hard armor steel, was found to break up uncapped shot striking obliquely and to turn capped shot so as to increase its angle of attack on the main armor. Anything in the space between like suspension housings had an unpredictable but mostly helpful effect; just occasionally it turned the shot back towards normal attack.

The key that opened the door to fabricated stressed-skin construction with single homogeneous plate was improvement in welding techniques. The Third Reich made the switch early, accepting the risk of coming apart at the seams (which quite often happened). The USSR I believe made it earlier still, shaping joints to protect the welds against direct ballistic insult and as far as possible against shock loading. Britain and the United States, after massive wartime research, did not switch until they could achieve welds and weld-affected zones equaling — and later surpassing — the main plates in strength. In this era all protection evaluations were based on rolled plate. Castings were used where shape required it, sometimes in preference to plate in the United States. Their greater porosity and tolerance zones exact a weight penalty upwards of 5%.

Unless titanium becomes a drug in the market, I can see little prospect of a departure from stressed-skin steel construction for the basic shell of the heavier armored vehicles, the more so since the amount of metal needed for structural strength also conveniently provides basic all-around protection against non-specialized attack. Pioneered by the United States, light alloy plate and castings have proved enormously successful on light armored vehicles and on large vehicles which need only modest levels of protection like self-propelled artillery carriages. But the thickness needed still rules out light alloys for tanklike levels of structural strength and protection.

---

8 Backofen, *op. cit.*

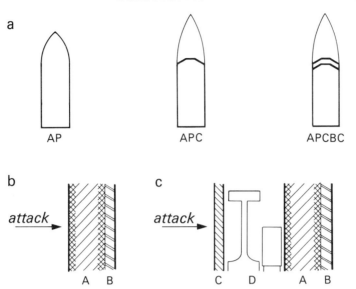

6. Historical attack and protection: (a) Solid shot — AP, APC, APCBC. (b) Case-hardened armor plate on mild steel structure ("D-skin construction"). (c) D-skin construction with skirt plate

More interesting to my mind, and certainly for the future, is the prolonged adherence to *single* plates or full-thickness castings. This was of course related to KE attack — by now mainly subcaliber. Use of excrescences on the outside of the armor like track links, bins and even the odd burster plate was accepted as a counter to HEP.[9] Major shaped charge attack was accepted as undefeatable other than by skirt plates and luck. We might note in passing that "luck" usually took the shape of running gear components; and I suspect the effect of these components may have helped provide the clue which led to Chobham armor and, as we now know, at least three other competing types of compound armor.

The switch to single plate was of course a complete reversal of earlier trends, maybe instigated by the rather low weight-effectiveness of the appliqué armor the Germans put on some of their World War II tanks. Certainly the combination of armor and structure in one piece of metal was a notable advance. But the conventional wisdom of the early fifties on this topic, as taught to me, was such a glib mathematical extrapolation from

9 High explosive plastic, British HESH — high explosive squashhead.

empirical formulas[10] that I have always suspected it and have
come to think it may have held back progress.[11]

If we think of the resistance of homogeneous steel plate as
"brawn", we can regard the destabilization of the penetrator at
the successive interfaces of a compound array as "brain". To the
penetrator, steel armor is like ploughing through a thicket or
rather maybe swimming through pitch. A compound armor array
is more like the ghost train in an amusement park — a series of
differing shocks — as we already saw in looking at case-hardened
plate. Whatever its precise arrangement, any compound armor
system is about interfaces and about exposing the penetrator to
the greatest possible number of changes of density, hardness and
ductility. There are two reasons for the greatest drawback of
current Western arrays — bulk. Air creates valuable interfaces
because it is so different in density from the other materials and is
fluid. And destabilization needs a finite time and hence a certain
distance in which to become effective.

We can assume that any compound armor will use some
arrangement of ultrahard ceramics, tough metal and air, all
sandwiched between two steel plates. The outer plate, sometimes
referred to as a burster plate, must protect the array against
nonspecialized attack and initiate explosive forms of antiarmor
attack. In terms of homogeneous steel plate, the nominal
thickness needed within the conventional frontal arc of a tank
(page 55) is 10 to 12 times that for basic all-around protection.
So, allowing for the inner and outer plates, the weight available
for compound armor arrays is 80% of the frontal armor weight or
around 17.5% of the vehicle's battle weight. Within self-evident
extremes, the depth available is whatever the user is prepared to
trade off in the way of handiness and indirect protection (cf. pls. 4
and 8). A tank with compound armor may be better at keeping
hits out than a conventional one: *in the present state of the art it
is also significantly more likely to be spotted and to be hit.*

The "bulk-weight effectiveness" of compound armor evidently
depends on the number of interfaces that can be incorporated
and on the degradation of the attack that each can achieve. The
work of Poncelet and others[12] has shown reasonable similarities in

---

10 As taught to me, from the Milne de Marre formula, but could be applied *mutatis
mutandis* to any of the penetration formulas (*see* Backofen, *op. cit.*). The effect of the
argument is that sustained resistance to hydrodynamic flow is more effective than a
repeated "destabilize/flow" cycle. In practical terms the question is to what extent
destabilization at an interface both takes up energy and spoils the attack on the next layer.

11 In fairness, however, one has to admit that the adoption of a cast silica-cored hull
front for M60 proved to be an enormously expensive nonevent.

12 *See* Backofen, *op. cit.*

the penetration mechanisms of long rods and shaped charge jets against steel plate, but there is at least one fundamental difference in their encounter with a compound array. The long rod penetrator is a solid body which arrives bringing the full energy of attack with it. Unless it glances off or comes out sideways from the array, all this energy must be transferred to the target. The array may indeed succeed in absorbing this energy safely over a finite time and distance, like the crush zones of a modern automobile. But no way can any passive system prevent this transfer of energy.

With shaped charge the jet is formed at the target and its tip must travel a certain distance to reach full velocity and hence energy; this distance is often greater than the standoff that can be provided in a projectile of high ballistic performance. So destabilization can spoil the attack before its full energy has developed. Being built up from particles so minute that it effectively behaves like a fluid, the jet can be deflected or even brought into a swirling motion far more easily than the rod can be turned through a few degrees. Likewise the jet can be disrupted far more easily than the rod can be broken up. This deliberately simplistic explanation will I hope serve to indicate how compound armor can provide balanced protection against shaped charge and KE attack delivered from guns of similar caliber and how this balance can be varied to take account of ATGM warheads of larger diameters.

We are currently looking at first-generation compound armors on conventional turreted tanks for which their bulk makes these armors rather unsuitable. Even where slopes of 60° to the vertical can be achieved with this configuration, warheads with angles of arrival of 20° or more, reducing obliquity to 40°, are going to cause problems. Partly thanks to compound armor, there is no sign of the "death of the tank" in the sense that journalists so often love to proclaim it. But the now conventional expression of the broad concept "tank" looks like being on its way out at least in the West; and we shall be examining later in this book the continuing validity of the narrower concept "main battle tank". So it makes better sense to look at developments in compound armor in relation to novel configurations like S Tank (pl. 9), the Swedish Marder/105-mm test vehicle (pl. 2) or the United States HIMAG test vehicle (pls. 10a, 10b) and HSTV-L prototype (pl. 11). The characteristic of all these is that sloping up to 75°, giving a net obliquity of at least 55° against helicopter attack, can be maintained over the upper front and side of the main armored envelope. Additionally all these novel configurations have a much smaller armored volume than their conventional equivalents.

Predictable middle-term trends in compound armor look like broadly following the classical development cycle of naval and other armors. We might start with two things that may in fact have happened in T72 or are highly likely to happen in its successor, "M80/T82" or whatever.[13] One is the reduction of armored volume to the point where the conventional compound array (fig. 7a), whatever exact form it may take, can in effect be turned inside out (fig. 7b) and built *inwards* from the structural shell. The baseplate or shell (A, 7a) replaces the burster plate (B, 7a) outside the array (C) and is itself replaced by a thin backing or stop plate (D, 7b). As we shall see later, predictable forms of explosive attack on compound armor may well force designers to put the main plate outside the array if they are to maintain balanced protection.

The reader may wonder, as I often do, what has happened to the "catcher" plate, the mild steel structural plate (B, 6b). As I have written elsewhere[14] a relatively thin layer of boronated polyethylene or such (E, 7a and b) would be a logical addition to both conventional and inverted arrays. Quite apart from markedly reducing the lethality of marginal attack, this would provide a useful measure of neutron attenuation, improve thermal insulation and cut down the incidence of everyday minor injuries to the crew.

The next step advance, once configuration allows it, is the classical one of using the space within the protective system to house expendables like fuel and even major subsystems like the power train. This is done to some extent in S Tank and more deliberately in the Israeli Merkava (fig. 7c). Interposing the power train may require housings, pipework and the like to be "hardened" somewhat (*see also below*), but I believe significant hardening could be achieved at no cost except in money and not too much of that. Additionally the self-sealing principle would need to be extended from fuel tanks to all reservoirs. With this useful hardware and necessary airspace forming part of the protective system, the array (C) can be reduced. Evidently the backing plate needs to be divided (D_1, D_2), one "layer" of it forming the bulkhead and stop plate (D_2). Once again the crew compartment can be lined (E).

Evidently we can expect the usual dingdong battle between

13 Cf. *Tank Warfare*, Chapter 17.
14 *Tank Warfare*, pages 117-118.

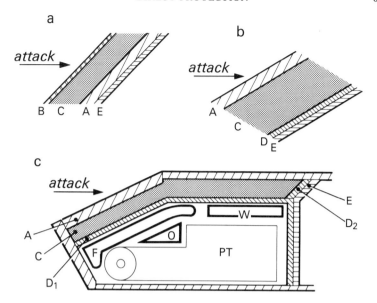

7. Schematics of composite arrays. A = main shell, B = burster plate, C = array, D = stopper, E = boronated polyethylene liner, F = fuel, O = oil, PT = power train, W = coolant
(a) First-generation array. (b) Rearrangement with main plate outside. (c) Inclusion of ("hardened") main subsystems in protective system

attack and protection, with advances in penetrators and modes of explosive attack on the one hand, and improvements in armor materials and arrangement on the other. It could be that the next step will be the reduction of energy transfer by dissipating or actively countering the energy of attack. But we need first to look briefly inside the armored envelope.

Internal measures to reduce lethality

Logically I suppose, any part of the vehicle that reduces the lethality of an attack should be considered part of the protective system — from a headlight guard or a big wrench lying in a bin to, in one case I recall, the field dressing in a tank commander's hip pocket. But it is convenient to think of the armor system as the shell put there to keep the armored envelope inviolate, and to look separately at what can be done once this envelope is broached.

By far the greatest hazard is ammunition. Already the United

States has followed Sweden in putting this in externally vented jettisonable magazines (S Tank, Abrams); the Soviets have gone at least some way in this direction in T72; and the Germans, although seemingly still willing to accept very high ammunition fire risks, have an autoloader which gives them this capability. So I am going to treat the ammunition fire problem as solved, with the remark that forcing a tank to jettison its magazines constitutes an F kill unless immediate backup is available. A developed fuel fire adds up to a K kill, though the crew probably has time to get out. But DERV and AVTUR (JP3) are not easy to ignite; nor, given a firefighting system of adequate capacity and redundancy, are they too hard to contain.

The next step is to contain minor projectile fragments and spall, and to reduce the tendency of primary and secondary material to ricochet by the "soft" plastic lining I described above (E, fig. 7). Then comes a move which would greatly reduce the risk of subsystem damage and the production of secondary fragments; additionally it ties in with use of the power train as part of the protective system. This is the "hardening" of housings, conduits, pipelines and the like (*see also above*). Maybe to help ensure built-in obsolescence, most commercial housings and cases are now made of pressed die-cast light alloys, extruded plastic or frangible plastic sheeting; and this practice spills over to many dedicated military products. I believe the technology now exists to replace all these by armor-type light alloy castings and fabricated plate boxes, or as the case may be by tough nonfrangible plastics, with metal reinforcement if needed for mechanical strength. I do not know how one could put a figure on the payoff, but my instincts tell me it would be considerable — specially when the respective states of the relevant arts can be expected to lead to a dominance of marginal KE attacks on armored vehicles.

As a tanker, I personally do not believe in shielding the crew beyond the helmets and padded clothing needed to protect them during cross-country movement and/or NBC protective clothing. Some unconventional layouts are in any case tending to isolate crew stations from one another, and shields round a crewman have two major drawbacks. Psychologically they produce a feeling of isolation and claustrophobia. Physically they cut off alternative escape routes if a crewman's own hatch jams, a problem which produces a substantial psychological kickback in war.

Dynamic armor

I pulled this term out of my memory where it is linked to a far-out
United States project of the fifties. I don't suppose its originators
or anybody else too much wants to recall the scheme in its then
form; but the notion of "micro-counterattack" provides a useful
point of departure for the last two sections of this chapter. The
first question to address here is whether one-shot armor is
acceptable. Now that the principle of armoring has switched
from the "brawn" of steel to the "brain" of composite arrays, we
look to be in for a battle of wits between chemical energy attack
and armor defense. By contrast, as I remarked above, there is no
way these clever passive armors can persuade a long rod
penetrator to eat itself or otherwise reduce the transfer of energy
from projectile to target. So we need to look at active or dynamic
armor systems; and these by their nature are going to be one-shot.
So I would ask the reader to accept the principle for a moment
subject to three conditions — and then go back and weigh
critically both the principle and the conditions.

If the "dynamic" element is contained within an array, we can
forget about the risk of fortuitous triggering and the hazard to
friendly forces. The first requirement then becomes the
maintenance of a meaningful level of residual protection once the
dynamic element has gone. Second, the system must be
compartmentalized so as to limit the surface area over which
protection is reduced by one strike. Third, the system must be
quick and easy to "recharge", preferably by the crew with on-
vehicle stores.

One first needs to be clear that the bulk of the protective effect
will have to be passive, both to satisfy these conditions and to keep
the dynamic element within controllable limits. This said, one
might approach the problem highly speculatively at two levels —
dissipation of some of the energy of the attack, with the possibility
of disrupting it; and disruption *per se*. At the level of dissipation,
one would almost dismiss the possibility of getting into a
meaningful ballpark were it not for the proven success of
pressurized sleeve ammunition containers. These sleeves contain
a suitable liquid under carbon dioxide or nitrogen pressure.
When a fragment or a shaped charged jet penetrates the sleeve,
the liquid discharges itself through the hole into the cartridge
case and either quenches the fire or removes enough heat to stop
the charge "cooking off". Sure, one is dealing only with residual
energy of attack here; but trials demonstrated success up to
rather high energy levels of both jet and fragment attack.

Experiments on fuel tank safety generally show similar positive effects as long as the tank is full or the strike is below the surface of the liquid; a hot shot or a jet into a vapor-filled space is apt to produce an explosion, unless that space is filled with nitrogen.

So for starters one is thinking — not for the first time in the context of ballistic and nuclear protection — about reserve fuel and water. This follows the classical pattern of making use of the space within protective systems but puts the liquids to double use. Again, one is thinking of materials with high thermal conductivity and high latent heats of fusion, vaporization or sublimation, and even of fast endothermic chemical reactions. With KE penetrators one is looking for removal from the target of a significant albeit small proportion of the energy of attack; and he is hoping for rapid removal of enough heat from a section of the penetrator to produce acute internal stresses and/or metallurgical destabilization. With jets one is looking to interrupt them, hoping to quench them and to provide a cooling and extinguishing follow-through. All in all there is a good deal of evidence to suggest that "steam armor" may one day be good for more than a horselaugh.

At the level of disruption one is into controlled explosions in a chamber with a "burster" device to limit pressure — maybe by blowing out the remnant of the charge unit and leaving its seating ready for reloading. A small linear shaped charge (shades of the original project I mentioned!) fired along a narrow chamber within and parallel to the armor array — that is, as nearly as possible normal to the path of attack — might well offer the requisite speed of initiation and intensity of local effect without producing an uncontrollable explosive force. A strike produces, at and immediately behind the inner surface of the burster plate, a number of effects which could be used for initiation. If the parameters were right, one can envision a simple and easily replaceable explosive device.

Active protection against the overhead threat

The kites I just flew were about active protection against *fast* antiarmor attack like APDSFS or HEATFS[15] from a tank gun. For any number of reasons I believe such protection needs to be confined within the bounds of a compound armor array — apart of course from the discharge of vapor or products of combustion.

---

15 High explosive antitank, fin stabilized, i.e. shaped charge; British hollow charge.

Its possible benefits are reduction of the weight and bulk of armor arrays and maybe holding of the energy transferred by KE attack to within the limit for system survival.

We saw (page 56) how the extension of the threat in the vertical plane imposed severe problems of armor distribution within the available weight. We noted too that this overhead threat consisted of major shaped charge attack from helicopter-delivered ATGMs and guided shells; minor shaped charge attack from submunitions; and minor KE attack from self-forming fragment (SFF) warheads, either the primary munitions of manportable systems like STAFF or submunitions of cluster shell and bombs like SADARM. Fact is, this overhead threat consists almost entirely of systems that telegraph their punch by flashing the target up, probably these days with millimeter wave (MMW) or some kind of laser beam. This signal may be used for detection and/or marking and/or homing.[16] An across-the-board transponder system can very easily pick up these or any other usable electromagnetic signals, including visible light and IR. So we need to examine whether the tank designer can use the transponder output to help solve his weight problem.

Way back in the trial period of that man-size Anglo-Australian missile Malkara, there was much discussion and a certain amount of experimentation on countering it. Malkara was a subsonic wire command link missile, so detection depended on visual observation. The indications — I would not like to call them conclusions — that came out of all this were that there was a useful chance of spotting a missile in time to respond in one of two ways. White phosphorous (WP) local smoke from the normal cups might screen the target in time but had two drawbacks. A determined controller could use his reticle to keep the missile on course unless the target had time to move (which was unlikely); and the firing of local smoke by every tank that felt itself threatened would cause chaos and give away the tactical layout. Second, if the target tank had a canister round[17] loaded, and the gun was already within, say, 30° of the missile's line of flight, the missile could be engaged with a high chance of success. By the same token it has recently been calculated that a tank with, say, an HE/HEP round loaded would have time to get a shot usefully close to an attack helicopter firing a transonic/low supersonic

16 We need to distinguish between marking a target to indicate it to somebody else, which can be rather brief, and marking for homing or for both purposes, which lasts much longer.

17 A grapeshot round for mass man-killing at short ranges, developed for the British 77-mm, 17-pr, 20-pr and (low pressure) 76-mm gun, and for the NATO 105-mm tank gun.

nonautonomous missile from a range of 2000 m or beyond. With a shell of muzzle velocity around Mach 2 I have to say I find this problematical.

Nonetheless these examples serve to illustrate that we are in a ballpark worthy of further investigation. The modern situation offers two notable advantages to the target. MMW and laser beams are narrow with minimal scatter, so there is little doubt about which vehicle is the target. Second, the firer or controller cannot use determination and a reticle to get the missile through; if the reflected signal is spoiled in time, the attack is at least degraded. But once again we need to consider two levels of response — spoiling the signal and attacking the missile or whatever.

Normal smoke will not do for MMW or the lower laser frequencies. The requirement is for a screen of "rope"[18] or at least metallic particles as well as a visual block. For helicopter-delivered ATGMs, primary artillery munitions like Copperhead and submunitions descending at parachute speed like SADARM this combined screen should suffice. Since a system like this is nonlethal to friendly forces, it can be fired automatically, so there should be no difficulty in deploying it in time.

Nonetheless most projectiles and missiles will either tend or be programmed to maintain their course if the guidance signal is lost. And in short-range systems like STAFF, target acquisition takes place close-in and is very rapidly followed by detonation. So there is a case for replacing the metallic particles or rope in the screen by buckshot or ball bearings discharged from forward-bursting multipurpose grenades. These could be fired at a fairly high angle and would not be lethal when spent. A more sophisticated antimissile projectile combining SFF and smoke is likewise conceivable. But since any aggressive system is potentially lethal to man, it must be fired manually or at least have a manual inhibit device.

Since the cups of any such system would need to point in a quite different direction than the normal smoke cups — in fact in an upward-facing ring offset towards the most probable arc of attack — one can envision this entire device as a separate roof-mounted subsystem. Unless countersunk it would be something of an excrescence; but if analysis shows that the parameters are right, this active protection might go a long way towards solving the problem of armoring the large roof area against the spectrum

---

18 British "chaff" (as in World War II Window).

of overhead threats and thus allow the level of protection of the horizontal frontal arc to be maintained.

Conclusions

Since this part of the book seeks to establish a target scenario for the rest, I guess I should attempt to draw some broad conclusions from this (Yes, I agree!) very long and complex chapter.

- The "overhead threat" will force designers to *extend the frontal arc vertically and laterally, probably onto the large roof area.* This requirement may impose reduction of the level of protection over the conventional frontal arc, and/or raising of the risk threshold for full protection.

- The establishment and maintenance of user confidence in antiarmor weapon systems requires them to have a *very high F kill lethality.*

- The P kill requirement reinforces the call in the previous chapter for *antiarmor weapon systems to be capable of firing multipurpose explosive munitions accurately out to extreme direct-fire ranges.*

- Further development of compound armor, combined with the trend away from the conventional turreted tank, will enable *high levels of direct protection to be achieved at decreasing cost in indirect protection.*

- One can expect a series of small swings of the pendulum between explosive (chemical energy) attack and compound armor, but a point may be reached at which *explosive attack will achieve useful lethality only by disruption.*

- Far out as it seems, the use of *"dynamic armor" to spoil KE attack and reduce energy transfer* is by no means unthinkable in the context of compound armor developments.

- Likewise armored vehicle designers may well resort to *"active protection" by upward-facing projectiles deploying smoke and/or "rope" and/or fragments* to counter the overhead threat, thus partially solving the problem of the extended frontal arc.

5

Protection against
nonballistic attack

The chemical threat

At one time there was considerable discussion of the possibility of
the Soviets using dedicated antivehicle chemical agents.
Nonspecific corrosive gases would be relatively slow acting; they
might have a part in a war of attrition, but seem irrelevant to the
pace and running time of current scenarios. For quick results the
obvious point of attack is the engine air intake. The enormous
quantities of air swallowed by modern tank engines provide a
mechanism for concentrating an agent, rather like the marine
food chain does radioactivity but many times faster. With
carbureted spark ignition engines some kind of smothering effect
might have been feasible; with compression ignition engines
several possibilities remain (Chapter 9).

If this type of attack was considered a worthwhile dilution of
the antipersonnel chemical effort or adopted as a "nonescalatory"
form of chemical warfare, it would not be easy to counter. Engine
air filtration is already a critical point in modern tank automotive
systems; the addition of a counterchemical filtration stage would
impair aspiration seriously and maybe critically. Likewise the
development of protective fuel and/or oil additives might prove
difficult, since the range of possible agents is large. In any event
the logistic repercussions of introducing additives would be
awkward to say the least. At present a commonsensical view
might be that this threat is too improbable to justify the effort
and tradeoff required to counter it.

A second specific chemical threat is attack on some or all
elements of the filters of the vehicle's NBC protective system.
Corrosion apart, there is no very evident means of attacking the
physical elements of these filters — nor indeed any great purpose
in so doing. But the stages in the filter which act chemically are

another thing again. These become saturated or spent after a time when fulfilling their normal function without interference; it should not be too difficult to accelerate this process. And some at least of the filter's substances, active carbon for instance, could be neutralized almost instantaneously. By contrast this filtration system is handling infinitesimal volumes of air compared with the engine intake, and some increase in the system's pumping power would be tolerable in the framework of modern vehicle electrics. Likewise the *raison d'être* of the system is the removal of chemical agents; the addition of an extra filter element is in tune with this. The question is, though, how far it is worth taking this or any other game of "counter measures to the nth".

The primary chemical threat is of course to the crew; although nonspecific this is a very serious one. Apart from the risk of being caught out by a new class of agent, there is no problem whatever about keeping toxic agents out of the armored envelope or about maintaining enough overpressure to allow at least one hatch to be opened without risk of contamination. Existing NBC collective protection systems are entirely adequate when the vehicle is out of contact; should the system break down, the crew would have time to don respirators and protective clothing.

In battle the combination of ballistic and chemical threat puts rather a different light on things. Most if not all major armies have now adopted the practice of wearing individual protective clothing, except maybe the respirator itself, inside armored vehicles when in contact, even if the threat of chemical warfare remains unfulfilled. The most evident but maybe the least important of the reasons for double protection is the risk of the armored envelope being broached. If the hole was too large for overpressure to be maintained, the chemical threat would be the least of the crew's worries! A more serious risk is breakdown of the collective system from direct battle damage or failure of its electrical supply. Additionally the crew may have to dismount in a hurry.

This policy of wearing individual protection has led some to question whether the resulting design penalties could not be partly offset by abandoning the collective protective system. Unfortunately designers and politicians are apt to forget that armored vehicles mostly have to be lived in as well as fought in. At physical and psychological levels alike, collective protection is an enormous asset to habitability in waiting periods and during out-of-contact movement. Keeping the vehicle's interior virtually dust-free improves reliability and life of the more delicate

subsystems and may even allow certain types or designs of device
to be used where they otherwise could not be. More importantly
still, once persistent chemical agents or radioactive dust enter an
armored vehicle, it is next to impossible to get rid of them; the
vehicle just stays contaminated.

Before full collective systems were introduced, the Americans
and the British fitted — or at least developed — small blower
units for each crewman. These units provided some prefiltration
and delivered air under pressure to the respirator intake through
a flexible hose. Since the principle of double protection has
become accepted, some collective systems have this facility too.
Now the mounting likelihood of mechanized operations with
a chemical or even a nuclear setting in subtropical climates
calls for an extension of this principle (page 20). Under Mideast
conditions a degree of air conditioning may be necessary to
prevent heat exhaustion if crews are to spend long periods
buttoned up and wearing protective clothing. The NBC
protection system provides an excellent basis for air conditioning
despite a rather alarming power requirement. An add-on pack of
this kind was in fact developed for the various versions of
Chieftain destined for Iran. I don't know how thoroughly modern
protective clothing has been trialed under subtropical conditions,
but I strongly suspect that wearing of it by crews would impose a
high risk of heat exhaustion in a rather short time. So it may well
be necessary to feed cooled and dried air from the collective
system direct to the interior of these suits.

All this is adding up to a considerable design penalty. Crew
stations and all instruments and controls must be suitable for use
by men wearing protective clothing including gloves and
respirators. What is more each man must be able to don and shed
protective clothing reasonably quickly and without risk of
damaging it, and to carry out personal decontamination
procedures on remounting. This problem will be more acute in
some of the novel configurations which tend to isolate the crew
from one another and provide no "communal" space like the
conventional loader's station. The collective protection system,
probably extended to include air conditioning, has to be
accommodated under armor and supplied with power. Its intake
has to be positioned where it can pick up air with a low dust
content and will not impair ballistic protection. Additionally it
may now be necessary to feed cooled and dried air to the crew's
protective suits, and maybe pressurized air to their respirators. In
the conventional tank layout and many others, this will involve a

choice of ducting air between turret and hull or using a combination of a collective system and individual blower units drawing air from the clean micro-environment.

Once again the message for the antiarmor side is clear. *Mounting a broad spectrum chemical threat against the crew will force the tank designer to make tradeoffs in other directions.* Whatever these are, they are going to degrade the tank's primary characteristics in some way. Dedicated chemical threats against engines or the filters of the NBC collective protective systems might significantly raise the ante.

The nuclear threat

Given that the filters of the collective protection system exclude fine particles, the discussion above also covers the threat of radiological contamination from fallout or ground bursts. The risk of the Warsaw Pact escalating land operations in Europe to tactical nuclear level seems to be increasing (page 17). Unfashionable as it may be to say so, nobody can I think reasonably doubt that both the Warsaw Pact and NATO would be far readier to go nuclear in a theater where population densities are low, the peoples are noncaucasian and the risk of escalation to a strategic exchange is hardly credible. Additionally we have postulated (page 14) that the Poor South, or at least the Islamic part of it, might well resort to any nuclear capability it possessed without too much regard for the consequences of retaliation. What is more, by developing and now also producing enhanced radiation weapons (the "neutron bomb") the United States has pitched in a dedicated antiarmor nuclear threat. So it may be timely to take a fresh look at the philosophy of protecting armored vehicles against immediate nuclear effects — in fact against immediate radiation, or more precisely still against *gamma radiation and neutrons.*

This kind of discussion has dropped so far into the background that we should maybe refresh our memories at qualitative level on a few of the basic facts. A "normal" fission weapon produces a certain mix of gamma radiation and neutron emission. Near ground zero the neutron threat is the more "intense" (if I may use that word loosely to avoid protracted explanations), but this decays very rapidly with distance (fig. 8). The gamma threat is less "intense" at the epicenter, but gamma radiation decays far more slowly with distance than neutron emission. So at a certain

distance from ground zero, gamma takes over from neutrons as
the greater threat. The distance of this crossover point from
ground zero evidently depends on yield. For near-"nominal"
yields (20 kilotons) the minimum range at which a tank survives
blast makes gamma the critical fraction of the radiation dose. For
low yield (unit kilotons) and fractional yield (under 1 kiloton)
weapons, neutrons are likely to be critical.

Published information about *enhanced radiation weapons* is
naturally scant. All kinds of tricks can now be played with nuclear
devices; it could be that the proportion and/or energy level of
neutrons in the total emission is raised. Probably, though, these
weapons simply yield much less blast and heat flash in proportion
to radiation as a whole. Thus the critical range for armored
vehicles is reduced to the point where neutrons dominate —
whence the popular name. Since both sides' "normal" tactical
nuclear weapons are likely to be low yield, maybe 1-5 kilotons, the
probability of neutrons being the critical type of radiation is now
rather high.

Gamma radiation and neutrons are quite different in nature,
so it is not surprising that they need to be countered in quite
different ways. The attenuation of gamma depends on the density
of the material it traverses. We can thus think of the "half
thickness" of a material — the thickness that reduces gamma by
50% — as a function of the material's weight per unit area. This
half thickness concept also allows for any "soft" secondary gamma
produced.

The ability of substances to stop neutrons depends on a specific
property of atoms known as *neutron capture cross section* — a
concept very easily envisioned in terms of tennis balls and
different sized rackets. Capture of a neutron may also trigger
secondary radiation. Among elements with high neutron capture
cross-sections are hydrogen and boron. Hydrogen makes up a
large proportion of the atoms in fuel, water and plastics; and
boron can be very easily introduced into most plastics (page 68).

Hitherto the philosophy has been acceptance of the fact that a
tank was a better place than most to be when a nuclear weapon
went off but that not much could be done to make it better still.
This made entire sense given gamma as the main threat and steel
armor. A neutron-dominated attack and compound armor adds
up to a whole new ballgame. It could be that maximum use
within the array of materials with high neutron capture cross-
sections, notably hydrogenous liquids (page 70), combined with
a boronated polyethylene inner skin would enhance protection

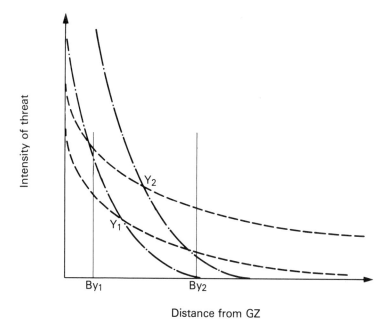

Distance from GZ

8. Gamma radiation and neutron threats. At ground zero neutron effects (*chain-dotted lines*) are critical, but these decay with distance more rapidly than gamma (*broken lines*), crossing over as indicated for a very low yield (Y1) and a higher yield (Y2). Suppose B_{Y1} and B_{Y2} (*full vertical lines*) to be the radii at which an armored vehicle survives blast at these yields. Then for yield Y1 neutrons are critical, for Y2 gamma. In an enhanced radiation weapon the blast survival radius B is evidently reduced (*full vertical lines moved to the left*) with respect to the radiation effects. It may also be that the neutron effect is increased with respect to the gamma (*chain-dotted lines moved to the right*)

against neutrons in a tactically significant degree with only minor tradeoffs or — for once — even none at all. Only when this possibility has been looked at technically could one say whether it might influence other aspects of protection. But the perspective I suggested above — optimization without tradeoffs — feels about right.

Mines

As we shall see (Chapter 14) antitank mines are apt to come in two kinds — disruptive and penetrative — and two sizes — laid and scatterable ("minelets"). One must surely discount the massive mines often used by irregular forces, which may contain 250 kg or more of explosive and cause disruption, the more so since they are apt to be detonated by remote control right under the vehicle's belly. Likewise both hand lifting and clearance systems like explosive hose, artillery fire and dedicated vehicles are irrelevant here. The only types of clearance we need to look at because they involve tradeoffs in other characteristics of the tank are plows and the like.

Here there is a flat conflict of evidence. The Soviets have developed what purports to be a highly successful series of plows and rollers fitted to a proportion of tanks in normal combat subunits. The latest known versions, KMT4 and 5 (pl. 12), are issued on a scale of 30 and 3 respectively per designated "break-in" regiment, or around one per tank platoon. And the Soviet Army has SOPs to match.

A great deal of similar work, among it the copying of Soviet devices, has been done in the West with complete lack of success. Let us suppose for a moment that the Soviet devices work. Evidently they seriously hamper mobility, not least because they increase width by as much as 0.75 m, length by over 3 m in the case of the KMT5 and weight by up to 7.5 t. My subjective view is that this penalty may be justified for a force which is on the strategic and operational offensive and which has enough numerical superiority to earmark specialized tank units. It is not justified for a numerically inferior defender.

So we come down to looking at passive protection. The most probable threat is now the *track-cutting mine of scatterable size*. Here the general disruptive effect is nil. By contrast, cutting of or at least severe damage to a track link cannot be prevented. In the days of lumbering monsters strengthening of the track might just have been worthwhile to force the other side to scatter larger and thus fewer minelets. But with modern levels of mobility the effect on track dynamics — not to mention weight — would be disastrous. *Deliberately laid mines* are hard to protect against directly. The traditional modest thickening up of the front half of the belly can easily be countered by multipressure fuzes. Likewise it is customary to angle the lower hull sides in to keep the side/belly welds out of the primary blast cone of a circular mine going off under the track. But this is partially countered by laying long mines, like the British bar mine, transversely to the expected path of the vehicle. Additionally both these protective measures are nullified by remote fuzes.

Remote fuzes, however, add significantly to the logistic load and greatly to the effort required for laying. So they are more likely to be associated with *penetrative or shaped charge mines*.

The laid shaped charge mine with one or more electromechanical remote fuzes is almost the only type of attack on a tank that offers a calculable chance of a K kill; and there is no means of protecting against it. Shaped charges with gross overmatch, both circular and linear in form, are well within the size, cost and effort limits of practical mines. The attack is normal to the belly; and the combination of the vehicle's ground clearance and burial of the mine gives a standoff of 600-700 mm on which charge design can easily be optimized.

Shaped charge minelets are designed to roll on landing and settle the right way up, or possibly to stick into the ground like mini-javelins. The first type evidently cannot have a mechanical fuze, and a fuze rod would make the second rather conspicuous. So there is a strong case, both with these minelets and with large shaped charge mines, for an influence fuze. This has the added advantage that it will detonate only underneath the vehicle, where the signature is roughly uniform; a laterally remoted fuze has an even chance of detonating the mine underneath the vehicle or to one side of it unless each fuze is linked to two mines. Influence mine fuzes represent about the only use for an armored vehicle's magnetic signature (page 49). But this signature could rather easily be simulated by a forward- and downward-looking device mounted on the hull front, which would detonate the mine harmlessly in front of the vehicle.

Clearance devices apart, we can thus define two areas where the armored vehicle designer has room to maneuver in countering mines. One is in outwitting the shaped charge minelet. The second is in localizing damage from large track-cutting mines. There is a divergence of Western and Soviet practice here. The West pays a penalty in height and weight to mount everything, notably the crew, clear of the belly. The belly plate can be severely dished without affecting the tank's performance, and no undamped shock accelerations are transmitted to the crew or the more sensitive subsystems. The Soviets mount seats and major subsystems direct onto the floor, evidently relying on clearing mines with their various devices. Looked at this way the choice between Western protective techniques and Soviet emphasis on clearance is a near-run thing.

6

System survivability[1]

Having explored in some depth the present and predictable characteristics of armored vehicle targets, I now want to draw up a balance sheet in an effort to see where within the broad and complex spectrum of the attack of armor the payoffs might lie. First, however, I must digress from this narrower field to reemphasize yet again that the greatest single factor in mobile operations is one which lies outside the scope of this book — *air*. The fixed-wing threat is a nonspecific one but has a high and mounting antiarmor potential in its own right; and the air situation will in some measure influence the operation of attack helicopters. Trials have suggested that this interaction is less than might be supposed; but certainly the kind of bold "top cover" tactics the Soviets seem to envision for large machines like Hind D and F would be suicidal in an adverse local air situation.

Unfortunately this key area is also the one of greatest disparity between the Warsaw Pact and NATO, at least where tactical air defense is concerned. No solution is perfect, and few people as yet have much feel for the impact of modern electronic warfare. But the Soviets look to have got it right at the levels of doctrine, force structure and hardware alike. The way they are equipped and organized and the way they deploy leave no doubt that *the goal of Soviet tactical air defense is the protection of their maneuver force.* NATO faces a numerically superior opponent operating on central lines; the Alliance's failure to solve the tactical air defense problem correctly — or indeed at all — puts its maneuver force on a hiding to nothing.

This said, we need to weigh up the relative importance for the future of direct and indirect protection. Compound armor is a notable advance, a major swing in favor of the tank. But to the very extent that it neutralizes the least lethal and energetic mode of attack, shaped charge, it may militate against system

---

1 Being in effect a summary, this chapter is not cross-referred.

survivability by encouraging extremely powerful KE attack and by channeling explosive attack into forms that will release rather large amounts of energy, maybe within the confined space of the armor array. As I indicated earlier, I see the next step as a *"battle of the burster plate"*, a move away from the external pack and main inner shell towards an external structural and protective plate with a sophisticated backup system comprehending reserves of fuel and water and hardened major subsystems. What we now think of as the "array" may become a specialized, possibly changeable insert behind the main plate.

Advances in the bulk-weight effectiveness of armor will be partly offset by lateral and vertical extension of the conventional frontal arc. This may even lead to a reduction in existing levels of frontal protection against surface-to-surface attack. Massive shaped charges delivered by ATGM from helicopters will continue to overmatch any foreseeable protective system. Another threat which we shall be evaluating later in this book lies in dedicated artillery shell, submunitions and short-range downward-looking attack — all directed against the vehicle's roof. My guess is that the contest between attack and direct protection will remain a dingdong one — the more so since, whether the local attack succeeds or fails, increased power of attack inevitably reduces the chance of system survival. Interpreting this in a rather different way, ballpark figures for F kill lethality of matching attack will most probably go on ranging between 30 and 70% and meaning around the 50% (minus) mark.

It is in the sphere of indirect protection that we can expect a dramatic swing in favor of the armored vehicle, because there are three major trends marching hand in hand. For so modern a phenomenon the tank generates an astonishing amount of emotion and entrenched conservatism,[2] even maybe among the farsighted Germans and the rational Soviets. Now, though, military opinion is on the move. The American story of MBT70 — XM803 — XM1 (Abrams) is a cliffhanger despite its relatively happy ending. It is hard to believe that the Bundeswehr is exactly enchanted with the Wagnerian weight and bulk of Leopard 2. And the British cancellation of the MBT80 project, linked to a surge of opinion among British armor officers now coming into decision-making positions, are hopeful signs that the ultimate proponent of the slugfest is starting to waver. The existence of the

2 I am indebted for this insight to Bryan Watkins, in his review of *Tank Warfare* in the *RUSI Journal.*

HIMAG test vehicle and its German counterparts is a milestone in itself.

But the most important two facts in the whole Western armored scene at this time are these. *The HIMAG test vehicle is made up of proven automotive subsystems* — the engine and transmission of the rejected version of XM1 and a hydro-pneumatic suspension modified for experimental purposes from one developed for the M60 series. Second, HIMAG's demonstrated mobility *reduces movement exposure times to a point where they overlap acquisition and even engagement times,* while the vehicle's agility looks like *posing severe problems in hitting it.* If we suppose that a certain antiarmor weapon system under battle conditions has an 80% chance of acquiring a moving M60 target, a 70% hit chance and 50% lethality, then we have a figure of rather under 30%, say between 3 and 4 to 1 against, that a potential target will suffer an F kill. If we reduce the first two figures for a HIMAG-type target to 25% (acquisition) and 50% (hit), we have an overall figure of 6% or over 15 to 1 against. Even if we discount this to 10 to 1 it remains too striking to need comment.

If the moving target is going to get much harder to hit, *the firing tank may altogether cease to present a direct fire target to surface-to-surface systems.* We saw that the firing exposure time of a tank first observed when it moves up to fire is lower than the engagement time of its opponent. The concept exemplified by the Swedish Marder/105-mm test vehicle (pl. 2) would be based on technology that is not just proven but well established. If the Swedes are running this option as second or equal first string in the S Tank successor stakes, we can take it that the practical problems have been exhaustively probed. And Western user opinion is at last on the move in a direction that makes abandonment of the vehicle commander's superior position at least thinkable.

Some figures recalled from long ago[3] suggest that the tank targets offered to a defender might be made up of two turret targets, putatively firing tanks, to one hull-up target, probably a mover. I would expect Soviet densities and tactics to shift this ratio somewhat in the direction of moving tanks; and if we add in the 75% of nontank priority hard targets in the Warpac mix, we arrive at a proportion around 1 to 1. Suppose the chance of a

---

3 I hope I have not misremembered these. They link in my mind with the early fifties, and either with range of engagement trials or with weapon effectiveness studies; but I would have no idea where to start looking for them.

potential moving target being killed to be reduced by a factor of 4 and firing targets to be largely eliminated. The advances in indirect protection now predictable for the nineties improve system survivability in face of surface attack by a factor of around 8. No matter whether this factor is 5 or 10 or even 3, it wreaks havoc with the exchange rates on which NATO's hopes of winning the antitank battle are based.

Evidently like all other swings this imbalance will be redressed, maybe even before it happens. The ways of redressing it, taking account of compound armor arrangements too, stand out rather clearly as signposts for antiarmor development.

The *primary surface-to-surface antiarmor system* will be a KE gun-ammunition system backed up by an excellent, more particularly a fast fire-control system. The key advance to be looked for in fire control is *automatic target acquisition.* This primary system, along with any lesser systems of the same kind, must be equally well adapted to delivering fast, accurate fire out to full antitank range with explosive munitions. This capability is needed both to inflict P kills on priority hard targets other than weapon platforms, and to neutralize "nontargets". The key advance in firepower *per se* would be *"over the crest" direct fire* against these nontargets. We will explore this particular piece of Irish later; from first principles any such capability would have to be based on explosive attack.

Sophisticated manportable systems (like STAFF), capable of attacking the weaker aspects of the target from a fire position within the target's frontal arc, are evidently most desirable, both in their own right as a counter to compound armor and as a threat that is highly embarrassing to the armored vehicle designer. They remain an unproven if not unknown quantity. In any event the continuing validity of *simple hand-held shaped charge systems fired from outside the frontal arc* should not be overlooked.

The importance of *indirect antiarmor fire* is evidently on the increase. Primary artillery munitions like Copperhead raise a number of questions which we shall examine later. But cluster projectiles — shells or bombs — with all types of submunitions are extremely interesting. Here we need to consider both immediate effect munitions delivering near-vertical shaped charge and KE attack; and track-cutting and shaped charge minelets.

The *attack helicopter's* task is evidently to deliver massive shaped charge and maybe disruptive attack over as wide an arc and at as high an angle of arrival as tactically feasible. But this

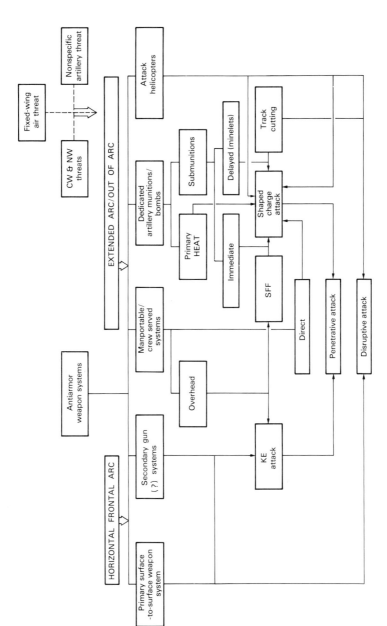

9. Antiarmor weapon system complex

88

threat is subject to severe counterthreats in the shape of tactical air defense, electronic warfare and target response. Target marking and/or autonomous missiles remain a possibility; but our examination of target characteristics suggests that the third of these counterthreats alone is enough to knock a considerable dent in the credibility of the attack helicopter's part in the battle between mechanized main forces. *It looks like the helicopter needs to be able to guide command link missiles while remaining in rotor defilade.*

PART 2

The Attack of Armor

7

Penetrative attack

Quite apart from the fact that it has been excellently done already[1] I see little merit in an historical approach to the penetrative attack of armor. It is enough to note that, thanks partly to common origins in German work before and during World War II, an extensive and largely agreed technological base is shared by the United States, European NATO members and the Soviet Union. The fact that all concerned have taken over half a century to get where they are today is due on the one hand to the point of departure — full caliber spin-stabilized shot and shell — and on the other to problems of engineering, notably production engineering, and raw materials.

Arguing from first principles, if we want to punch a hole in a piece of material with the least possible expenditure of energy, we need to pack this energy into the smallest possible area. This is true no matter how we produce the energy and no matter whether it is pure kinetic energy (KE) or a mixture of KE and thermal ("chemical") energy (CE). So in the KE case we start by thinking of an infinitely long needle of infinitely small diameter made of infinitely dense material and traveling at the speed of light. Or in the CE case of a jet of similar proportions and velocity, in which lack of density is made up for by available thermal energy. In remarking that neither of these notions precisely constitutes a practical weapon system, we should also note that, even if it did, its chance of achieving any damage after penetration would be rather small. It would be a needle in a haystack-sized wax image. We should have fallen into "the trap ... of demonstration of expertise in attacking the armor envelope".[2]

---

1 Summed up in: Backofen and Williams, "Soviet kinetic energy penetrators — technology/deployment", and Backofen, "Kinetic energy penetrators versus armor": see Bibliography.
2 Backofen, *op. cit.*

Attack mechanism

We observed earlier one difference between the KE penetrator (fig. 10a) and the shaped charge jet (fig. 10b) — that the jet might be prevented from developing its full energy (page 67). A second evident difference is that the heat contained in the jet probably brings the armor material to or near the point of fusion, thus greatly reducing its mechanical resistance to pressure from the kinetic energy of the jet tip. But as far as is known the mechanism of penetration of both types of attack is rather similar. It can best be seen in the case of an attack that just fails to penetrate (fig. 10c).[2]

> *Stage 1.*   On initial impact both penetrator and plate will undergo compressive shock loading of an intense but rather unpredictable kind. One can probably consider this impact phase as lasting until the shoulder of the penetrator has passed the outer surface of the target. During this phase any one of several phenomena may occur. One is *shot shatter*, compressive failure of the leading part of the projectile or the whole of it. Another is the initiation of *shot breakup,* associated with oblique attack and caused by nonuniform compressive loading across the shoulder section.[3] A third — and a key one in oblique attack — is *setting up* (Fig. 10d). This depends on the ogive angle (a, fig. 10a(1)); sometimes on the presence and nature of a windshield or ballistic cap; or again on a penetrating cap now known as a *plug* contained between the sheath and the core of the penetrator. We can envision a ballistic cap or plug of ductile material deforming on impact to build a collar round the nose of the penetrator. Likewise we can picture the penetrator pivoting about its tip on impact. If the projectile is flying true, either or both these effects will tend to "turn in" towards the normal a projectile which strikes obliquely[4] and so help counter the effects of sloped armor. Once stage 2 starts, flow of the target material may enlarge this "collar", thus contributing to the setting up effect. So stage 1 may have any of three outcomes — the penetrator may be broken up or destabilized; it may be turned in; or initial impact

---

3 In their conventional AP/HE projectiles with a bursting charge, the Soviets use two grooves, known as "localizers", to protect the weaker sections at the rear of the projectile from this effect.

4 By contrast a projectile with an excessive yaw or angle of incidence may turn away from the normal, topple and be deflected.

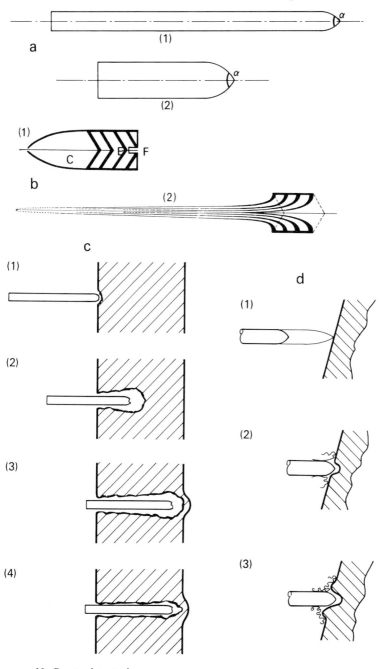

10. Penetrative attack
    (a) (1) and (2) Long rod and spin-stabilized KE penetrators
    (b) Shaped charge principle: C = cone, E = explosive charge, F = fuze
    (c) (1)-(4) Penetration mechanism
    (d) (1)-(3) Setting up effect

may be uneventful. Shaped charge jets are less liable to surface destabilization of the tip, probably because they are fluid and resistance on impact is reduced by the thermal effect. By contrast they are more susceptible than KE penetrators to deflection of the jet and/or destabilization down its length at the interfaces of arrays (page 67).

Stage 2. This main stage of penetration consists in the application of a calculable pressure by the jet or penetrator to the target material and the progressive transfer to the target of the energy of attack. The basic mechanism is one of hydrodynamic flow of the target material, both within the yield point (elastic) and beyond it (plastic). A notable feature is that because of cavitation, the sides of a solid penetrator are not as a rule subject to friction. With a jet, energy losses are likely to occur from turbulent flow in the boundary layer and superfluous heat transfer.

Stage 3. In the third stage of "afterflow" the target material continues to deform after the penetrator or jet has spent its energy and come to rest or dissipated.

Stage 4. Finally, the target material reasserts itself to some extent.

In a successful attack penetration is completed at some point during stage 2. The first two stages are of course repeated at each interface of an array, the ultimate residual energy of attack being available for behind armor effects. When penetration succeeds, the back bulge in the armor (fig. 10c(3)) does not reassert itself (stage 4) but breaks away to form spall — the first element in target response (page 60).

With an understanding of this basic mechanism we can go on to consider the characteristics of KE penetrators and shaped charge warheads; the restrictions they may impose on the systems projecting them; and ways of improving the lethality of penetrative attack.

KE penetrators

The *length/diameter ratio* (L/D) of a solid spin-stabilized projectile is limited to around 4:1 (fig. 10a(2)). Fin stabilization allows L/D ratios up to 20:1, the limiting factor probably being stability against toppling on impact. A switch to fin stabilization thus allows the *subcaliber ratio* (penetrator diameter/gun caliber) to be reduced from 40-45% to 30% or less without undue sacrifice of penetrator mass. Theoretically it would be possible to fire and stabilize penetrators of much higher L/D ratios, as exemplified by the longbow arrow. But the gain in penetration from concentration of the attack into a smaller area starts to be outweighed by acute loss of lethality; and the mechanical strength of the penetrator on firing and on impact starts to present problems. State-of-the-art penetrators have L/D ratios of between 12 and 16 to 1 and subcaliber ratios of 30-35%.

Leaving aside add-ons like windshields, fins or kill mechanisms, there are three basic options for material and construction. The classical one is sintered tungsten carbide sheathed in steel; this has the advantage that the sheath can be made to form the windshield and a cunningly shaped plug of ductile material enclosed in this to help setting up. Sources conflict, but the 125-mm APDSFS penetrator of the Soviet T72 tank gun is probably sheathed tungsten carbide; it has an L/D ratio of around 12:1. By contrast its predecessor for the 115-mm T62 tank gun was steel. Although the tungsten carbide technology is fully at their disposal, the American DARPA/ARES team started with steel for their "long rods". They have now moved to depleted uranium (DU), a material previously used in American work on spin-stabilized penetrators.[5] Since DU offers several clear-cut advantages in terms of density and ease of engineering, it is very hard to know why the Soviets have not (seemingly) opted for it. They have the technology[6] and surely cannot lack the material.

Fin-stabilized penetrators can be fired with equal ease from rifled guns, using a slipping driving band on the sabot, or from smoothbore tubes. Since fin-stabilized projectiles in fact require a *slow* spin for optimum stability, penetrators designed for rifled guns have straight fins and acquire this spin by residual friction across the driving band. Smoothbore projectiles have a very slight pitch on their fins and/or have spin imparted to them at the moment of separation of the sabot. It may thus be that

---

5 At one time the media dubbed this earlier project as "the atomic tank-killer" or such. It needs to be spelled out that *depleted* uranium has near-zero radioactivity and there is *no* "atomic" effect. There is a pyrophoric effect behind armor, which we will touch on a little later.

6 The Germans in fact had the technology back in World War II. When they ran out of tungsten, a large quantity of uranium was earmarked for antitank projectiles (Backofen/Williams, *op. cit.*).

"decoupled" projectiles fired from rifled tubes are marginally the more reliable and consistent.

I shall not discuss separation of the sabot because this no longer seems to present any problem. But long rod penetrators offer two interesting options for ammunition design. One, used by the Soviets in their 125-mm smoothbore, is the inclusion of a "secondary cartridge". This consists of a supplementary propellant change in a bag or combustible case which is attached to the projectile, fitting into the spaces between the fins and between penetrator and sabot. It presumably travels up the bore with the projectile like a kind of in-tube boost motor. I do not know whether this trick has been or can be played with a decoupled round. If it can it offers extremely interesting possibilities by way of increasing the charge weight within a chamber standardized on existing conventional KE and explosive munitions (Chapter 10).

The other option, used in fact in the DARPA/ARES project, is to reduce the length of the complete round almost to that of the penetrator. This offers notable design advantages, specially in association with autoloaders and high rates of fire.

Shaped charge warheads

Although not applied to antiarmor weapon systems until the late thirties, the shaped, hollow or "beehive"[7] charge principle has been around quite a while. The technology and penetrative performance is well known and I shall not probe it in detail. One great feature is lightness; a 1.5-2 kg charge of 75 mm diameter easily penetrates any arrangement of steel armor feasible on a tank. For a given design, penetration is a function of cone diameter and the thickness/obliquity relationship follows the cosine law.[8] As mentioned above, shaped charge is far less subject to destabilization or inconsistency of performance during the first stage of penetration; by the same token it is normally unaffected by spaced plates of conventional steel armor.

Shaped charges can be custom-built with some precision. Up to the advent of compound armor it was customary to design for suboptimal penetration and enhanced lethality — in plain words

---

7 This is the name given to shaped charges in field and civil engineering, *not* to be confused with the United States Beehive flechette shell.

8 i.e. sloping makes no difference to the weight of conventional armor needed to protect a given vertical area against horizontal attack — more generally, a given area against normal (0° obliquity) attack.

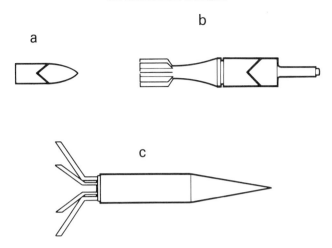

11. HEAT projectiles: (a) Classical ogive. (b) Spike nose, HEATFS (rigid fins). (c) Long nose-cone, HEATFS (collapsible fins, rocket-assisted)

a thicker jet making a larger hole. Kill mechanisms (of which more in a moment) aside, there are four main design variables. The first is *cone angle* (C, fig. 10b) which we might think of as loosely analogous to the ogive or nosecone angle of a KE penetrator — although the shaped charge cone points away from the target, of course! The second is the use or omission of a *liner* (on the front of the cone), thickness of the liner and the choice of liner material between copper and ductile copper alloys on the one hand and aluminum/light alloys on the other. The third variable is the inclusion or otherwise of a conical or paraboloid resonator on the back of the charge; the tamping and focusing effect of this is self-evident. A variant in vogue at one time was the use of a backup shaped charge, a wide-angle cone or shallow parabola in form, fitting the back of the main charge and detonating fractionally later.

The fourth parameter, *standoff,* derives from the chosen combination of the first three. Unless I misremember, the tip of a shaped charge jet tuned for optimum penetration can reach velocities upwards of 9000 m/sec (roughly Mach 27). Evidently it will take a finite time and space to do so. Because of the configuration of a shaped charge, the classical ogive of a shell or the nosecone of a low velocity rocket will provide a standoff of 2-3 calibers; the spike nose of a high velocity rigid-fin-stabilized shell for a tank gun rather more; and the nose cone of a flipout-finned projectile up to 5 calibers (fig. 11).[9] For cone diameters over 100 mm this is probably enough, but in some ATGMs the shaped charge warhead is set back and the space in front of it occupied by a donut-shaped electronics pack with a hole large enough not to interfere with the jet — a doubly convenient arrangement if the missile has a homing or TV head. This problem of standoff is the first constraint imposed by shaped charges on ammunition design.

The second constraint lies in the way shaped charge penetration is degraded by spin (fig. 12).[10] This degradation can be overcome by providing the cone with a liner fluted (like the teeth of a ratchet wheel) to induce opposed spin; but this adds up to an awkward production problem, and small irregularities in the fluting are apt to spoil jet formation. In the French *obus G* ("G shell") the shaped charge floats on bearings inside a spin-stabilized casing. The United States development of a decoupled HEATFS round for the 105-mm (rifled) tank gun was one of the most protracted and agonizing minor programs I ever encountered. It finally achieved complete success shortly after the Soviets fielded their T62 with its 115-mm smoothbore firing APDSFS and HEATFS. Fin stabilization is also preferred for terminally guided shaped charge artillery shell, both to avoid degradation and to eliminate the guidance synchronization problems associated with fast spin; these projectiles too can be satisfactorily fired from conventional rifled tubes in the decoupled mode. As with APDSFS this caters for the slow spin[11] needed to iron out the effects of imbalances arising from production tolerances. Otherwise this spin is provided by canting the fins.

Kill mechanisms

We already noted (page 60) that the lethality of KE penetrators peaks at, say, $20 \pm \%$ overmatch and then falls off rapidly, while that of shaped charge normally increases with overmatch until a quasi-disruptive effect is achieved. Over the past decade or two lethality has proved to be the most obstinate of the parameters for the attack of armor — aside, that is, from acquisition time which designer and user alike are only too glad to let slip discreetly away

---

9 Scaled from German 120-mm Mz round and 75-mm rocket-assisted Helbard round; from Germershausen and Romer, "Flügelstabilisierte Geschosse", *see* Bibliography.
10 Germershausen and Romer, *op. cit.*
11 Of the order of 10^1 rpm as against the 10^4 rpm of spin stabilization.

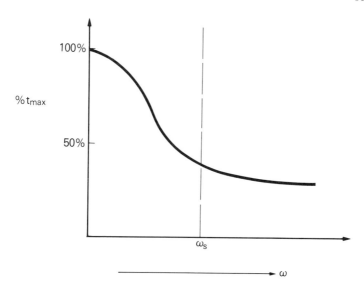

100%

% t_max

50%

ω_s

ω

12. Degradation of shaped charge with spin

from the party as the other's baby. On published information I would still ballpark the F kill lethality figure for KE attack at $(40+)\%$; and for shaped charge around the 30% mark at the kind of margin its own gun would have over a conventionally armored tank.

We saw that, before compound armor, shaped charge was often degraded to achieve a net boost in lethality. Likewise it could be necessary to bring KE penetrators back from L/D ratios of 16 or 18 to 1 towards the 12:1 of the Soviet 125-mm APDSFS or even less. Here maybe the user needs to step in, though. The shot designer, faced with substantial overmatch, may be tempted to fatten up his rod so as to get nearer to the lethality called for. This is fine as long as there is no risk whatever of failing to penetrate. But now it is the user's turn to play the Victorian bridegroom. F kill or no, the chaos caused inside a tank by a penetration of the fighting compartment is utter; and the sag in morale of a tank or antitank crew which hits with no apparent effect is deep.

Here, though, I want to consider mechanisms included in KE and shaped charge projectiles to enhance lethality without trading off penetration. At first sight making the KE penetrator of DU gives it an inbuilt kill mechanism in the shape of pyrophoric effect. Problem is trials suggest that this seeming plus-value is exciting, but negligible in real terms. So we need to look at the penetrator's two ends. The Germans back in World War II[12] experimented with rather blunt penetrators and ballistic caps of magnesium or solid aluminum aimed at an incendiary effect. The magnesium would flash spontaneously at high temperatures, and the aluminum might be expected to give a thermitelike effect[13] on breaking up and mingling with ferrous armor spall. These caps do not seem to have worked much. Later evidence suggests that the material would have dispersed on impact, set on the outer surface of the armor (*cf.* fig. 10d) or burned up early in stage 2 penetration (page 96).

It is hard to envision a bursting charge being accommodated in the tail of a long rod penetrator or achieving much if it was. But until they went for long rods, the Soviets used a bursting charge in the base of almost all their AP shot at calibers of 45 mm upwards. We are talking here of spin-stabilized penetrators with L/D ratios of 3 or 4 to 1, and there is evidence to suggest that detonation might occur during stage 2 penetration at a depth of around one shot diameter.[14] So it is hard to see how this small charge could contribute with HE or incendiary effect to a roughly matching attack. What charges like this can do is to make a gross overmatch, like 100-mm APC/T[15] *v* M113, extremely lethal in terms of F and P kills alike. I guess, though, the next chapter is the place to have the AP/HE argument.

Any attempt to increase the lethality of shaped charge is going some way or other to degrade its penetration, and this may or may not be affordable in face of compound armor. My personal guess is that it may pay to go for the highest possible degree of overmatch (residual energy) and leave it at that. We already mentioned playing with the cone angle to thicken the jet. Some success has been achieved in making the residual jet fan out after penetration. But this depends on fairly narrow assumptions about the degree of overmatch; and the fanned out "spray" does not seem too effective either in causing damage or in triggering secondary effects.

A more promising approach, fairly widely employed where overmatch permits, is to use a liner and arrange for this to form a smaller number of larger particles than would otherwise be the

12 On their "composite rigid" projectiles, otherwise known as "arrowhead" or "*Pfeilgeschoss*".

13 Thermite is the mixture of powdered aluminum and iron oxide used in welding and in incendiary devices.

14 Backofen/Williams, *op. cit.*

15 T = tracer. This was the main antiarmor nature of the Soviet T54/55 tank gun.

case, along with a larger than normal "plug". The hope is that these particles and the plug will cool and harden enough to ricochet and generally behave like fragments of shot and spall. Again, I think it was the Swiss who designed a shaped charge warhead with a quite separate follow-through KE projectile fired from a kind of miniature "gun" back of the shaped charge. Trouble was they never, so far as I know, persuaded it to go through the hole.

All in all it looks like the most effective way of improving "engagement lethality" is to go for multiple strikes. The DARPA/ARES project in fact provides for large-caliber automatic fire. But here again user common sense needs to step in. Firing 105-mm or even 75-mm ammunition in bursts adds up to increased complexity, reduced battle endurance and a whole nest of logistic problems. I can envision circumstances in which I would face up to these problems to get improved *hit* chance. But I cannot see any user accepting them just to turn a genuine penetration into a textbook F kill. Small-caliber multiple strikes are another thing again; we shall be looking at them in the next chapter.

8

Disruptive and mixed attack

Historically attack and protection of warships and armored vehicles alike focused mainly on penetration of the armored envelope and achievement of primary and secondary effects behind armor. So we have first to consider both the meaning of "disruption" and the need for it. The phrase from which I have drawn the term is "total disruption", understood as "blowing a ship out of the water" or "blowing a vehicle to pieces". But as I see it, disruptive attack is about any of four things.

External damage, serious and widespread enough to make the vehicle inoperable to the extent of an F kill. "F" needs to be interpreted here to cover not just guns or launchers but sensors and fire-control communications links (in AD vehicles for instance).[1]

Structural/subsystem damage. This is about energy transfer and shock accelerations and is also an element in penetrative KE attack (page 54). Racking forces may cause structural deformation or even failure. (We noted, for instance, how the Wehrmacht's Pzkw III and IV were apt to come apart at the seams.) Shock accelerations high enough and long enough in duration to defeat resilient mountings may cause internal structural failure, most of all in optical, electronic and optronic subsystems.

For purposes of argument, we need to draw a somewhat arbitrary distinction between the above effect, which will often be primarily due to kinetic energy, and the next.

---

1 The term "E" (equipment) kill is sometimes used, but logically these systems are concerned with firepower.

Local structural collapse. This effect can best be envisioned in terms of blowing in a plate on a light armored vehicle — the surest way of getting a P kill — or stripping to its base a substantial area of a compound armor array. It is essentially an explosive effect. Defeat of compound armor may require a second strike in the same area.

Total disruption. This amounts to gross overkill; like all forms of K kill it has to be regarded as a bonus — but an important one because of morale effect. It may be caused by kinetic energy. I have seen an inert 120-mm trials shell fired from Chieftain at 670 m/sec take the turret off the target tank. Records of the Arab–Israeli wars suggest that Soviet turrets come off rather easily too; in fact the Israelis deliberately inerted or removed the warheads of Maverick air-to-surface missiles so that the impact knocked out the crew, maybe removing the turret, but left the tank fit for reclamation and reuse. Or again total disruption may result from explosive effect. In conventional tanks this is normally associated with tamping by an HE pocket (fig. 13); but the probable effect of a shell with high brisance bursting inside a compound armor array gives rise to interesting speculation.

Having set up the how of disruptive attack we need to look at the why. The general support role is always with us, specially with Mideast scenarios looming; but looking a development cycle ahead I can see three other reasons. The first is the number of *nontank hard targets*. If we got our target priorities right (page 30), the key targets are apt to be helicopters, or relatively lightly armored vehicles whose main importance rests either in unarmored excrescences like antennas or in the men they carry. Penetrative attack against choppers is a nonstarter; the hit

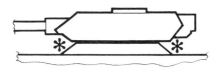

13. HE pocket

chance at the most probable ranges is absurdly low, and even if it was not, lethality would be negligible for KE attack and low for a shaped charge.

By contrast in the current state of antitank missilery a shell detonating on the ground or against a tree or building near the target stands a good chance of achieving neutralization and maybe damage at the longer ranges.[2] For reasons we saw in the last chapter, penetrative attack is not a good way of dealing with the priority vehicle targets. Even shaped charge is far from optimal; but the characteristic of these targets and the types of damage required make them a natural for disruptive attack.

As to heavy armored vehicles, I have gone along with the general opinion that penetrative attack will keep marginally ahead of protection — or at least that massive KE attack will produce a low chance of system survival. But with everybody into the compound armor ballgame and the Soviets so strong on materials technology we cannot count on this. Here, for once, I agree with the traditional British view that NATO must have a disruptive mode of attack as a backup — though HEP as we now know it is no longer relevant. This option may be needed either as an alternative in its own right or as the first phase in a composite attack (strip — kill).[3]

The third and strongest reason is the "nontarget" (pl. 2b and page 86). KE attack is evidently out. If gun-based antiarmor weapon systems go on carrying HEATFS at all, they certainly cannot carry a "fast HEAT" for direct-fire targets and a "slow HEAT" to get over the crest; and in any event the angle of attack would be unfavorable. Likewise neutralization by blinding fire on the crest — the only expedient now available — is not enough. If however, we take the upper part of the Marder/105-mm test vehicle (pl. 2a) as a typical configuration for an external mounting and note that the principle depends on a top sensor array, we can see that the superstructure is particularly vulnerable to disruptive attack. The chance of an F kill should be reasonably high; and the chance of knocking the sensors out and forcing the vehicle to come turret up should be very high indeed.

---

2 Earlier I said I disbelieved the estimate that an engagement of this kind could succeed at 2000 m, but the minimum range is largely a matter of the relative speeds of shell and missiles.

3 See also *Tank Warfare*, page 90; *Mechanized Infantry*, page 83.

The KE element

I included the word "mixed" in the title of this chapter on two counts. One was that disruptive attack may penetrate targets it overmatches, specially if it is designed to get in among compound armor arrays. The second was to remind myself and the reader of the part played by kinetic energy in the modes of attack we normally regard as explosive. I mentioned two examples just now, and systematic trials with inert 105-mm or 120-mm shell against both tanklike and light armored targets might be very interesting.[4]

So I make no apology for reverting to and extending my favorite example. KE attack from a modern tank gun just about equals in energy an M60 tank traveling at 50-55 kph. A 105-mm HE/HEP shell or a 40-kg missile averaging Mach 1 equivalates to a European family car traveling at the same speed — no mean impact! Even if this kinetic energy is applied to the target only instantaneously before the projectile detonates, its effect is by no means negligible.

Maybe the most forceful evidence of the KE effect in disruptive attack was the results of trials of the gatlinglike Vulcan gun with its very high cyclic rate against a tank turret front.[5] Naturally these AP/HE rounds did not penetrate. A few caused specific damage of a more or less serious nature, like jamming the mantlet or smashing a sight head. But in almost every trial the result was assessed as an F kill because a cumulation of minor damage, mainly to instruments and the like, made the tank incapable of firing effectively. Since much of this damage was internal, we are talking here of general energy transfer. For reasons I believe I brought out clearly enough in earlier chapters, I incline to the Soviet view that one good thump is better than a lot of pinpricks even against light targets. Certainly I am convinced it is wrong to extrapolate these Vulcan results to a single-tubed automatic cannon with a much lower cyclic rate. But if this multistrike approach does not offer a sound means of disruptive surface-to-surface attack on hard targets, it suggests interesting possibilities for the "Gatling" gun of attack helicopters against the softer aspects of armored vehicles.

---

4 I have a feeling data like this exists, but I have no idea where. It may be very old results on solid shot.

5 Cf. *Mechanized Infantry*, page 51. I am not sure whether the tank was an M48 or an early M60, but no matter.

Explosive shell

The requirement for a disruptive/general support round is going to be a complex one, so maybe we should start by stating some constraints and then bracket in on it from known natures. Suppose we postulate a caliber range of 85 to 125 mm and work on the midpoint — 105 mm, which everyone in the West can easily envision. Suppose we also, without prejudice to the arguments of Chapter 10, agree to think about a full-caliber, spin-stabilized round. I suggest this because there is a vast body of naval and land force knowledge about the ballistics, design and construction of shell of this kind. By contrast I can find no firm reference other than some German World War II work on flak to Western investigation of fin-stabilized designs of full charge fragmenting shell.

The Soviets of course have a 125-mm HEFS for the T72, but all I know about it is that the report refers to it as "new", and that it has flipout fins and a nose fuze, probably with percussion and VT options.[6] The existence of this round will serve as evidence of feasibility. I still in fact suspect that fin stabilization may offer more scope for the kind of shell we are looking for.[7] Nonetheless I prefer now to stay with the known so as to avoid arguments that are not too relevant to this issue.

It is extremely interesting that the Soviet Army is prepared to develop and stow a general support round for its dedicated tank guns. The US Army and the Bundeswehr, by contrast, accept the 105-mm and 120-mm HEATFS projectiles despite proven shortcomings in this role. Even at 152 mm caliber, considerable argumentation went on before a HEAT shell was accepted as the unguided partner of the Shillelagh missile on General Sheridan and M60A2. Shaped charge projectiles are normally thin-walled for lightness and maximum charge diameter, so there is little material available for fragmentation. They throw all their energy forward in a narrow parallel-sided jet; the result is devastating localized overkill but little in the way of spread. Going to war with tanks stowed with only APDSFS, HEATFS and smoke might arguably be a justifiable risk in the NATO center now — at least if one stays with the narrow view that the opposition's MBTs are the sole important target. On the target spectrum described in Chapter 2, this policy could be as wrong in Germany as it certainly would be in the other scenarios we looked at.

---

6 VT = variable time, also called "proximity fuze". Such fuzes act at a predetermined distance before impact.

7 Cf. *Tank Warfare*, pages 92, 93.

While the 105-mm HE/HEP round evidently will not fill the bill for disruption of compound armor arrays or of tanks with externally-mounted guns lurking in turret defilade, it is an excellent shell for disruptive attack of light armored vehicles and an adequate one for general support. This is a base-fuzed shell which from its nature tends to burst forward. One can get a good idea of its effectiveness against soft and area targets from the commonly accepted yardstick that, for a shell fired direct with tank gun accuracy, 90 mm is the optimum caliber for conventional HE and 105 mm for HE/HEP, 120 mm being extravagantly large even for HE/HEP. Some believe that initial splinter velocity is lower for HE/HEP than for normal HE because the tamping effect is reduced unless the shell sets on armor. Whether this is so or not, HE/HEP splinters are smaller, so that their higher surface/volume ratio makes them lose speed more rapidly. All this adds up to lower lethal radius (whence the increase of one-sixth in optimum caliber), lower fragment lethality and more rapid decay of lethality outside the nominal lethal radius. Fuzing and point of burst problems aside, all this adds up to poor suitability for the antihelicopter role. So the HE/HEP shell meets only two of the requirements.

Self-formed fragments (SFF) attack looks attractive for the three specific roles. But this is a new field and I have to admit that, if there is much published information on it, I have not come across it. So I simply do not know whether the principle is in the right ballpark for either feasibility or effectiveness. In any event SFF could be the head for one or more of the other clubs in the antiarmor bag and provides essentially penetrative rather than disruptive attack.

Fact is a conventional HE shell — like those of the American 75-, 76- and 90-mm tank guns or the British 77-mm and 17- and 20-prs — comes nearer than any of these more modern solutions to filling this bill. If it has a VT or skip airburst fuze option, so much the better for the antipersonnel and antihelicopter roles. It might even get in among some first-generation compound armor arrays; but keeping this level of attack out is just what I referred to as the "battle of the burster plate". Nonetheless we can line this shell up as one of three points of departure. The others are solid shot, or better the Soviet AP/T or APC/T projectile with its bursting charge in the base; and conventional naval AP shell (normally in rather larger calibers, it is true). The aspects we have to examine are muzzle velocity, the "HE:AP ratio" (as I shall loosely call it) and fuzing.

The muzzle velocity (MV) of the 105-mm HE/HEP shell is limited to 700 m/sec by the critical striking velocity for HEP. The most recent Soviet 100-mm APC/T projectile (before, that is, they switched to subcaliber), the BR-412D, has a MV of 900 m/sec. Densitywise this projectile is near to solid shot, so the MV probably lines up with the maximum muzzle energy of the D-10 series of tank guns. Tankers like fast ammunition. The anti-helicopter role calls for it in order to reduce the minimum range at which the tank can respond in time. As we shall see in a moment we want to get the most out of the KE effect. Again as we shall see, fuzing problems favor a fast shell. The case against a fast shell rests on the "over the crest" target.

Consider the side view of an external gun tank with top sensors like the Marder/105 mm (pl. 2) in a fire position (fig. 14). If it is to engage a target at zero or negative angle of site with hypervelocity KE ammunition, parts of the gun housing and superstructure must be on and above the horizontal plane of the crest. Sure, they are invisible to the target; and light cover, even grass, may make them invisible even to opponents in overlooking positions. But they are there; theoretically a projectile which grazed the crest on a flat trajectory would hit them. The nub of the problem is not (as appears at first sight) angle of descent, but angle of attack. The gun housing could rather easily be given a nacellelike shape that would present a KE penetrator or a high velocity HEATFS projectile with an unmanageable compound angle of obliquity. By contrast, given the right fuzing, a disruptive round might either be initiated on the crest and burst onto the superstructure front, or glance off the superstructure and burst over the hull rear. We can also see from this schematic that to lob a shell over the crest in the accepted sense of that term and get a frontal strike at a reasonable angle of obliquity would call for a MV far too low to be acceptable in the other roles.

So let's ballpark the MV of this disruptive round at 1000 m/sec. This is getting much more interesting for the antihelicopter role. For a gun firing at 35-75% full charge and backed by a modern fire-control system it is near the optimum for accuracy out to full antitank range; and the KE element is substantial. Suppose by extrapolation from known natures that, if either existed, a 105-mm full bore steel shot (APCBC) would weigh almost 18 kg and a conventional HE shell around 7 kg.[8] Then for a fifty-fifty "AP:HE ratio" we might assume a weight of 12 kg. On the analogy of an

8 Rather heavier than the HE/HEP shell.

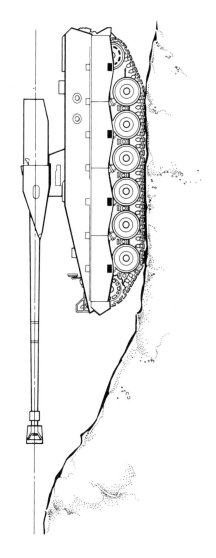

14. External gun tank in fire position. With high-velocity ammunition (little superelevation) and a zero or negative angle of site, a small area of the tank will in fact be exposed to an opponent at the same level (*broken line*) on a bare crest. Even where this area is behind visual cover (as in pl. 2b) it is vulnerable to attack "over the crest". The problem is less one of angle of descent (as pl. 2b might suggest) than one of excessive obliquity of attack

M60 tank (APDS) and a family car (HE/HEP) traveling at 50-55 kph, this shell would equivalate to a 32-t articulated truck.[9]

The next aspect to look at in getting a feel for the "AP:HE ratio" is the likely thickness of the outer or burster plates of compound armor arrays. On guestimates we used in Chapter 4, this could be around 50 mm at normal on a first generation array, rising to 100 mm or more at normal in possible "inverted" arrays (page 68). Extrapolating again very loosely from known data, we might line this up with an "AP:HE ratio" of 1:2 or a 105-mm shell of around 10 kg. We might also note that this thickness correlates with the yardstick of "detonation after one caliber of penetration" quoted for Soviet AP/HE. The next question, though, is whether a shell like this would be strong enough mechanically to reach the inside of the array and still be intact enough to detonate effectively. This is maybe the point at which I should admit to lacking the expertise, the data and the resources needed for a closer approach. I would not like to call my efforts even ballpark figuring, more like doodling on the back of an envelope. But a solution just has to exist somewhere within an area so firmly enveloped by the parameters of solid shot, HE shell and naval shell — all of them founded on a vast body of knowledge of design and ballistics alike.

I mentioned above that the Soviet 125 mm HEFS had a VT fuze option. I am puzzled, though, as to how a turret crew of two with an autoloader could set a fuze manually; and I cannot see the payoff justifying the complexity of an automatic fuze setter.[10] In any event, while either instantaneous percussion or VT will do for the general support role, neither suits the three specific roles predicated for this disruptive shell. For starters a shell which is to penetrate by KE effect before detonating evidently has to have a base fuze. We saw that the attack of a turret-down tank calls for a skip effect; and it hardly needs saying that getting a shell to burst in an array or behind light armor requires delay. Again I do not have the resources to figure it out, but it looks like a delay of 1-2 milliseconds might be in the right ballpark. The shell must detonate when its shoulder skips on the ground or its nose brushes, say, dense foliage or branches; and when the nose strikes armor. The fuze would thus need to actuate over a very wide range of decelerations; and my pocket calculator hints, I hope

---

9 This will mean more to European readers than to American, as it happens to be the "normal" GVW limit under EEC regulations.

10 I know the Soviets used to stow explosive main armament natures unfuzed, but I can't believe they still do this.

rightly, that a delay varying between set limits inversely with deceleration would be an advantage.

To sum up I would see future gun-based antiarmor weapon systems as having three main natures available — APDSFS, HEATFS and this disruptive AP/HE shell — but normally carrying only one explosive nature at any one time. A few rounds of bursting smoke are a must, but these will probably have to be stowed separately and manually loaded (as in S Tank). I am convinced of the need for this third disruptive nature, the more so as it could probably be fairly easily developed by combining existing naval technology with ballistic data for HE and HE/HEP shells for tank guns.

ATGM warheads

In looking at this multipurpose shell optimized for disruptive attack of compound and light armor I moved towards a "mixed attack" — a semipenetrative solution with a substantial KE content — for three reasons. First, the projection parameters suggested there would be a deal of KE around; so why waste it? Second, these antiarmor requirements called for two-phase attack; and the history of two-stage explosive attack within one small projectile is mainly one of the head eating the tail. Third, keeping one jump ahead in the antiarmor game is largely a matter of having the maximum number and variety of clubs in the bag — or at least in the clubhouse locker. SFF warheads or submunitions and three gun natures offer four distinct modes of attack; with optional penetrative and disruptive warheads, ATGMs could add two more. If it is true that winning the antiarmor battle is going to be the name of the game on land, six options is none too many. By contrast only four or even three might be deployed at any given point in time and space.

A 40-kg air-to-surface missile like Hellfire could pack a 10-kg 200 mm warhead.[11] This is rather over twice the warhead weight of even the larger current ATGMSs. The penetrative and disruptive effects of a shaped charge of this size should give a high chance of at least an F kill on any feasible armored vehicle, specially if the attack is delivered at a significant angle of descent. The Anglo-Australian Malkara was the only example I know of an ATGM using disruptive (HEP) attack; that warhead weighed

---

11 Though if Congressional pressure to use Hellfire as a surface-to-surface system is soundly based, the warhead may be only 7-7.5 kg.

A - I

13.6 kg and would not be adequate today. For a number of reasons a primary ATGM just has to hit and has to kill. To allow for penetrative and disruptive attack options with high assured lethality against armored vehicles of the nineties, I would like to see 20 kg allotted to the warhead. At present this means an air-to-surface missile weighing 80 kg and a surface-to-surface missile of 110 kg; and the improvement curve for the warhead weight/missile weight ratio is flattening out.

The payload trend for helicopters in general and attack helicopters in particular suggests that even Western attack helicopters, let alone the successor to the massive Hind, could comfortably handle a load of missiles like this. By contrast direct experience of trying to mount Malkara or even Swingfire and vicarious hindsight of continental systems and the United States ITV (Improved TOW Vehicle) suggest to me that an ATGM like Hellfire, let alone one almost three times as large, is a very awkward thing to field in the direct fire zone.

The value of systems like TOW, MILAN, Hot or Sagger, whether in vehicle-mounted or crew served forms, is based on the overmatching power of attack of small shaped charge warheads against steel armor. What I believe compound armor does is to *drive the ATGMS out of the middle ground of the antiarmor defense.* The helicopter-delivered systems must and can have assured overmatch. At the other extreme systems using overhead SFF attack may supplant crew served shaped charge ATGMSs in the main defense. And existing manportable systems will remain valid for use outside the tank's frontal arc — in enfilade positions, ambushes and tank-hunting patrols. The *Catch 22* problem, of which more later, is what form the primary surface-to-surface ATGMS should take.

9

Neutralizing and nonspecialized attack

When armored folks talk about the firepower of a tank or whatever, they are apt to mean the maximum energy of attack it can deliver in one shot. Power, though, means the *rate* of application of energy, and that is another thing again. This established misuse of the word "power" often leads to a piece of elliptical thinking which equates the ability to knock out a given target with the ability to stop an attack. It is only when we start to spell out — and work out — rates of exchange for own losses, space and time that we really see the danger of a numerically inferior defense being obliterated, overrun or swamped.

Although the role of artillery in the mechanized battle is seemingly on the upgrade, this resurgence is mainly in terms of observed fire. By the same token the Warpac tactical air defense leaves little scope for fixed- or rotary-wing attack on mechanized forces in depth. So we cannot expect much slowing down or thinning out of the attack beyond the back of the direct-fire zone unless nuclear weapons are used. This is the significance for the defense at tactical level of nuclear weapons and more particularly of enhanced radiation weapons. They are the only *area* weapons lethal to armor.

Whatever the defense doctrine at operational and tactical levels, we can pan in on time and space to a point where a low-level group is occupying a position where it has to stand and fight.[1] The chips are down. Within a depth of 3000-4000 m and a time of maybe 45 minutes, this small group has to reduce the odds facing it from 10 to 1 to something below the traditional 3 to 1. These defenders are eyeball-to-eyeball not just with a mass of Soviet armor but with the three exchange rates. The performance of the weapon systems this book is about does its best to minimize

---

1 Livsey, "The active defense": *see* Bibliography.

115

own losses. But by definition each direct-fire weapon system and
— electronic warfare permitting — each laser-equipped forward
observer can only engage one target at a time. These guys may
well be saying "Stop the world, we want to get off." They just
have to be saying "Stop the world." And this is precisely what
neutralizing attack on mechanized forces is about — *to gain time,
and with it space, for the lethal antiarmor weapon systems to
operate.*

Soldiers, specially tankers and infantrymen, seem to be very
sceptical about neutralization, all the more if it does not carry a
lethal threat with it. Both in procurement and on the battlefield
they are loath to divert human and material resources from
actually or potentially lethal systems. Maybe they regard such
systems as a departure from the concept of war as the ultimate
test of physical strength. If a nonnuclear area weapon lethal
against armor existed, it would evidently be preferable to a
nonlethal one. But it doesn't — now or foreseeably. *So
neutralizing area antiarmor weapon systems are an essential
complement to lethal pinpoint systems.*

Chemical attack

Speaking generally chemical warfare is not merely lethal; it could
well bring hostilities to an end by producing conditions
intolerable to the troops of both sides. But within our terms of
reference — armored vehicle crews trained, warned and doubly
protected (page 77) — we have to regard toxic agents not just as
a nonlethal form of attack but as an indifferent means of short-
haul neutralization. We therefore need to look at chemical attack
on the vehicle. Many will question whether this is a worthwhile
dilution of the antipersonnel chemical effort. I suggest it may be
because, as noted earlier, both points of attack provide
convenient mechanisms of concentrating the antimateriel agent.

Maybe we should look first at the less promising option,
*spoiling of the chemical filter elements in the collective NBC
protection system.* I have not probed this personally in detail, nor
would I think a published document the place to do so. Suffice
it to say that parts of the filter could either be rendered inopera-
tive or have the rate at which they become saturated by antipersonnel agents dramatically increased. This approach has three
drawbacks. The volume of air aspirated by the NBC protective
system is small in relation to engine air, so the rate of enrichment
of antimateriel agent is lower. Likewise the addition of an anti-

antimateriel filter element should present no great problem. In any event putting the chemical side of the collective filters out of action simply throws the crew back on individual protection. My own guess is that this form of attack is not worthwhile in temperate climates but could well be so in a desert or tropical setting. There the conditions for crewmen in protective clothing might quickly become intolerable if support from the collective protection system was withdrawn (*cf.* page 78).

Of greater interest is the *engine air intake*. Modern tank engines breathe in upwards of 700 litres of air per second, offering an opportunity for extremely rapid concentration of an agent present in very low dosages in ambient air. Compression ignition engines are not easy to attack. One possibility is to modify the combustion characteristic of the fuel; but since the fuel is accessible only in the combustion chamber, there is no opportunity to build up a concentration of agent. By contrast, an agent which survives combustion or is effective in oxidized form could be deposited on the cylinder walls and attack the lubricating oil. This might bring vehicles to a standstill in a few minutes. Gas turbine power plants do not have a convenient interface between working substance and lubricating oil, but turbines have a centrifuging action. The compressor turbine blades are vulnerable to corrosion by an unoxidized agent, and the drive and power turbine blades by combustion products.

This threat is hard to evaluate. It is certainly feasible and came into fashion several times during the sixties and seventies. But I know of no firm proposals or experimental results, maybe because a number of potential antimateriel agents are disabling or even lethal antipersonnel agents too. It would be worth studying in the context of providing NATO with an offensive chemical capability — a decision that may well have been taken by the time this book is published.

Blinding attack

Currently both sides seem to be declaring their intention to cover the battlefield in smoke (page 17). Presumably the Pact would use it in accordance with Soviet doctrine — to screen assembly, to shorten the direct-fire zone and to neutralize known defended localities. I have to admit to having failed to elucidate NATO's rationale or technique — the more so since everybody with experience of fighting or exercising under European conditions knows how much reduced visibility favors the attacker. Sure, there are many occasions, like neutralizing a firing tank you cannot engage, for *quick, localized* defensive and tactical screens. But for the defense a more interesting option by far is to blind attacking armored vehicles while leaving them exposed as targets.

Maybe this possibility gets overlooked because it is nonlethal and because the real requirement is so modest it hardly seems worth doing. Yet I do not think anyone with experience of beating off an armored attack or trying to block a bypassing force will question the value of bringing the advancing tanks to rest, unable to fire, for 5 minutes or even 2. With free play a modern gun-based antiarmor weapon system could take out at least eight attacking vehicles in two minutes — as opposed to three if it is forced to adjust position after each shot. And in two minutes a modern attacker could move 1 km or more if not forced to halt. Naturally it wouldn't be quite like that for real. But the idea of even a short period with the first wave presented as sitting ducks and the overwatching support smoked off could have a dramatic effect on the space and time exchange rates.

Delivery and dispersion of a liquid agent by VT fuzed shell would be no problem, and a mixed concentration of this shell and percussion fuzed HE could result in a useful mingling of "black rain" and dust at just about cupola height. Likewise HE would stop commanders and drivers unbuttoning. Looking at the number of commercially available products like contact-setting paints, adhesives and fillers, I find it hard to believe that a suitable agent would be difficult or costly to develop. Sure, a solvent in the wash-wipe systems of sight and vision heads might get most of it off again. But the defense doesn't even need the "5 minutes more" of the World War II song to turn the scales. As a bonus, this form of attack would also obscure respirator visors or eyepieces.

I mentioned earlier the soldier's psychological block on nonlethal weapons. I have to admit that, as a serving officer concerned with armor/antiarmor policy, I looked at the idea of blinding several times, discussed it with others and rejected it. With standoff the proposition looks rather different; and it is one which just has to favor the side which is thinner on the ground.

Track-cutting mines and minelets

Whatever their size and however they are delivered, shaped charge mines constitute a lethal weapon system. The only advantage in covering them with fire is to inhibit clearance; and this can be done almost as well by antilift devices[2] and by mingling in large numbers of minimal antipersonnel mines. Track-cutting mines of any size are only incidentally lethal, even in the limited sense of an M kill. They are essentially a neutralizing weapon system and need to be covered by antiarmor and HE fire to destroy the vehicles they immobilize and to inhibit mine clearance and track repair.

Having delivered myself of that earthshaking cliché, which I first heard at least 40 years back, I want to diverge sharply from conventional wisdom, old and new alike. If the Pact is gentleman enough to give NATO the 10 days or so warning it expects, there is a place for massive deliberately laid minefields in linking and deepening natural obstacles to form an obstacle belt. At the other extreme there is great morale and some tactical value in the mines which platoons or even squads throw out round themselves for local defense.

By contrast, given the tempo of future mechanized operations, the use of deliberately laid minefields in defensive positions adds up not just to telegraphing a punch but to holding your hand up and telling the other guy what's coming to him. Again, I am all for using every kind of mobility denial munition, dispensed from the air or delivered by missile or tubed artillery, on the opposition's approach routes where we have no intention of going and where these devices may delay and soften the first punch. But as I see it, scattering mines on the probable routes of spearheads after a breakthrough is a double-edged tactic. So is their use by an attacker to block counterpenetration moves at a point where operations are still completely fluid.

Maybe we should stop talking about "scatterable" mines and "delayed effect" munitions and just use the term "instant mines". For I believe the best use of artillery-delivered minelets is going to be right in among the defensive fires of the main defended positions or killing zones. These minelets need to go down so close in front of the attacker that he has no time to respond, let alone to clear them. The other role I see for instant mines, probably helicopter-delivered, is the creation of something resembling a pivot of maneuver for contain-and-destroy operations by attack helicopters. Economy apart, this concept of putting down mines just when and where they are needed has two great and related

---

2 Since the fuzing of HEAT minelets is fairly complex anyway, there should be no problem in making them actuate if moved once they are armed, even if the primary fuze is an influence one. Minelets like this are in fact under development, maybe already in production in the USA.

merits. The defense knows where the mines are. It sees them go
down; and if all goes well the area is immediately marked by
knocked-out vehicles. Then again, mines used in this way can
have very short self-sterilization times.

Antitank mine technology is well established and seems to be
keeping one jump ahead of clearance techniques; and the
interfaces of antitank mines with their targets are rather sharply
defined (page 82). Thus I see no point in discussing the state of
the art in detail. But I would utter one plea, which I believe goes
with the trend of United States opinion and against the views of
European NATO members. It is for a virtually complete switch of
development and production effort from mines designed for
deliberate laying to "instant" minelets. No matter whether these
are thrown across a covered approach from an IFV as the
maneuver squad dismounts, dispersed from fixed- and rotary-
wing aircraft or delivered by shell and missiles, getting the best
out of them and their delivery means requires these minelets to be
put down *where* the opposition has to go because he is already
there; and *when* it is too late for him to evade them, clear them or
even check in front of them. Instant mines turn the old cliché
inside out. It is no longer a question of minefields being covered
by fire but of instant minefields being used to support the direct-
fire antiarmor defense.

The neutralizing concentration

United States and Soviet doctrine are marching in the same
direction over the part of surface-to-surface artillery in the
mechanized battle. Fact is future hard target characteristics make
this trend inevitable. The extent to which artillery will be able to
deliver lethal attack on armored vehicles is an open question
which we shall address in Chapters 10 and 14. What is crystal
clear is the ability of defensive fires to set up targets for the direct-
fire antiarmor defense — and the acute need for them to do so.

In this chapter I have suggested various means of neutralization
— some short-lived some extended in time, some well established
some far out. Doubtless there are other possibilities too. No
matter, for the impression I want to leave is a broader one — of a
mix of neutralizing natures of artillery shell, or better maybe of a
neutralizing shell carrying a mix of antiarmor devices. Combined
into an on-call fire plan highly concentrated in time and space,
these munitions must halt the first attacking wave, isolate it and
hopefully silence its weapons for just enough time to allow the

direct-fire antiarmor systems to turn the odds in the defense's favor.

This is so important that I believe it calls for a new look at artillery deployment. Artillery can now go straight to fire for effect and needs to stand off enough to mass its fire. Against this no radio link can be counted on in an electronic warfare environment. The timing, accuracy and above all the certainty of neutralizing defensive fires like this are literally vital to the defense. Maybe it would be worth following Soviet practice and having an artillery subunit placed where it could fire direct, if needs be on call by signal flares. This is just one example of the way technological advance may become self-defeating and force armies back on to long-discarded techniques.

PART 3

Means of Delivery

10

Direct-fire guns

Before we move into the complex of arguments to be had about high-pressure guns, I want to touch on fire-control systems. I believe what I wrote 2 years back on powered mountings and fire-control systems stands,[1] but our investigation of target characteristics leaves two points to be highlighted and one to be explored in greater depth. The first concerns *laser range finders.* There is a mounting likelihood of some kind of active response from the target, but the transponders used to trigger this reaction are unlikely to operate reliably in the visible light spectrum, at least during the day. So there is a case for range-finding lasers to use this spectrum despite any technical arguments for going to a rather longer wavelength. Under certain circumstances the white light option may guard against detection at night too. Certainly visible light is best for the "identification/acquisition boost" to passive image intensification (which I suspect is regaining favor over thermal imaging). Additionally it will be important for the interval between laser flash and firing to be minimized by putting range finding as late as possible in the engagement sequence.

This leads into the second point to be taken *en passant.* I am now sure (as I was not 2 years back) that the time has come to abandon any direct mechanical link between fire-control/sighting system and gun mounting in favor of *slaving.* This possibility has long sent shivers down users' spines; for once — maybe like anyone who has experienced transmissions of the selsyn[2] type in an armored vehicle vibration environment — I have to vote with the conservatives here. But the kind of electronic control now available and the ease with which redundancy can be built into it adds up to a whole new ballgame. Now that there looks like being an immediate payoff in firepower and indirect protection (from putting the laser flash late in the sequence) as well as the self-evident advantages in vehicle design,

1 *Tank Warfare,* pages 93-99.
2 British "magslip".

the time has surely come to wave goodbye to any pretence of an emergency mechanical gun-sight link.

The aspect I now want to probe rather more deeply maximizes the firepower payoff of slaving. It is the Parthian shot I fired in the relevant section of *Tank Warfare — namely automatic target acquisition round the clock.* Since thermal imaging will do the job reasonably well in most conditions by night, the real problem is the daytime one — the more so since I am skeptical enough to think that the tempo of battle will still be slower by night than by day. I believe I demonstrated (page 42) that, as soon as mean firing and movement exposure times start to come down towards mean acquisition time — let alone fall below it — the chance that a target offered will be killed starts to fall dramatically. As I stressed in Chapter 3, though, the figures I used for acquisition times are shaky, from old age if nothing else. And aside from its probable complexity and cost, an automatic acquisition system could impair indirect protection and would certainly revolutionize the art of tank commanding. So the first need is to establish some valid up-to-date figures on acquisition times in modern fields of surveillance and fire for a layout with duplicated commander's and gunner's stations.

Here one has to discover first the times for systematic but "unintelligent" visual scanning of the kind a device or an untrained man might perform; then the improvement to be had from two trained brains and pairs of eyes reading the ground and making use of knowledge of the opposition's tactics, local combat intelligence and indications like the marginal visual signatures of armored vehicles and helicopters. A set of figures like this would not only confirm or disprove the need for an automatic system but show whether the requirement is for a whole-field scan or for narrow-arc, even fixed, monitoring of selected azimuths.

If the requirement for an automatic system is confirmed, the display will need very careful thought if it is not to interfere with visual scanning and action on visually acquired targets. As a user I would envision a polar display showing the range and azimuth (with respect to the gun) of numbered target blips updated or cancelled scan by scan. This could either be a look-down screen combined with an audio warning in the commander's headset when a new target was acquired; or a permanent or on-call head-up display in his primary vision instrument. The commander would need push buttons to allow him to retrieve any target serial and either lock his own primary vision system onto it or pass it to the gunner. Ideally these facilities should be available in both turret stations, but never activated in both at once. I can even envision a system of automatic target acquisition combined with slaving which would allow three successive targets to be engaged in the same time as it now takes to get three shots off at the same target — in other words without necessarily adjusting position.

Rifled tube or smooth bore

The whole question of rifled and smoothbore guns has become emotionally charged and politically loaded to the point of absurdity; additionally, apart from tubed air-defense systems, it has been linked to the conventional concept of a turreted tank. One needs to look first at the fundamental pros and cons of the two types of gun, then at their versatility *vis-à-vis* existing and predictable operational requirements, then at their ease of installation.

Surprisingly maybe, rifled tubes are the easier to make because of the high finish required of the smooth bore and the disastrous effects on accuracy of any blemish, irregularity or incipient failure of the lining. One does not know what problems the Soviets had in engineering their 100- and 115-mm smoothbore tubes; strong as they are on metallurgy, this may have been one reason for the surprisingly early change from 115 to 125 mm. Certainly the tendency of plated bore surfaces to collapse put a number of Western projects out of court as recently as the fifties and sixties. Despite the success of the German 120-mm smoothbore, the weight of British armored opinion and American user opinion still hangs a question mark over its reliability under battle conditions. Following the step advance in wear reduction brought about by the use of "Swedish additives" and the minimization of effective full charges (EFC) fired once satisfactory high-velocity training ammunition became available, the life of rifled tubes only remains a problem if one makes absurdly optimistic assumptions about exchange rates in war. Conversely tube life has never been adduced, publicly at least, as an argument for modern smoothbores.

Tube weight for a given caliber, shot travel and pressure somewhat favors the smoothbore. From first principles one would expect projectile acceleration in a smoothbore tube to be higher, so that a smoothbore gun could be shorter for a given muzzle velocity. The Soviet 125 mm (T72) and the German 120 mm (Leopard 2) bear this out (*see* Table 1, p. 131). Principles and practice agree that, everything else being constant, a smoothbore gun will impart around 15% more energy to the projectile for a given chamber volume and trunnion reaction than a rifled gun firing a spin-stabilized projectile. In state-of-the-art tank guns this adds up to a 15-20-mm advantage in caliber for given mounting parameters. By contrast much of this energy difference is probably accounted for by rotational acceleration of the spin-stabilized projectile. In decoupled rounds fired from rifled tubes only the driving band rotates at a significant speed; fair inferences from the published results of the DARPA/ARES project[3] and the action taken on the ARES gun confirm that decoupling nullifies much of the smoothbore's advantage in efficiency. Fact is confirmation and extension to lower calibers of the provisional results on decoupled APDSFS obtained in the sixties with the 125-mm XM150 gun (MBT70) swings the whole issue back in favor of rifled guns. Decoupling could present problems at muzzle velocities above 2000 m/sec, but this figure is 15-20% beyond what has so far been achieved — or at least published.

On the other side of the coin, one of the arguments formerly put forward for the rifled gun was versatility — that it would fire any spin-stabilized nature required as well as decoupled APDSFS and HEATFS. I myself have never been able to see why a smoothbore should not fire fin-stabilized HE, HEP, AP/HE or whatever with acceptable accuracy; or why, within the overall restriction of muzzle energy, higher L/D ratios should not be exploited to deliver rather large quantities of explosive. The successful development of the Soviet 125-mm HEFS seems to bear this view out. In terms of L/D ratio and muzzle energy alone, a 120-mm smoothbore optimized for long rod APDSFS should be able to throw a 30-35-kg projectile at 1000 m/sec. Since the parasitic weight of the fins and their carrier is more than offset by the reduction in case thickness the absence of rotational forces permits, we are talking of charge weights which are extremely interesting in terms of disruption by surface-bursting HEP — which are in fact well over the "safe overmatch" weight of 20 kg I postulated for a disruptive ATGM warhead (page 114). I know this would be a massive round to stow and load, but the projectile weight is around the same as the weight of the old British 120-mm (Conqueror) cartridge case with full (APDS) charge. This was considered to be — and was — just around the limit for manual

---

3 *See* Bibliography, "The US Army's armoured combat vehicle technology program", etc. (Furlong, Ogorkiewicz).

loading; but even the complete round weight should present no problem to an autoloader.

Then again there is the question of accuracy. Along with velocity drop, accuracy and consistency beyond 1500 m or so were long thought to be a limiting factor in fin-stabilized ammunition. Now APDSFS has achieved accuracies which offer an acceptable hit on a turret target (1 m square) at 4000 or 5000 m. I do not know — and I doubt anyone in the West does — whether a massive fin-stabilized explosive round could achieve this kind of accuracy at all direct-fire ranges. But even if it could, this may not be good enough for explosive antiarmor projectiles. As we saw (page 106), there may be a requirement to hit twice in the same place (strip — kill); and that is another thing again. There seems to be a general feeling among users and technologists alike that, in the current state of the arts concerned, the best accuracy is to be had from a spin-stabilized projectile fired from a rifled tube at between, say, 35% and 75% of maximum muzzle energy.

I hope the discussion above, read in conjunction with the relevant passages of Chapters 8 and 9, conveys an impression that for antiarmor gun-ammunition systems considered in isolation, the choice between rifled and smooth bore is a very open one. The crunch — along with the aura of overheated emotion it generates — comes when you try to mount the gun in a tank.

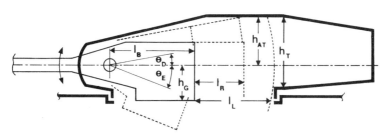

15. Constraints of turret mounting
I_B = length of breech (to rear of trunnions)
I_R = recoil length
I_L = loading length
θ_D = angle of depression
h_T = turret height
h_G = height of trunnions above turret ring
h_{AT} = height above trunnions
θ_E = angle of elevation

Fact is a conventional turreted tank faces the gun designer and through him the ballistician with just about the worst sort of constraints imaginable (fig. 15). The schematic I think speaks for itself,[4] even though it does not show the tendency of the trunnion

---

4 See also *Tank Warfare*, pages 129-132.

reaction (recoil force), acting in a plane well above the vehicle's center of mass, to rock the vehicle and in the extreme to topple it backwards. It is this set of constraints and the complex and rigid envelope of mounting parameters they generate which currently seem to give the smoothbore gun an edge — or even a 15-20% advantage — *as the armament of a conventional turreted tank.* The ability of a smoothbore gun to generate a given proportion of its theoretical maximum muzzle energy over a shorter shot travel is important too. A conventional modern tank traversing an optimized rifled gun might sweep a circle up to 15 m in diameter; and the forward overhang of a gun like this would give an embarrassingly poor net angle of attack.[5]

The moment we fix the gun in the hull (S Tank, pl. 9) or mount it externally (Marder/105 mm, pl. 2) this rigid envelope of constraints collapses like a house of cards. With a ready round or main magazine fixed relative to the gun, loading length can be what we like. We can bring the trunnion reaction and its attendant pitching couple right down by extending recoil length to artillerylike proportions. And we can reduce gun overhang and swept radius by mounting the gun (or its traversing base) well back in the hull.

So I suggest the rifled *v* smoothbore argument has become a new way of fighting the longer-standing conflict over conventional *v* radical vehicle configurations, and that much of the heat carries over from that. If the requirement is to pack the greatest possible power of antiarmor attack within a turret, it makes sense to maximize caliber and go smoothbore. Unconventional configurations allow designers to optimize the gun-ammunition system and go on from there. Given certainty of being able to fire decoupled KE projectiles, freedom to go for a long tube, the possible need to hit the same spot twice and the available body of knowledge on the ballistics of spin-stabilized shell, I guess an optimized high-pressure gun still has grooves in it.

Caliber and shot travel

In a review of *Tank Warfare*[6] I was very properly taken to task for suggesting a composite platoon that needed to be fed with three different calibers of main armament ammunition. I have to admit that my attitude to logistic problems always was that logisticians and engineers are hired to solve them and let the

---

5 i.e. the angle from the forward point of contact of the track to the gun muzzle, the true angle of attack being the slope of the track from front roadwheel to idler or sprocket.

6 By Brigadier Bryan Watkins in the *RUSI Journal.*

combat crews get on with their job. Nonetheless the familiar scenario of a muddy woodland trail on a dark wet night will always remain a fact of life for tankers and their colleagues in the maneuver element. Under these conditions three or even two natures, let alone different calibers, spark enough problems, specially when you throw in machinegun ammunition, smoke grenades and the rest. A lot of folks' thought is currently moving towards a hi-lo profile; and this has so far implied a mix of calibers — say 120 mm and 90 mm or 105 mm and 75 mm — within the company and maybe within the platoon. So I asked myself whether one couldn't have a hi-lo profile with a common caliber and even common natures.

As we saw above, within the constraints imposed by a turreted tank, about the only way to increase muzzle energy is to go up in caliber. Freed from these shackles, another way is to play around with shot travel. To examine this approach we need the concept of *caliber-lengths* so loved by the Germans —

$$\text{caliber-length (L)} = \text{shot travel/caliber}$$

With two exceptions (marked *) the caliber-length values in Table 1 are scaled from published schematics or photos; and shot travel is back-calculated from this figure.

TABLE 1 — *Gun calibers and caliber-lengths*

Country	Vehicle	Caliber (mm)	L	Shot travel (mm)
Rifled guns for turreted tanks				
Third Reich	Panther	75	70	5250
USA	M48	90	53	4770
USSR	T54/55	100	51	5100
UK/USA/NATO	Centurion, M60, Leopard 1	105	51*	5355
UK	Chieftain	120	51	6120
Other rifled guns				
USA	(HIMAG, HSTV-L)	75	72	5400
Sweden	S Tank	105	62*	6510
(postulated design, see below)		105	72	7560
Smoothbore guns				
USSR	T62, T64	115	47	5405
USSR	T72	125	44	5500
FRG, ?USA	Leopard 2, ?XM1	120	46	5520

For conventional turreted tanks there seems to be a general consensus of feeling that a swept circle of not more than 12 m (corresponding to a shot travel of 5-5.5 m) and a net angle of attack (gun level, 12 o'clock) of not less than 25° are sound empirical limits. Chieftain is outside both these — and it shows in handling. A smoothbore gun allows the Soviets to go to 125 mm and stay just within 12 m, though their low trunnion heights make T62, T64 and T72 marginal on angle of attack.[7] I believe this analysis provides striking confirmation of my point that the switch to smoothbore is limited to a turreted tank.

Turning away from convention, we can suppose that the DARPA/ARES team didn't go to 72 L or so and the incon-venience of an intermediate tube bearing just for kicks. In fact the shot travel of this gun is just about on the NATO 105-mm/ 51 L norm. But the HSTV-L configuration[8] gives a swept circle well under 9 m and a net angle of attack better than 45°, matching in fact the angle of attack of the track. Let us note at this point that the standard 105-mm/L51 gun on HSTV-L would give roughly the same figures.

S Tank as it stands is marginal on net angle of attack, although by design the limit is imposed by the bottom edge of the hull front in order to protect the gun. However, given an ideal point turn, S Tank sweeps only 7.75 m. For reasons unconnected with this argument we can suppose that a future vehicle of S Tank configuration would have an additional roadwheel station. Holding the running gear geometry constant, we arrive at an increase in length of, say, 730 mm or 7 caliber-lengths at 105 mm. The S Tank's gun is already 62 L, so we come to 69 L. To dispose of argument, one could in fact get to 72 L by adopting the chamber form and ammunition design of the ARES 75-mm gun. But the arguments for staying with the standard 105-mm chamber and cartridge case and increasing charge weight — as in the Soviet 125-mm — by using the space within the sabot for a "secondary cartridge" are extremely strong. So an extra 315 mm (just over 1 ft) of tube length have to be accommodated. The angle of attack could be held by raising the bore-axis height (the equivalent of trunnion height) by 220 mm; and the swept circle would still be under 10 m. This is enough to demonstrate feasibility; evidently an appropriate redesign could do much better.

---

7 In fact the two schematics I have of T72 put the angle at 23° (+) in one case and just on 25° in the other.

8 I have failed to find a good enough schematic of the HIMAG test vehicle to scale from. In any event this is not an operational design.

For the same recoil length, I guestimate the trunnion reaction of the 105-mm/L51 firing an APDSFS round optimized for a 72 L gun at upwards of 17,500 kgf as against the 9000 kgf of the 75-mm ARES gun fired in its "hard recoil" (in-battery) mode. By happenstance — or maybe not — the trunnion height of HSTV-L is just half the length of track on ground. So if the vehicle's center of mass is over the midpoint of the track plan, this trunnion reaction will start to topple the 17-t vehicle with the gun level and do a whole lot more than that to it with the gun depressed and the vehicle on an uphill gradient. By contrast we can count on Swedish homework and assume that the hull of the 26-t Marder stays upright with the 105-mm/L51 gun firing normal APDS and mounted rather high (pl. 2). Going one stage further, we can put our money on the 35-40-t hull of the fixed gun tank postulated above providing a stable platform for a 105-mm/L51 gun externally mounted above it.

We are now in a ballpark of the very highest interest. If the APDSFS projectile of the 75-mm/72 L ARES gun defeats the current frontal arc target and an equivalent gun of 90 mm will do for the beyond, a 105-mm/72 L gun should offer a better than 100% reserve in the short haul and a 60% reserve later on. By the same token, because it is going into at least the first batch of XM1 (Abrams) tanks, we know that the 105-mm/L51 with the M774 APDSFS round satisfies the middle-term requirement. There is already the XM833 round to back this up; and the optimized "upscaled ARES" round I have postulated would presumably be more powerful still. So it seems safe, even conservative, to suppose that the 105-mm/L51 gun can meet the antitank requirement in the nineties, at least at short and medium ranges. *This "long and the short of it" offers a pair of guns suitable for a tank destroyer and a fire support tank (the hi-lo profile) firing the same ammunition and making use of existing 105-mm explosive and miscellaneous natures.*

This line of attack is attractive enough in itself. But it offers another powerful club in the bag. We know from the Leopard 2/XM1 exercises that the German 120-mm/46 L smoothbore and the 105-mm/51 L have compatible mounting parameters. We also know that the S Tank successor is currently being designed on this or a very similar gun; and we have demonstrated that it could accommodate the length of a 105-mm/72 L gun. Should the need arise, the tank destroyer of the pair could be regunned with a 120-mm smoothbore, extended if needs be to some 63 L.

Fact is, the West has a very powerful solution to the problem of the primary antiarmor gun in its hands for the asking if it is prepared to move away from a turreted tank — to say nothing of the other advantages this shift will bring. What is more the program is a cheap one with a high degree of assurance. The DARPA/ARES project could readily be switched back to the 105-mm caliber in which it started and is in fact still working. The XM833 APDSFS round (which will probably be type classified by the time this book appears) is an adequate short-term expedient to say the least; and its HEATFS partner is a proven round. Likewise the Germans have proven the APDSFS and HEATFS rounds for their 120-mm smoothbore. Add to all this the fact that future Soviet tanks may have to trade off conventional frontal arc protection to accommodate an extended arc (page 56) and the next moves in penetrative attack can be evolutionary.

With this gun program go two clearly defined R & D programs for disruptive attack of armor (Chapter 8) — an AP/HE spin-stabilized 105-mm round; and a massive fin-stabilized shell, probably based on HE/HEP and disruption by explosive power alone, in the 120-mm caliber.

This is the solution for the primary gun-based anti-armor weapon system I shall use in the rest of this book — long and short (i.e. standard) 105-mm rifled guns, with a 120-mm smoothbore as a backup. Using exactly the same arguments, I shall also assume a "long and the short of it" solution for a light mechanized force. This will be based on the DARPA/ARES *Super 75*[9] and, if required, a matching gun of around 50 caliber-lengths. In going this way, we should make a mental note that a rethink at around 90 mm might be needed in the longer term.

---

9 i.e. with rotating chambers and automatic "soft recoil" mode.

11

Guidance and communications in the sophisticated combat environment

We all pay lip service to the gravity of the electronic warfare (EW) threat and fling EW countermeasures to the nth to and fro across staff college tables and round the upper and lower control levels of CPXs.[1] Airmen, sailors and signallers take this threat seriously in training; but for combat soldiers it is something that happens to the other guy. In exercises overdependence on electronic links which are vulnerable to countermeasures is no more than a peccadillo — maybe even a plus because it enhances the value of the training in many ways. One might even say that good radio communications freely used are the best aid to bringing troops up to a standard where they can operate on radio silence. Disregarding EW in the statement of requirements for and development of weapon systems is another thing again; it could take a decade to put right.

While I would concede an outside chance that the Warsaw Pact will not go chemical, at least initially, I can see no way of ducking the EW threat. My impression is that EW favors the attacker at sea and in the air; so the Pact is going to use it there and NATO is going to retaliate. On land I reckon an EW environment favors the defense; since EW has no political overtones, NATO will surely resort to it — and the Pact will retaliate. So one way or another the NATO maneuver force is going to have to fight under EW conditions.

Maybe the best confirmation of this lies in Soviet movement

---

1 Command post exercises.

techniques, tactics and training. Whether moving in columns and packets or deployed, they are generally at high enough densities to use hand or flag signals, and this is just what they do.[2] Again, I see no reason for risking modern self-propelled artillery in the direct-fire zone only 5-6 km behind the FEBA[3] when it is controlled by a forward observer anyway. So maybe the justification for the direct-fire platoon (page 17) is having some artillery in visual contact if radio cannot be used. Yet again there is (at least as I write) no published indication that the Soviets are shifting away from wire command link ATGMSs.[4]

I suggest *en passant* that these points exemplify a basic difference between Soviet and Western equipment philosophy. When the Soviets hit a snag, they home in on it and either solve the problem or find a way round it. Only in extreme cases do they abandon their existing approach; and since they stay firmly within the state of the art, extreme cases are few and far between. By contrast policymakers and technologists in the West, most of all maybe in the United States, are always looking for an excuse to innovate. There is a host of new ideas waiting in the wings; if the star of the moment falters, even in rehearsal, somebody quite different leaps under the spotlight and into fashion. Result is some shows never quite get around to opening.

My suspicion — to say the least — is that several existing antiarmor weapon systems and a whole lot more proposed ones are incapable of facing up to an EW environment, let alone to dedicated countermeasures superimposed on this (page 72). For this reason I hesitated before putting forward the notion of an automatic target acquisition device (page 126), because this would evidently have to be active to achieve target identification, even maybe detection of small low-contrast stationary targets. I felt, though, that a system which scanned a whole sector might act as a counter-countermeasure, triggering any transponder which operated within its band on every target it scanned. The opposition would then be forced to switch these devices off or risk having his whole layout disclosed.

In the section on fire-control systems I likewise stressed the need for the laser range finder to operate as late in the firing sequence as possible. Since the gun is by nature a fire-and-forget

---

2 The most recent confirmation I personally have of this is a Soviet recruiting film probably made in the early/mid-sixties.

3 Forward edge of the battle area.

4 The recent reduction in the scale of Sagger on BMP from 1 per vehicle to 1 per platoon is probably based on quite different considerations.

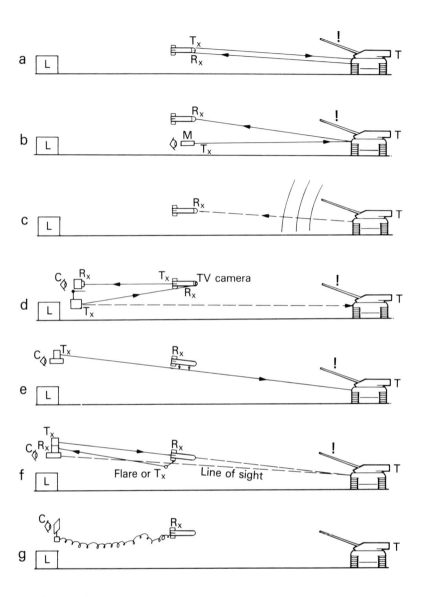

16. Schematic of ATGMS guidance principles
    C = controller, L = launcher, M = marker, T = target,
    R_x = receiver of radiation, T_x = transmitter of radiation, ! = target warned
    (a) Active homing
    (b) Semiactive homing
    (c) Passive homing (feasibility doubtful)
    (d) Manual command link with TV head
    (e) Beam riding
    (f) Semiautomatic command link
    (g) Manual wire command link

weapon and the time of flight of an APDS projectile is extremely short, target reaction to the laser flash would not then matter. Additionally, to prevent repeated false alarms (such as might be caused by an automatic target acquisition system or incident sunlight reflected from a windshield), an active protection system would need to integrate signals over a finite time before reacting.

Active or even semiactive millimeter wave (MMW) homing may be acceptable for terminal guidance, provided the time between first pulse and impact is too short for the target to take evasive action. But I always believed laser target marking, outside a very short terminal guidance phase, to be an illusion. A brief flash following a talkdown in handing a target over from a ground observer to a helicopter — a kind of visual "No, *that* one" — may be acceptable. But the duration and time to impact of a marker signal used as the sole means of handover and/or for full trajectory guidance of an ATGM lay this technique wide open to countermeasures in the shape of active protection of the target and offensive action against the source of the radiation.

I know I am moving further and further into an area of subjective opinions; but the questions we are addressing are too important to the success of the antiarmor defense to be hidden under the carpet. I hope someone can convince me otherwise, but until they do I hold to the view that full trajectory homing guidance must be passive if it is to succeed on future battlefields. We saw (page 43) that the visual signature of an armored vehicle is the only one that will do for passive homing. So to my mind full trajectory "homing" for ATGMSs means a vidicon head and manual command guidance. Beam riding likewise involves protracted illumination of the target from a pinpoint source and will thus alert it. By contrast, spoiling or bending the beam is not a simple business within the constraints of bulk and power imposed by a tank. Beam riding, though, has never been a favored technique for surface-to-surface cruise missilery.

Because it is less specialized (in the evolutionary sense) the infrared tracking and/or command link system used in several semiautomatic weapon systems of the TOW generation is less susceptible to countermeasures. The only thing that reaches the target before the missile is the command link beam with its characteristically coded signals. There is evidence to suggest that this excitation is not particularly easy to detect and identify. Nonetheless the possibility is there; so could be a response by way of saturating the tracker. Going back a step further down the line of evolution, we come to manual guidance with a radio or IR command link. Here again there is a signal which the target can detect and respond to, but the responses available are limited to blinding the controller by dazzle or obscuration, and physical attack on the missile. So we come back to square one, *wire command link manual guidance* — which is right where the Soviets look like staying!

When the United States first moved away from a wire link with Shillelagh[5] and the run-in to TOW (which finally came out wire-guided), wits in France and Britain suggested that the Americans reckoned any opposing infantry who happened to be around might whip out their "Swiss Army" knives or the equivalent and cut the wire before the missile reached the target. This could be; but in fact there are three more serious objections to a wire command link. The first and most substantial of these is the kind of basic engineering problem that modern Western technologists on both sides of the Atlantic will go to the wildest heights of electronic sophistication to duck. At near sonic or transonic missile speeds the wire is apt to break as it comes off the dispenser.

Anybody who stayed with Chapter 3 or battled through to the later pages of Chapter 4 will need no explanation of the gravity of this limitation. Dearly, and rightly, as the user would like missiles flying at around Mach 2 or better — in the same ballpark as a 105-mm HE/HEP shell — the effect on missile dimensions and weight would be rather dramatic. This is no way to go when one is asking for a large disruptive warhead as a fallback (page 113). Additionally there is a point probably around Mach 1.25-1.5 at which the controller encounters difficulties even with second-generation manual control.[6] We can return to this aspect in a moment; but a sustainer phase or glide speed of that kind, with times of flight of unit seconds to most ranges, would certainly make for a much more battleworthy system. So here we have a clearly-defined mechanical problem — develop a wire and a dispenser which will give, say, 98% reliability at high confidence limits for a missile speed of Mach 1.5. The British and French did a fair amount of work back in the sixties on using the sustainer

---

5 The missile of the 152-mm gun-launcher system fitted to General Sheridan and M60A2.

6 Everybody, specially the Germans, calls the current systems like TOW, MILAN or Hot "second generation". Fact is the jump from the acceleration control of SS10 to the velocity control of SS11, Bantam, Vigilant, Swingfire and the rest was a far more significant advance than the introduction of semiautomatic control or the abandonment of wire.

motor gases to spin the dispenser reel, but as far as I know this work was never taken to a conclusion.

We now come to the point of controller selection and training for manual guidance — a topic of which one might say that never had so many argued so much to so little effect. There are two related issues here — the difficulty of the task and the effect of battle stress on performance. Aside from remarking that controlling a missile manually is a single-skill as opposed to a multiskill task, I would like to deal with the first point by a reminiscence and an analogy. I recall watching a controller rated as marginal — a judgment to which I would entirely subscribe — on the ranges with Swingfire. On his first ever live firing the automatic gather failed and the missile sailed on upwards at 20° or whatever. When nothing appeared in his field of view, the controller lifted his eyes to heaven, saw the missile and proceeded to pull it down at 45-50° onto a target at a shade over 2000 m. I dare to tell this story because the days of the trials of the SS series, Malkara and Swingfire brought up case upon case where a human controller fully in the loop pulled back a missile that had gone way beyond the scope of any semiautomatic or automatic system. While giving the soldier every sophisticated aid, we should do well to keep firmly in mind the human ability to "pull something out of the bag".

My analogy is the story of the US Army and the Soviet rocket launcher. The initial assessment of a captured launcher, presumably one of the RPG7 models, was that the hit chance was so low as to make it a useless antiarmor weapon. Luckily somebody told the trials team to go away and try again, using Soviet training techniques. The second trial was a complete success. I do not wish to labor this point, but it leads neatly into the subject of battle stress. Israel's principal opponent in the Yom Kippur War was a nation not widely reputed (ancient times apart) as possessing *il dono di coraggio* or notable attainments in manual skill. Israeli soldiers are generally accepted to be the most effective and among the bravest in the world. But the Soviet ATGMSs, with their manual wire command link guidance, came very close to winning the war for the Arabs and convincing the world that the tank was dead.

Western trials using battle effects suggest that controllers remain virtually unaffected unless they are physically disturbed by having their line of sight interrupted or partially obscured, or by being jolted or displaced. These results, though, have only limited validity because the subject knew he was at no real risk. In the early sixties the United States Human Resources Research Organization (HumRRO) in conjunction with a number of universities attempted to assess the effect of battle stress on performance of combat tasks.[7] The situations used bore no great resemblance to that of a guided-missile controller, but the result tended to bear out experience. An active participant in an exciting combat task takes a lot of putting off. I believe the continuing demand for autonomous missiles stems from quantitative evaluations of the vulnerability associated with long exposure times rather than from user anxieties about battle stress.

Certainly one theme that runs through debriefings on trials and training firings of manually controlled missiles is the feeling of being "up there flying the missile". This is probably why controllers of manual systems are relatively immune to battle stress. It also links to the third objection to the manual system, protracted exposure of the controller and his mount — specially if he is the expensive pilot or the gunner of an expensive attack helicopter. I have to admit to an unAmerican — and maybe unGerman — preference for putting my money on a man rather than a machine. This aside, though, I hope I have a reasonably objective approach. So maybe I can also admit to utter puzzlement at the total unresponsiveness of other NATO members to the Swingfire system with its facility for *"semiindirect fire"* — the separation of launcher and controller (pls. 13 and 14). Maybe it is relevant if nostalgic to trace a lineage from the British World War II technique of semiindirect fire from tanks through Swingfire to the current British project (of which more later) for a "mast-mounted sight" for attack helicopters.

Sure, deploying Swingfire in the semiindirect mode is a circumstantial and rather unarmorlike affair. Likewise the elevated sight for choppers is expensive and problem-fraught. And both devices expose to observation a sight head which is fairly large and, once spotted, pinpoints the "over the crest" target discussed in Chapter 10. If we link the need to improve system survivability by avoiding protracted and predictable exposure to the merits of letting the controller feel he's "right up there flyin' it", one technical solution leaps out — *a vidicon tube in the missile with a wire link serving both to give the sight picture to the controller and to carry his command signals.*

---

7 Unfortunately I cannot now trace the documentation, although I obtained some of it and worked on it in 1967. My recall is that the project was named Project or Task Fighter, that the trials were carried out with US Combat Development Command and that results were published through Columbia University, New York: see also *Tank Warfare,* page 154.

This system — sometimes with a radio frequency rather than a wire link — has long been a proven and successful technique in air-to-surface missiles or "guided bombs". I guess the reasons everybody shies away from its use in the antiarmor role are low rate of fire, lack of battleworthiness and high cost. Unless we are prepared to accept the very grave drawbacks of an autonomous missile — when somebody gets around to developing one — in an EW environment and in face of active protection systems, we can forget about the rate-of-fire problem and accept that ATGMSs are slow compared with gun-based systems. We can then address the other questions.

I see three arguments for a system working in the visible light spectrum. First, it provides the best possible data to the human eye and thus offers the best chance of exploiting those "hidden" human resources. Second, it is hard to jam (blind), and any source attempting this is instantly visible to everybody on the battlefield. Third, if smoke is used to block the line of sight, the user exposes himself to all the associated problems (pages 17 and 117). Sure, a TV-based ATGMS optimized for round-the-clock use calls for a combination of tube characteristics rather different than any existing requirement. The camera head needs to accommodate automatically to the entire range of light levels normally covered by standard and low light-level tubes. Additionally the response at all light levels needs to spread well into the near-IR band to minimize the effects of deliberate smoke or the "fog of war". But all this — indeed an entire system of this kind — is entirely within the current state of the art. Problem is, it is probably too old hat to interest designers and manufacturers much — even if it should happen to be the answer the user really needs.

From the time armies first began to take spin-off from aviation and later aerospace technology, the innovators have had to fight an unending battle over cost. Fact is sums of money which are run-of-the-mill in the aerospace ballpark as a whole and which represent a minute fraction of aerospace system costs look plain unacceptable in land-force terms. We can begin to get a feel for this by noting that the electronics, optronics and the like currently add up to some 60% of the cost of a main battle tank.[8] I recall some discussion of TV-based systems back in the early days of ATGMS. The idea of expending a "TV camera" with every shot left the financiers open mouthed. As to user reaction, I

8 von Senger und Etterlin, Introduction to *Taschenbuch der Panzer 1976*: see Bibliography.

suspect the real rub was the gross indecency of having a "TV set" in a tank.[9]

So we need to look at cost in real terms. For starters we can forget about the on-vehicle part of the system. Most probably a display tube already installed for some other purpose can be used; even if not the monitor is a drop in the ocean of the avionics/optronics/electronics as a whole. The on-missile unit may be more expensive than those of other guidance systems used in the antitank field. But if this unit maximizes real-kill chance and saves the firing vehicle or helicopter from becoming a direct fire target, the system has to be cost-effective. Theoretically, by use of a modification of target grid procedure,[10] an ATGMS with a TV head could be fired indirect — that is, without any exposure of any part of the weapon platform.

This possibility, however, highlights the second major question mark which hangs over operations in an EW environment — the possibility of losing all net radio communications. Nobody much cares to think about this because of the effect on command and control. But everybody knows that's the way it is — whence my earlier suggestion of calling artillery fire down by flare (page 121). The Soviet Army has motorcycle subunits which double in the reconnaissance and dispatch-riding roles, scaled to provide an alternative means of communication down to company level. Bundeswehr units have organic DRs. But the British and (as far as I know) US Armies lack this backup. In any event DRs and at higher level light helicopters can maintain communications for command and control purposes at some cost in tempo. *These means cannot be used to call for or correct fire, still less as substitutes for a radio link within a weapon system.*

Links based on directional beams like radio relay or lasers are harder to cut than omnidirectional radiations. And as one moves up in frequency along the electromagnetic spectrum jamming proper gives way to capture and then to swamping or blinding — in other words the power required for countermeasures rises and their effective range falls. But we have to face the fact that any

---

9 I recall how, after one meeting in which this possibility was mentioned, a very senior British tank officer linked it to the story of the Battle of Beda Fom (Libya, 1941), when 2nd Royal Tank Regiment captured an Italian tank with two women crammed into the loader's station.

10 *Target grid procedure* allows an observer to bring down artillery fire by passing just his position, the target bearing from him ("OT bearing") and its estimated distance from him. A simple converter then gives the gun (or launcher) target azimuth ("GT bearing") and range. Likewise the observer gives corrections of fire as he sees them.

"wireless" link can sometimes at least be blocked. I myself have always believed this possibility should rule out all ATGMS *guidance* systems but wire command link. I admit this is an extreme view, but I believe most users would go along with me in excluding any form of guidance link the failure of which could lead to a missile going wild and endangering friendly forces.

Fire-control radio links present rather a different problem which we need to address at two levels — without and with an EW environment. In the first case normal artillery communications are evidently acceptable. If we treat spoiling of the attack by target reaction as a separate problem, there is no objection as far as communications are concerned to the use of an observer with a target-marking device for terminally guided systems like Copperhead which present no hazard to friendly forces even if guidance fails.

I have nonetheless always regarded with grave suspicion the "two-stage" ATGMSs which have been discussed many times over the past two decades and which will doubtless come into vogue again as compound armor targets call for missiles which are at least Hellfire-sized and maybe mansized like the old Malkara. In the two stage system (fig. 17) launchers are sited either individually or grouped like a battery of guns behind the direct-fire zone under an artillerylike command post! "Forward controllers" in positions of observation call for a missile by giving simply an observer-target bearing. Stage 1 of the system puts the missile over the forward controller's head within certain limits of lateral and vertical dispersion and of heading error.

The forward controller then gathers the missile and (stage 2) brings it down tangentially onto his line of sight (or adopts some other flight profile appropriate to the missile's turn rate). I guess it doesn't need too much imagination to envision what is likely to happen when an attacking combat team breaks cover and comes fast down a forward slope. Calling up of missiles by forward controllers, designation of missiles to them and synchronization of gathering signals with the arrival of the missile over their heads has to add up to one big snafu — quite apart from the problem of ensuring that this long-range ATGMS and the direct fire antiarmor systems closer in do not engage the same target.[11] One

---

11 In a hitherto unpublished paper by de Gaulle quoted by Huard (*see* Bibliography), one of de Gaulle's strongest objections to the 1939 French doctrine of dividing the tank force into "mass attack" and "infantry support" elements was that each had its own artillery support and chaos would thus ensue when one passed through the other.

1. Dongolas Pass, Keren, Eritrea

2a. Swedish Marder/105-mm test vehicle: three-quarter view

2b. Marder/105-mm in fire position

3. Soviet T72 tank

5. (*Upper and lower right*) Two views of the US M60A2 tank

4. British Chieftain Mark 5 tank with Chobham armor

6. US M60 tank

7. Soviet Josef Stalin heavy tank

8. British FV4030/3

9. S Tank

10a. US HIMAG test vehicle in basic form

10b. HIMAG with 75-mm ARES gun

11a. US HSTV-L prototype/test vehicle in a tactical setting

11b. HSTV-L instrumented for test

12 a and b. Soviet KMT 4 and 5 mine-clearance rollers/plow

13. British Striker vehicle with Swingfire

14. Swingfire combined sight (mounted/dismounted, day/night)

15. US TOW ATGMS

16. Franco-German MILAN ATGMS

17a. Soviet Sagger ATGMS in case

17b. Sagger in action (missile is to right of sight and operators)

18. Soviet BMP1 infantry fighting vehicle

19. Soviet RPG7V: (a) launcher; (b) complete round

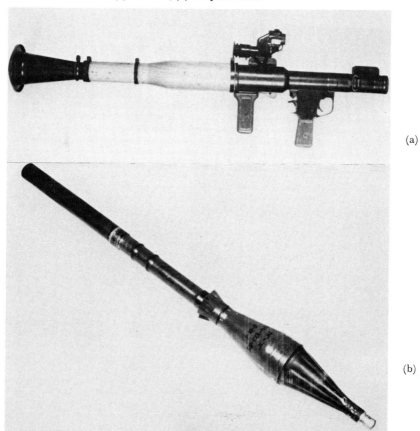

(a)

(b)

20. Swedish Carl-Gustav M2-550 with HEAT round

21. Soviet RKG3 antitank grenade

22. British rigid limpet assault mine

23. French Alouette 3 with SS11 ATGMS

24. Huey Cobra AH1G with TOW ATGMS

25. US advanced attack helicopter AH64

26. West German B0105 antitank helicopter (prototype)

27. Soviet Hind A

28a. Soviet Hind D being serviced

28b. Hind D in the assault

29. British Scorpion light/reconnaissance tank.

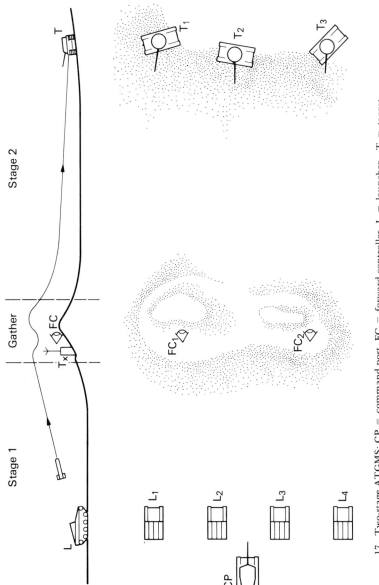

Stage 1   Gather   Stage 2

17. Two-stage ATGMS: CP = command post, FC = forward controller, L = launcher, T = target

145

can now see why there is at first sight a big payoff in a laser target marker combined with semiactive homing.

Moving back into an EW scenario, we need to consider how artillery fire can be called down and corrected with the command and artillery RT nets out. In the worst case there are just two options, both of them highly restrictive — *line* and *visual* communication. Tempowise, conventional methods of line laying are evidently just not in the same ballpark as the modern maneuver battle. Fast line laying by light helicopter is a possibility. But one objection to this is the risk of disclosing the defensive layout; another is the problem of linking line to an armored vehicle that wants to maneuver. It might be possible to establish *forward line terminals* to which VHF or UHF radios, or lasers, could work at very short range on nap-of-the-earth visual paths without interference from hostile jamming stations outside this visual path. But the complexities of such a system and the limitations its use would impose on maneuver are self-evident.

Since this topic belongs in the "countermeasures to the nth" ballgame, discussion of it is classified. I do not know what the official trends or solutions are — if indeed the problem has been squarely faced. It strikes me, though, that despite the extreme simplicity it imposes on message content and options, visual signaling may offer more scope for calling fire down. Additionally, as mentioned above, even though a very short-range broadcast net may be an impracticable though technically feasible form of counter-countermeasure, a highly directional UHF relay or laser link going back from command tank or forward observer looks a much better starter.

I go right along with the Soviet concept of bringing a *small amount* of artillery up to the back of the direct-fire zone. But to move the bulk of the artillery forward like this would add up to an enormous risk and nullify the prime advantage of indirect fire in the maneuver battle — its ability to mass. So maybe we should think in terms of a *"rear observer"* linked to the guns and rocket/missile launchers by fast-laid line. He would need to be far enough back — say 5-6 km behind the FEBA — and high enough up to have a field of visual observation with sufficient breadth and depth to give scope for company-level maneuver. Ideally he would be on the receiving or relaying end of a high-capacity communications system like laser beams running back from conventional forward observers and/or subunit headquarters. Failing this he could see and respond to visual signals and himself observe and correct fire.

We need then to examine the possibilities of visual signaling as a means of calling down prearranged fires and hopefully of target indication. Here we are on much more familiar ground because the problem is basically the same as visual communications between forward troops and ground-attack aircraft. Groups of three of the various standard signal and illuminating cartridges combined with observation of the approximate point of origin could provide an adequate though limited code for calling down planned defensive fires by "target number"; for indicating danger to friendly forces, as for instance from fire falling short; and for orders like "lift" or "cease fire". There would be a need for phased "gunlines" (by analogy with bomblines). Opportunity targets could be indicated by marker rounds of colored smoke, heavy machinegun/cannon tracer or the like.

I do not wish to probe too far into what are essentially artillery problems, but I hope this chapter has succeeded in highlighting three points about operating in an EW environment.

Using any kind of "wireless" link in the guidance system of an ATGMS adds up to a serious and I believe an avoidable risk.

If the maneuver element of the antiarmor defense is to stay in business, it must be prepared to maintain communications by "mechanized runners" when its radio nets are put out.

If indirect fire is to play the part in the antiarmor defense that many other factors suggest it now can and must, artillery too needs countermeasure-proof communications systems which will not expose it to undue risk or impair its ability to mass fire.

12

Guided and mixed systems

We already noted that compound armor would tend to push antitank guided missiles out of the middle ground of the antiarmor weapon spectrum towards the extremities where they first came in. The second clearly emerging trend in the state of the armored vehicle art, a series of step advances in mobility aimed primarily at reducing exposure times, is likely to reinforce this effect. For guided missiles are by nature a slow form of attack compared with the gun. Even with a conventional autoloader as opposed to the high-rate DARPA/ARES design, a tank can get three APDSFS rounds to a target at, say, 3500 m in the time of flight of one transonic missile. So even if gross differences in hit chance and lethality existed — which they do not — the gun would still be the faster system.

To examine the future of antitank missilery we need to borrow a term or two from other fields of the art. A distinction has to be drawn between the *cruise* type of missile with guidance over its whole flight and the *ballistic* missile with initial and/or terminal guidance; and in this second category between the rocket and the gun-delivered missile or "guided shell". I believe in fact we need to look at three types of ATGMS —

a ballistic system;

a "heavy" cruise system;

a "light" cruise system.

For a number of reasons, not least the question of warheads, I want to defer discussion of the third until we have looked at submunitions and to pick it up along with unguided crew-served weapons. So in this chapter we shall be concerned, for ground launch at least, with rather deliberate, artillerylike systems. A while back the British switched Swingfire on its various mounts from the Royal Armoured Corps to the Royal Artillery, thus once again demonstrating their knack of doing the right thing in the long haul for the worst possible reason in the short.

System cost-effectiveness

Lying on the borderline of land warfare and aerospace technology, ATGMSs are always specially vulnerable to arguments about cost. So before we probe any specific problems deeper I want to digress and come again at a point I nibbled at in the last chapter — what it is worth to destroy an enemy tank or IFV *which has reached a key position on the battlefield.* Sure, we can put a unit cost and a system unit cost[1] on a tank; and armies can and certainly should follow the practice of air forces and calculate a figure for the real cost of recruiting, selecting, training and maintaining crew. Suppose all this came to $5m — or any figure you like in that order. Certainly it will be high enough to make politicians tear their hair. Likewise suppose that this cost is the same for the Soviets, which is probably true to the extent that cost means resources — only it doesn't make the Politburo tear its collective hair. Then we have a T72 for $5m; so we can do the converse sum and argue that, with an overall kill chance from factory to target of, say, 20%, an ATGMS would be cost-effective at a real cost of a million dollars a shot.

But this is only half the story. When writing in *Tank Warfare*[2] of the movement of masses, in particular of the blitzkrieg, I tried to bring out the concept of *moment* or length of lever arm — the way the combat worth of a force increases with its distance beyond the enemy's center of mass. I now want to extend this thinking backwards. A T72 comes off the production line in the Soviet heartland east of the Urals. It passes down the issue channels and finally reaches a tank battalion, say near Kiev, where it is married up with a trained crew and brought to battleworthy condition. This process has, I suggest, added to the value of the tank in three ways. The vehicle has actually had subsystems like a radio added to it; and a series of inspections, tests and maintenance operations have debugged it. Additionally it has gained value as a realizable asset with respect to its *raison d'être* by being moved towards the point at which it may be deployed. Suppose the battalion holding this tank is then moved to say Magdeburg, ostensibly for maneuvers but in fact as a

1 i.e. respectively, the production cost of a vehicle, and the total financial cost of fielding it.
2 Pages 40 *et seq.*

reinforcement. Evidently the tank is now worth more to the Warsaw Pact high command.

So far this third gain in value is a fairly gradual one and probably quantifiable — say as a linear function of distance. (Figure 18 is an attempt to represent my point graphically — at qualitative level!) But now let us suppose the Pact attacks westwards directed onto the Rhine and with Bonn, Brussels and The Hague as its initial strategic objectives. Evidently the gain in value of this T72 now gets much faster; it also becomes imponderable, but maybe we can get a feel for it. There has to be a step advance as the tank crosses the frontier and joins battle; then the worth rises quasi-exponentially until the tank reaches the main NATO defenses. As it survives its way through these, the growth rate of value with respect to distance steepens yet again, to make another step advance if the tank breaks clear. After this the "moment" argument of the blitzkrieg applies. Maybe I can drive the point home by asking anyone in a responsible military or political position within NATO what they would pay to have this T72 destroyed as it sits on the Rhine bank looking across at Bonn.

In other words, I have never believed that cost-effectiveness had any *absolute* meaning in defense of the kind it has in commerce. Only in special circumstances, like when a government has to make a discrete financial tradeoff to secure supplies of a vital commodity like food or oil, do we get anywhere near to quantifying the financial cost of a political aim. Some argue that the percentage of the GNP or "gross alliance product" devoted to defense puts a value on preservation of the socio-political system. I do not think this is so, because the cost of even the most miniscule of warlike operations is completely out of scale with peacetime thinking.[3] Surely a defense budget is something between an insurance premium and a bet on an outsider — or buzzwordwise a subject for cost-benefit analysis rather than the straightforward cost-effectiveness treatment.

By contrast *relative* cost-effectiveness is of enormous importance because, as mentioned above, cost represents resources. In modern Western armies where manpower and equipment costs are apt to split around even, *manpower-effectiveness* is more important still; or rather it has to be a major factor in any comparison of real cost-effectiveness. *So relative cost-effectiveness is a genuine yardstick of combat worth and a valid means of comparing two systems,* whether like (say TOW and MILAN

---

3 For instance, some sources put the cost of the abortive United States attempt to rescue her hostages from Iran at $20m.

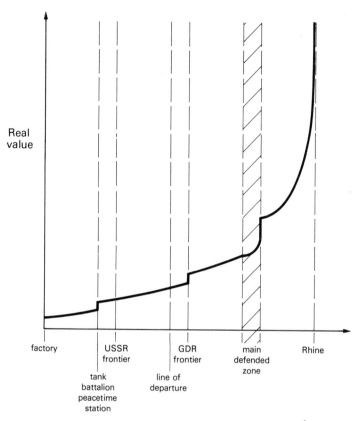

Real
value

factory   USSR   GDR   main   Rhine
              frontier   frontier   defended
                                         zone

              tank   line of
              battalion   departure
              peacetime
              station

(Distance from first strategic objective) $^{-1}$

18. Concept of "real value added" (*see* text for explanation)

or unlike (say TOW and M60A3). For the military man at least
"What is System X's cost per kill?" is the wrong question to ask;
the right one is "How do Systems X and Y match up in cost per
kill?"

Ballistic antitank missile options

Elsewhere in this book I refer to the ballistic category of ATGMS
as artillerylike or using "indirect fire"; but for an actually or
potentially moving target this definition will not quite do. A
direct-fire gun is *aimed at its target* with corrections set in, these
corrections including "lead" — in other words, at a predicted
target position derived from range input and tracking rate

feedback. A line-of-sight cruise ATGM is brought onto the line of sight to the target and constantly corrected onto it, whether this line of sight is fixed or changing.

Even should the target happen to be visible from the firing position, the trajectory of the type of missile I now have in mind is determined from quite a different principle. The projectile is fired on a trajectory designed to bring it to impact at *a certain point on the earth's surface.* This may be the actual target position, or some convenient reference point, or the datum point of a defensive fire concentration. Even if it happens to be the target position, this point cannot be determined by the observer or communicated to the firing position with sufficient accuracy to ensure a hit by, say, full-trajectory inertial guidance. Nor for that matter can the firing position be accurately enough determined.[4] So quite apart from cost, complexity and the like, initial or full-trajectory guidance is out.

Not until the projectile is "over the top" and its nose is pointed in the direction of the target can corrections usefully be applied. We are talking about a single free-flight ballistic projectile with *terminal guidance*; let us return in a moment to ways of launching it. By similar arguments, this terminal guidance has to be related to the precise position of the target at the time of impact. Since a projectile which is descending on a ballistic trajectory cannot be brought onto a surface-to-surface or low air-to-surface line of sight, this guidance has to be some form of homing. Currently, for reasons of cost and compactness, systems like Copperhead favor *semiactive homing with the target illuminated by a laser target marker* (fig. 16b).

At present this is a highly effective and economical system, with the added advantage that the use of an unspun shaped charge, a passive head on the projectile and a slipping driving band allow a shell of this kind to be fired by current techniques from a versatile projector, in fact a rifled gun of 152- or 155-mm caliber. But I believe several arguments put forward in earlier chapters call this kind of system in question for the longer term. One is evidently charge weight; but since one of the key features of ballistic systems is that they attack the weak top of the target, this is not too strong a one.

A much greater problem is the kind of active protection discussed in the last section of Chapter 4. Being mainly designed

---

4 Since some readers may question this, it may be worth reminding them that the greatest single problem in developing a submarine-launched ICBM system was said to be accurate enough location of the submarine.

against helicopter-launched line-of-sight missiles, such systems are likely to have a response time of around 10 seconds; within a further 5 seconds or so from activation the tank could start to move behind the system's screen. With artillery deployed conventionally for optimum massing capability and security, the time of flight of a medium shell is typically upwards of 20 seconds.[5] If we assume the observer to be on, or on relay to the firing battery net, take typical lag on an artillery net passing fire orders and allow minimal time for the order to be passed to the selected gun, we are talking of a lapse of 30 seconds at the very least between the observer's order to fire and the time of impact; and of something downwards of 20 seconds between the observer's hearing "On the way"[6] and impact. So if he is not to trigger the target's active protection in time for the attack to be spoiled, the observer must count down a number of seconds from hearing "On the way" before he illuminates the target. This alone could be awkward enough under battle conditions. But this system has an indispensable radio link in the firing sequence — a feature that our examination of the electronic warfare threat identified as a major weakness. Even if the observer could call a shot down by flare or whatever, he would be left from that moment on with his target marker switched on and glued to the target — not unlike the proverbial little Dutch boy with his finger in the hole of the dyke.

The only way round this is for the projectile to indicate its presence to the observer; and if this is done visually he must take his eye off the target. So we have pointer no. 1 towards an active system. Pointer no. 2 stems from the probable movement exposure times of future armored vehicle targets (page 36). We saw how, with a fast direct-fire system, the chance of a target offered being killed falls sharply as mean exposure time comes down towards mean acquisition time; and we were looking at a figure in the 25-30-second zone. Evidently an artillery observer will often have to acquire a target on one exposure, keep tabs on it by dust signature or such, and engage it on its second exposure. But even if he says "Fire" as the target comes into view again, he will need to choose occasions on which he can see that it will be exposed for at least 35-40 seconds. Sure, the time for which the target is in view of an observer on a hill is substantially longer than that enjoyed by the defending tanker tucked hull down in a

---

5 Reduction of this may be one reason for the reported Soviet tactic of bringing some artillery well forward.

6 British "Shot".

fold. By the same token, unless they can remain in full cover, targets in the impact area remain *permanently exposed to a projectile looking obliquely downwards.*

Certainly guided shell like Copperhead will remain a useful bonus as a complementary nature for tubed artillery. But whatever financiers may say about dispatching costly hardware on a one-way journey, I believe the future primary system has to be a *ballistic missile with terminal guidance by active homing.* The homing system should be triggered by an on-missile device during the last 10 seconds of flight and designed to revert the missile to ballistic flight on its last corrected heading if homing is spoiled. There are evidently a number of sensor options for a system of this kind, the choice between them probably depending on the fashion of the moment as much as any substantive factor.

What is more, this expensive projectile needs to carry a warhead massive enough to produce *total disruption of any foreseeable armored vehicle target.* There are four reasons for this, the first being quite simply that a high-cost system must have a payload which assures a kill. Second, it is uneconomical even if feasible to design for a K kill with direct fire KE attack, probably even with disruptive attack from a gun; yet a system with a K kill capability is valuable as a deterrent if it can be fielded.[7] Third, the penalties of a grossly overmatching warhead are less with this system than with a line-of-sight cruise ATGMS, specially a ground-launched one. Fourth, the power of attack should be sufficient for a near miss to give a reasonable chance of an F or P kill on the more lightly armored of the priority targets, and hopefully at least an M kill on a tank.

On ballpark figuring from basic parameters this projectile might just about be thrown from a 155-mm gun, but it "feels" much more like a rocket. Optimizing warhead mass-effectiveness will be easier without a restriction on diameter. Relatively low axial accelerations and no spin make the design of the homing head, its activating device and the fuze much easier, as well as allowing minimal case thickness. Additionally, if the reader will allow me to anticipate discussions we are going to have later, a rocket looks a better fit both in terms of the weapons family and organizationally. Suffice it to say for the moment that I envision this as the "heavy" equipment of a dedicated antiarmor artillery battalion (or the equipment of a dedicated battery); that with the

---

7 I recall the effect on morale of the British Crusader tank having its turret crushed in by field and medium HE shell, and of the very tough Matilda tank suffering crew casualties from heavy artillery.

possible exception of aerodynamic-control surfaces and the final links to them (if such a system were used) all the guidance and fuzing would be in the primary antiarmor warhead; and that the rocket would have alternate warheads in its basic free-flight form. With terminal guidance against pinpoint targets and free flight as an area weapon, one would hope to stay clear of accuracy problems up to the key main battle range, which I would put at around twice the depth of the direct-fire zone — at least 8 km and desirably 12 km. A considerably longer range would evidently be nice to have for massing fire and for the harassing role, but I believe this is "as long as a piece of string" and should be determined by optimization of technical factors.

Maybe I should make one closing point before readers familiar with the spoiling arguments of Western procurement systems throw the book out of the window — or at the financier who happens to be handiest. If this "ballistic" system succeeds, what I have called the "heavy cruise ATGMS" is superfluous in the surface-to-surface role and, like Hellfire, can be specialized for helicopter delivery. I see "ballistic" and "heavy cruise" systems not as complementary to one another but as *alternates,* either of them being complementary to the high-pressure gun, the attack helicopter and other dedicated and multipurpose delivery systems and munitions of the artillery. Frankly I cannot at this time see why, given scout choppers to spot for it with minimal exposure, this ballistic system should not also be an alternate to the attack helicopter in the main force defensive setting. But since the attack helicopter with its cruise missile is needed as the heavy punch of the light mechanized or airborne force, as a protagonist in quick counterpenetration and economy of force operations, maybe even as the weapon platform in a heliborne maneuver force, I do not need to stick my neck out quite that far.

"Heavy" cruise antitank missiles

I am going to assume then that the primary cruise missile system can be designed entirely for attack helicopters. On state-of-the-art parameters this allows a reduction in the missile/warhead mass ratio from around 5.5:1 to 4:1 or so. Either this payoff could be taken as such; or, other things being equal, the saving could be used to shorten time of flight by increasing sustained missile speed (or peak speed in a system with a boost/glide profile). Mainly on the arguments of earlier chapters, but partly because the autonomous missile concept is being actively examined in the

USA and the "mast-mounted sight" approach in the UK, I am likewise going to assume a missile with a "TV" head and a wire link along which the sight picture is passed to the controller and his manual command signals are sent back to the missile. The mast-mounted sight may nevertheless be worthwhile to allow observation and target acquisition without unmasking.

Fact is we set out the various requirements for this missile in Chapters 3, 8 and 11 and need only summarize them here. A warhead weighing around 10 kg and packing a massive improved shaped charge (like Hellfire) is sufficient in the short haul, but allowance of up to 20 kg for warhead weight should be made for successor systems. It is important to get missile speed up to 1.25 Mach and desirable to move towards 1.5 Mach. We do not at the moment know whether controller reaction time imposes a limit on speed with TV guidance in a low-level air-to-surface system; but if it exists at all the problem should be much less acute than with past and current manual command link systems based on the angular error subtended at the sight. The minimum range requirement is not critical in this application. Maximum range needs to be at least 4000 m — a range proven with wire control in Swingfire; 6000 m is evidently desirable.

There seems to me to be one improvement, though, which could radically improve the firing helicopter's survivability. With TV guidance the machine can remain in rotor defilade during the firing. But odds are somebody on the opposing side will know where it is lurking either from rotor or launch signature or from backtracking the missile — or again just from seeing the machine unmask briefly to acquire the target. We have seen that "over the crest" engagement is likely to become a feature of the direct-fire battle. So it would be healthy for the chopper to have some freedom of maneuver while the missile was on the way. TV guidance frees the controller from the need to remain on the line of sight; I reckon this freedom could be maintained even with wire control. For instance, the launcher could carry a spool of extra wire supplied with the missile. This could be spun up by a cartridge fired as the missile motor was ignited, or unwound as the helicopter moved by a small anchor weight which fell to the ground when the on-missile wire started to be dispensed. Or doubtless in many other ways. This is an important minor development. If it succeeded the TV guidance system would have a decisive edge on any other so far proposed — not "fire and forget" so much as "fight and run away".

As we proceed through this book with its very wide scope, I am increasingly trying to pan in on what strikes me as the key problem or possibility of advance within each subfield. Compound armor and elusive targets force the high-pressure gun back into its traditional pride of place and even beyond this. Compound armor pushes the antiarmor warhead designer right up in weight and maybe away from shaped charge to disruptive attack. Elusive targets and many other factors conspire to push the missile up in speed and thus further up in weight; and to impose severe constraints on guidance options.

As a tanker I fundamentally distrust indirect fire and, more than most, I enjoy teasing gunners. But looking at the nest of problems and being very familiar with the snags of handling large missiles both physically and tactically within the direct-fire zone, I have to concede that the answer may be to stand well back and surmount the problems with a neat ballistic hop — thus also taking the target from the angle at which it is weakest and most exposed to view.

Afternote

Research I carried out while this book was in press, notably discussion with Swedish experts, leaves me in no doubt about two things. The resolution obtainable from a TV-type system is critical both for the ATGMS discussed above and for the armored vehicle design concepts postulated in Chapter 15. At the moment the vidicon tube's performance is adequate for laying and tracking under reasonable conditions, but the system lacks penetration (of mist, dust, etc.) and is inferior in resolution to good optics, which thus remain indispensable for target acquisition. By the nineties, though, two advances can confidently be expected. One is a marked improvement in the vidicon tube's performance, notably resolution. The other is the incorporation of it into a multisensor head, the outputs from which are passed through an image processor to produce a combined image. This image can be optimized for any particular requirement (e.g. acquisition, laying, tracking) and to suit general ambient and local battlefield conditions.

13

Submunitions

I recall as a boy taking a potshot with an airgun at a pigeon on the wing. Being too young to have heard of statistics, I hit it. However, I soon learned the advantages of a shotgun. So I can see just how the notion of cluster projectiles and submunitions got itself extrapolated from the antipersonnel role through a rather devious route to attack on tanks. I used to fish too, and I soon discovered that a night line with a string of hooks left out for a lot of hours — an unsporting illegality to which all concerned turned a blind eye — made for a much better breakfast than a day's frantic casting. These childhood analogies, specially the second, make the key points about submunitions.

For the great merit of scatterable minelets ("delayed effect munitions") is that they require attack and target to coincide only in space, not in time as well. On the simplest of statistical models for scatter from carrier projectiles at burst and submunition characteristics, along with equally simple assumptions about formations and intervals between vehicles, one can work out the proportion of vehicles likely to be immobilized. Immediate effect submunitions have the odds far more heavily stacked against them even without the question mark that must hang over their lethality.

My impression from reading published literature, for instance on the United States Assault Breaker program,[1] is that technologists in government and industry are having themselves a ball on statistically thin ice, while the users admire the spectacle without knowing how thin the ice is. Life is difficult enough when success requires just one favorable outcome — as designers and users who have struggled for decades to give a tank gun an acceptable first-round-hit chance on a turret target know. When success means several things going the right way at once, it's apt to play hard to get (fig. 19). In, for instance, the bomblet version

---

1 e.g. "AUSA '79": *see* Bibliography.

of the Assault Breaker system, the pattern (with guestimated — I think generously — subsystem success chances) might be something like this:

		%
1.	arrival of "bus" missile over target area	85
	timely and successful burst and dispense	90
	whence chance of bomblet launch in target area =	77
2.	initiation of "smart" bomblet guidance	90
	initial trajectory within scope of guidance system	80
	timely acquisition of a target	50
	successful line-up or hit	60
	timely fuze initiation	85
	whence (from 1 and 2) hit chance =	14
3.	F or P kill lethality (see below)	20
	whence (from 1, 2 and 3) kill chance =	2.8

Thus a bus missile containing sixty-four bomblets might be expected to kill between one and two tanks. The claim that one bus missile could cause enough casualties to bring a tank or motor rifle company to a halt (or presumably reduce its worth by one tactical level) requires subsystem success chances that are not so much pipedreams as hallucinations.

What is more there is one massive tacit assumption behind all this, and we might take a first look at it now. The Assault Breaker concept requires an observation/fire-control aircraft to remain within a given piece of hostile airspace at a fair height — certainly divorced from terrain cover — for a significant time; and for part of this time to transmit signals establishing the "electronic basket" over the target area into which the bus missiles home. Additionally this aircraft has to transmit fire orders on RT to the missile battery and (as I read it) maintain a radio data link with the battery throughout preparation, launch and flight. I know the US Air Force is a good deal more optimistic about the tactical air situation than its British or German counterparts or most commentators are. Even so this aircraft's chance of accomplishing its mission in face of the combined air-to-air, surface-to-air and electronic warfare threats looks slender to say the least.

I thought it was taken for granted that ground attack aircraft operating in hostile airspace would adopt a lo-lo-lo (NOE) flight profile and laydown bombing, only — and very reluctantly —

going lo-lo-hi to the extent needed for toss bombing. The new American "counter-radar coating" for aircraft and missiles could change this policy; but one suspects that this, like all advances of its kind, will be no more than a temporary swing of the pendulum.

There may be answers to all these points, but without (necessarily classified) evidence on success chances I for one remain unconvinced. Nobody questions the need for harassment and destruction in depth of advancing hostile armor; specially in an electronic warfare environment it is hard to see how artillery can acquire accurate and full enough data on moving ground targets. But if fixed-wing manned aircraft are going to be used in this role and they need an alternative to direct rocket and cannon attack, then I would be surprised if a bomb analog of the ballistic antiarmor missile described in the previous chapter would not be a more effective and cost-effective solution than bomblet or "minimissile" attack. As a bomb this warhead with terminal guidance by active homing would be relatively light and compact; it could be launched onto an appropriate trajectory from the final "hi" section of the flight profile or by a modified toss bombing technique.

If we exclude bus missiles with "smart" bomblets ("smartlets") or terminally guided "minimissiles" from the weaponry for attack of armor in depth, we need to consider — for the moment in terms of hit chance — whether submunitions delivered by carrier shell or rocket over shorter ranges, as envisioned in the SADARM project, are a worthwhile option. On information available to me SADARM submunitions are unguided but descend on a special parachute that spins them so that their heat-seeking or MMW sensor head makes a helical scan of the ground. When a target is acquired within the standoff limits, the fuze is initiated. I cannot see where the hit chance analysis for a system like this differs in kind from the speculations I indulged in a page or two back. The critical factor in all these sophisticated immediate effect sub-munitions is the need to go for standoff rather than impact detonation in order to obtain worthwhile terminal effects. This requirement places even more stringent constraints on accuracy than a direct hit with impact fuzing and limits success to the occasions when orientation towards a target coincides in time with acceptable standoff. What is more, success depends on the absence *up to the moment of fuze initiation* of any spoiling effect such as an active protection system might provide.

All these forms of overhead and oblique attack impinge on the

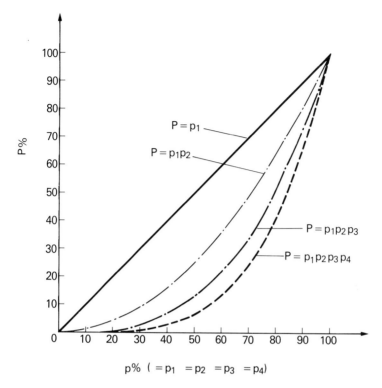

19. Success chance of multivariable systems. Success chance (P) for systems with two, three and four independent subsystems, each of which has the same individual success chance (p). The prospect of overall success falls away as the number of subsystems increases, unless *all* individual success chances are extremely (in fact unattainably) high

traditionally weak roof and rear of their target at low or medium obliquity. These aspects will almost certainly be toughened up at the expense of the traditional horizontal frontal arc (fig. 5); but bulk limits the kind of array armors which could be used on these surfaces. Frankly it is hard to see why, for angles of obliquity (in this case to the vertical) of 45° or less, the M42 51-mm (2 inch) HEAT/FRAG bomblet (currently delivered by the M483 155-mm round) will not do the job well enough, with an F kill lethality of maybe 15-20% or even 25% at normal. This is a cheap simple submunition with impact fuzing (whence high terminal reliability) and an antipersonnel bonus. It can be cheaply and accurately delivered in large quantities and is countermeasure proof. Carrier missiles or cluster bombs of the size of Assault Breaker's bus missile could saturate the target area with these bomblets. And there are evidently games to be played with optimization of overall kill chance by trading off shaped charge cone diameter (whence numbers whence hit chance) against lethality on future targets.

The question is whether sophistication can do better in terms of *tanks killed per weight of submunitions delivered* — specially when, on available information, these advanced systems require a submunition of at least twice the diameter of the M42 (upwards of 100 mm). Given delivery of the carrier to normal tubed artillery accuracy and predictable target densities, there has to be considerable doubt whether target seeking by a smaller number of sophisticated subprojectiles is likely to result in more hits than random dispersion of as many bomblets as possible. Additionally, as stressed above, any mode of attack which relies on proximity fuzing is going to reduce the chance of a "hit". So the name of the game is lethality. It is hard to see how any shaped charge submunition could attain an F or P kill lethality greater than that of a full bore HEATFS shell or warhead. So, as we saw above, we are looking at a maximum lethality of 20-25% for HEAT submunitions against the weaker aspects of the target, even with normal attack.

This is presumably one reason why the United States at least have gone for self-formed fragment (SFF) warheads.[2] I have left discussion of these over until this point both because information on them is scant and because the attack is completely bound up with the means of delivery. There are a number of possible designs and configurations; one that has been publicly demonstrated is shown schematically at fig. 20. When the sensor acquires a target within the limits of standoff, it initiates the fuze. The small discs of a ductile material like copper are projected at speeds claimed to be up to 7 Mach (say 2300-2400 m/sec). This phenomenon does not yet appear to be fully understood. One published explanation is that aerodynamic resistance fuses and reshapes the mini-projectile which then resolidifies (*cf.* fig. 20). A more probable hypothesis is based on shaped charges with a very wide angle and a relatively high-melting liner such as steel, which forms a single teardrop-shaped slug in place of a jet. This principle is already well known on a much larger scale (with a single projectile) in certain fougasse-like mines.

This technique has its own evident limitations. The surface/volume ratio has to be high enough for heat transfer to melt the entire slug; so size and thus mass are limited. The material

---

2 The acronym SFF is also expanded to "self-*forming* fragments" and "self-*forging* fragments". Take your pick!

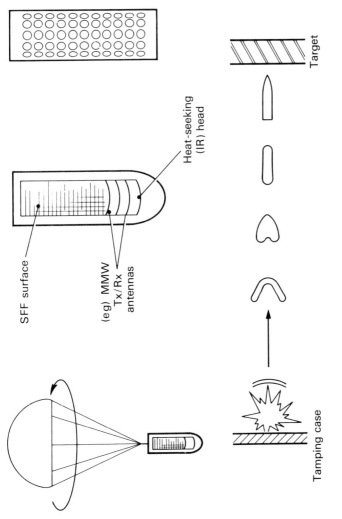

SFF surface

(eg) MMW
Tx/Rx
antennas

Heat-seeking
(IR) head

Tamping case

Target

20. Principle of SFF warhead (shown as parachute submunition). The sensor(s) and the SFF surface are laterally directional, the rest of the projectile wall serving merely to tamp and focus the bursting charge. Active (e.g. MMW) and/or passive (e.g. heat seeking) sensor systems may be used for initiation. The special parachute gives the projectile a slow spin as it falls, so that the sensor sweeps a helical pattern on the ground. There are a number of ways of achieving the "self-forming" effect (*see text*)

163

must be low-melting and ductile, in other words soft, although some work-hardening may take place. This slug could be expected to behave somewhere between a long rod penetrator and a shaped charge jet; but its speed on strike is likely to be only 25-30% of typical jet tip velocities. The energy required to deform the slug mechanically, to bring it to fusion point and then to apply the latent heat of fusion is considerable. This energy can only come from the slug's kinetic energy, so velocity drop over the first part of its flight will be acute. One might guestimate the remaining velocity at the point when the slug has achieved its final form as similar to the muzzle velocity of a modern long rod penetrator. In any event penetrations of around 100 mm of steel armor at zero obliquity and optimum standoff are claimed for SFF attack.

I suspect such attack would fare very badly, though, against the most elementary kind of unspaced array like steel/ceramic/steel/polyethylene that one would expect to find even on the roof and upper sides of major armored vehicles of the future. By contrast, it would be highly effective against vehicles with light steel armor, and the multistrike effect could well be similar to that of the Vulcan gun (page 107). It is hard to see how the F and P kill lethality could be much above 20%, but the effect on external fittings would evidently be more severe than that of HEAT. Without precise data one cannot be sure, but my feel is that sophistication is going to improve lethality marginally if at all, and that this gain may well be offset by reduced hit chance for a given weight of submunitions. In sum SFF attack could prove to be a particularly expensive way of falling between the stools of neutralizing and lethal antiarmor weapons.

If one is going to adopt immediate effect submunitions, he might do well to recall that the classical application of the Lanchester Equations was to arm the British Hurricane and Spitfire fighters with eight 30-caliber machineguns rather than 50-caliber machineguns or 20-mm cannon. In other words, it is the *number* of submunitions that matters.

There have to be situations in which the M483 shell or other artillery and air-to-surface carriers pay off over Copperhead, HEAT air-to-surface rockets and a pinpoint terminally guided missile or bomb. But I believe we have once more come up against the basic fact that looks like governing the attack of armor for quite a while yet. *Pinpoint weapons can produce a calculable chance only of an F or P kill, with a K kill as a bonus. Likewise*

area weapons can only assure neutralization, with an F or P kill as
a bonus.

This is not to say that immediate effect submunitions have no
place in the antiarmor family. Whichever facet of the antiarmor
defense one examines, one looks to be drawn towards a concept
of *a very high concentration of firepower in time.* Within this
concept neutralizing weapons have the role of setting up targets
and gaining time for the lethal weapon systems, direct and
indirect alike. The same combination applies *mutatis mutandis*
in the main defensive battle and in deep harassment by air
strikes.

This picture takes us back to another notion we discussed in
earlier chapters — extended neutralization. We saw a few pages
back how the minelet's success chance was improved because
attack and target needed to coincide only in space, not in time.
By the same token minelets provide extended neutralization. So
the choice of the mix of minelets, bomblets and other modes of
attack in the pattern of neutralizing fire calls for a judicious
balance between the double advantage of delayed effect munitions and the physical and psychological shock effect of a concentration of immediate effect weapons.

We can in fact give yet another twist to this tale. In Chapter 9
we discussed the use of scatterable mines by helicopters to provide
a kind of instant pivot of maneuver. If the lethal threat from
shaped charge and antipersonnel minelets in that mix was
thought to be inadequate, one could drop, lower or land
maroon-type weapons. By analogy with the jumping type of
antipersonnel mine,[3] these would scatter M42 bomblets or the
like; they could be initiated by short-range "wireless" command
and/or by tentacles of pneumatic pressure fuze.

Lack of published information on and feel for antiarmor
submunitions makes it hard to see them in any kind of perspective, harder still in the correct one. Sometimes desperation or
a particular constraint like bad flying weather will undoubtedly
result in their independent use for harassment. But coming new
to this subject and trying to think it through from scratch has
convinced me at least of three things. Pipedreams apart,
antiarmor submunitions are essentially neutralizing weapons with
a useful bonus of lethality. They will pay off best when used in
conjunction with lethal weapon systems as part of an all-arms fire

---

3 Like the Wehrmacht's S mine and the Bundeswehr's DM31.

plan, a fixed-wing air strike plan and maybe before too long a
helicopter fire plan. As long as these submunitions can achieve a
certain minimal level of effects, quantity not quality will count;
and quantity here means not just cheapness and simplicity but
above all lightness and compactness.

14

Crew served and short-range antitank weapons

The noises ammunition designers and analysts are now making increasingly suggest that enlarged and improved shaped charges v compound armors adds up to a good sporting contest likely to go the distance. By contrast, few would maintain that manportable weapon systems using shaped charge warheads are going to defeat the extended frontal arc of future tanks (fig. 5). But before we wave goodbye to crew served and individual antiarmor weapons or go pipedreaming, we need to get a few basic tactical points on record.

The first is the distinction between local defense and offensive or "tactical" firepower — firepower, that is, which can usefully be incorporated in a fire plan. I can best illustrate this distinction with an example outside the antiarmor field — by happenstance in a more controversial one still. APCs like M113 and FV432 carried a ring-mounted 30-caliber machinegun. I used to wonder whether its purpose in life was not to give the opposition a chance to shoot the commander — as the US Army in fact learned the hard way in Vietnam. Seriously though, this machinegun's role was limited to local defense or at most to covering the maneuver squad as it deployed. I do not see anybody lining these vehicles up to put down a curtain of fire. By contrast the stabilized 25-mm cannon on IFV (M2) makes several important contributions to the combat team's tactical capability and will be assigned defensive fire and/or antihelicopter tasks.[1] Likewise TOW, MILAN, Sagger, the 73-mm SPG9 gun-launcher on BMP1, RPG7V and Carl-Gustav (pls. 15-20) all currently play an important part in the pattern of antiarmor defensive fires. When it comes to confronting tanks with compound armor, all these weapon

---

1 This remains true whether or not a cannon as opposed to a larger gun is the best armament for an IFV.

systems have to be relegated to the local defense role or deployed in special ways. The other two points derive from this fact.

Short-range rocket launchers used against the tank's frontal arc are not rendered worthless but are degraded from lethal to neutralizing weapon systems. If a dismounted squad comes face to face with a tank on a sunken trail or a forest ride, thumping the front of the tank with a 70-90-mm HEAT rocket will give the men time to scatter and take cover, even if it only obscures the tank's line of sight. A lucky hit may do a good deal more — the lethality bonus is still there.

Fact is, aside from the crews of manportable ATGMSs, infantrymen should not be deployed to take tanks on frontally even if their weapons have enough power. The *tactically* correct use of the short-range weapons is in enfilade, ambush or tank hunting. In any event attempts to enhance protection of the upper hull front are more and more forcing designers to enlarge the vertical area projected by the lower front plate, to bring this plate nearer to the vertical and even to reduce its thickness (fig. 21). Extending the frontal arc upwards and sideways is going to encourage this trend; certainly one would not expect to see a major array on the lower hull front. So — with no disrespect — the worm's-eye view the good infantryman is apt to have of a tank offers him a target that his rocket launcher can defeat.

My guess is that inability to defeat the target's frontal arc, superimposed on some vulnerability to countermeasures, will eventually put paid to cumbersome and costly systems like TOW. MILAN's limited range makes it a borderline case too. But a really lightweight, simple, EW-proof, long-range system like Sagger will remain a must both for the dismountable element of the mechanized force and for the standard infantry battalion. Sure, its siting and fire planning will need a complete rethink; but skillfully deployed and tasked, a thoroughly serviceable system like this can still kill an awful lot of tanks.

Sad as it may be, users of most countries seem to agree that the Soviet RPG7V leads the rocket launcher league too; so maybe we should take it as an example of this class of weapon. Because of the gap in crew served weapon systems that may tend to appear in the middle ground of the antiarmor family, the rocket launcher will gain in importance even if it cannot defeat the tank's frontal arc. It is so easy to deploy in enfilade or ambush, or in elevated positions from which it can attack the target's roof and rear. And it is going to be deployed much more thoughtfully and aggressively than in the past. This is why I believe a handy

a b

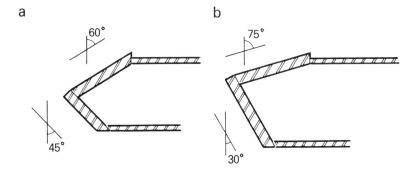

21. Tank hull fronts. (a) Conventional. (b) Modern

weapon like the RPG7V has a bigger future than a more cumbersome one like Carl-Gustav, despite the latter's greater range and versatility. There would be no problem in fielding an HE round for the RPG7V, but there is rather a lot of evidence from terrorist and urban guerrilla operations worldwide that the HEAT rocket does this job remarkably well!

Because the RPG7V will have to be used aggressively, I believe there is a need to provide for remote command and/or target actuated firing of it. This setup, which I learned to call a *fougasse,* is emplaced in the hedge or bank of a road and fires a projectile at short range at the side of a passing vehicle. One system of this kind is the French MIACAH F1 mine, said to have been "elaborated" — a very well-chosen word when one looks at its complexity and weight — from do-it-yourself rigs of the World War II bazooka. I cannot see why a very simple kit of wires and the odd pulley, which the infantryman could carry in his pocket, should not make the RPG7V into an excellent fougasse.

I doubt compound armor alters the position of antitank grenades, since most of these will not penetrate conventional tank fronts. The antitank rifle grenade has never seemed to me a particularly convincing weapon; seen alongside the RPG7V it looks even less so. By contrast weapons which allow use to be made of an armored vehicle's *blind zone* have always been underrated, maybe because few enough tankers, let alone infantrymen, are aware of the importance and extent of this blind zone. If, as seems likely, there is a trend towards guerrillalike tactics, hand grenades like the Soviet RKG3 series (pl. 21) and stick-on charges like the British "rigid limpet assault mine" (pl. 22) are going to increase in importance.

Since modern air-intake filters proof armored vehicles against Molotov cocktails and the like, the limpet mine is the semi-clandestine weapon I as a tanker feared most. Limpet mines designed for naval use would in any event require refuzing to provide much shorter delay; it looks like a minor development program aimed at a dedicated antiarmor limpet mine would pay off.

Finally, though, we need to address the question of a true successor to systems like TOW — a crew served ATGMS which will defeat the frontal arc of tanks with compound armor. Technically the answer lies in going for the roof, and this is just what the United States STAFF project does. It may be simplest to look at the projectile of STAFF first and then consider the delivery problem. The principle is SFF (fig. 20, page 163). A spun projectile shaped like a conventional shell has a sideways looking sensor and SFF element.[2] Because of design factors associated with the spin, lethality is rather down on SADARM (page 162); and initiation lag puts fairly narrow upper and lower limits on remaining velocity as the projectile passes the target. As the reader will by now have gathered, this shell needs to be placed over the target at an appropriate standoff.

Currently the intention appears to be to fire the STAFF projectile from a low-pressure gun or recoilless rifle, either of which could presumably be fielded on a light vehicle like a jeep or in manportable/crew served form. Even with a sophisticated fire-control system I cannot see this shell being placed over the target with sufficient accuracy; then there is the nest of multiple probabilities indicated at subhead 2 of our discussion of Assault Breaker (page 159); and once again lethality is questionable. If SFF attack is worth pursuing seriously, then TOW and Sagger (the latter modified for preferred plane roll stabilization) would seem to be excellent vehicles for it. With an SFF warhead having to be presented at optimum standoff above the target, semi-automatic control with wire guidance might be preferable to manual control despite its vulnerability to countermeasures. The requisite displacement could then be built into the system, allowing the operator to perform the more natural task of aiming for a hit.

I am far from convinced, however, that the pursuit of a technical solution for a major crew served weapon system is the best response to compound armors. In the main mechanized

2 A fin-stabilized projectile will not do because it in fact has a slow spin, traversing several hundred meters in each revolution.

force men on their feet fight alongside rotary-wing and vehicular
weapon platforms, and should complement rather than attempt
to duplicate these heavier weapons' capabilities. Antiarmor
firepower in a light mechanized force is a different ballgame; we
shall be looking at it briefly in Chapter 20. And if infantry
operating on a manpack basis had to confront armor in a
positional battle — a rather unrealistic situation — they would
have to rely on helicopter-mounted or heliborne support.

In sum — however little innovative Western technologists may
like it — the situation over crew served and short-range antiarmor
weapons looks to be one in which, with minor exceptions, tactics
and organization should adapt to a static or slowly evolving state
of the art.

PART 4

Weapon Systems

15

Tank or tank destroyer?

In an attempt to hold this unwieldy and divergent topic of antiarmor defense together and to pull it into some kind of shape, I have put forward a number of judgments that kinder readers will call subjective and others arbitrary. Likewise in this part of the book I want not just to move via complete weapon systems towards a family of antiarmor weapons but to hack my way through a number of quasi-philosophical issues so as to get a clean run in to a concept of operations.

When I wrote *Tank Warfare* I felt I was banging my head against a brick wall — or rather against the heaviest plates of an impenetrable and unshakable "main battle tank" (MBT). When I put together the proposal for this book, I offered the title of this chapter as one of its crunch points. Even when I wrote the Introduction (which oddly enough I am apt to do first) I still reckoned the future of the MBT was a major issue. Now the thesis I put forward in *Tank Warfare* looks to have the tide starting to flow under it.

The United States is going slow ahead with XM1 but making a determined bid for reduced weight and dramatically improved mobility with a hi-lo profile of tank destroyer (TD) and fire-support tank (FST). Sweden, the first country to break out of the "vicious spiral of tank design", looks like steering back towards mid-channel by pairing a straight S Tank successor with an external gun tank (pl. 2). This notion of hiving off top traverse in one case and the commander's superior position in the other, then compensating for the complementary drawbacks by a grassroots mix of the two configurations, is a particularly elegant solution — the more so as it makes both vehicles near nontargets when in a fire position.

After the disappointments of her mid-sixties analyses and trials on ultrahigh mobility vehicles, which were ahead of the then state of the art, the FRG fell back onto Leopard 2 with a good grace but a measure of chagrin. She is looking hard at radical solutions for the half-generation to replace Leopard 1 in the nineties. Even Britain — in my not very humble opinion a decade too late — has abandoned her MBT80 dinosaur in favor of a half-fleet reequipment of BAOR with FV4030/3 (Chieftain with the 1200-bhp engine and Chobham armor, pl. 8) and "probably some kind of collaborative project for the future". With their tank's battle weight running at around 40 t and a quantum jump in mobility almost certainly up their sleeve, the Soviets could well stay with the turreted configuration for one more half-generation after "M80/T82"; or again they could up-engine T72 and hold over its successor for half a decade.

So maybe a better question to ask at this time is whether the "MBT" is in fact still with us. Or whether Chieftain, T72, Leopard 2 and XM1 are in reality tank destroyers dressed up as tanks at an enormous cost in money, fuel consumption and trafficability in the Western designs — and of fightability in the Soviet vehicle. Navies and air forces are used to having their primary equipment concepts, force structures and terminologies turned upside down by technological advance. For armies the concept "soldier" provides a remarkably fine focus for conservatism; once hardware concepts succeed in making any real impact on military thought, they are apt to become similarly enshrined.

One can trace, as I did in *Tank Warfare* and shall not do again here, a direct lineage from T34/76 through Panther, Pershing M26 and Centurion to Leopard 1 and M60A3. With the sole exception of the S Tank, tank design moved in a purely evolutionary way for half a century in name and rather longer in practice. The British Conqueror was a heavy tank in name and in nature. It was precisely what we are now coming to understand by the term tank destroyer, capable of fighting only in conjunction with the handier and more versatile (though equally slow) Centurion. User insistence on making a "tank" of it resulted in a vehicle almost as disastrous as it was expensive. Chieftain was the successor to Centurion in name but owed much to Conqueror in nature. A concept which required the MBT to mount the primary gun-based antiarmor weapon system forced the FRG and the USA to move in the same direction, albeit with a far greater advance in some aspects of mobility. With T62 as a halfway house, the Soviets moved in the direction of keeping weight down and increasing firepower by accepting even harsher tradeoffs in habitability and probably other aspects of fightability — for them an entirely rational move.

Like so many of today's problems, the MBT concept was, I suggest, an accident of history, technology and opinion which has now outlived its usefulness, maybe even its reality. From the long 75 mm of Panther to the 105 mm of Centurion (and M60 and Leopard 1) the caliber of the largest high-pressure gun which could be mounted in a tank happened to coincide with the optimum caliber for direct general support fire with HE and then HE/HEP (page 109). The kind of sophistication tanks now have for the antitank role (General von Senger und Etterlin's "electronic revolution") was not available. So the state of the art made for a versatile vehicle. I hope American, and for that matter any Soviet readers will admit that, for a decade or more after World War II, Britain had a world lead in achieved tank performance; so she set the pace for a while. The dominant military figure in postwar Britain was that most dogged of infantrymen, Montgomery, who absolutely insisted on a "universal tank" — "universal" meaning above all capable of supporting infantry and cumbersome enough to ensure the battle was fought at the tempo of the boot.

I believe then we can start with a clean sheet in postulating the family of major armored vehicles which, in the era of compound armor and hence the second dynasty of the high-pressure gun, is going to carry the maneuver force and so provide the nub of the antiarmor defense. If further proof were needed, Table 2 leaves little doubt of what this nub should be. But we saw right back in Chapters 7 and 8, and again in Chapter 10, that a machine dedicated entirely to thumping long rod penetrators across the battlefield in a precise but rather simplistic manner will not do. The *primary antiarmor role itself* now calls for a disruptive attack option against compound armor and the ability to deal with "over the crest" targets, if necessary by neutralization. *This adds up to something very like the combination of punch and versatility that characterizes the firepower of a main battle tank.* To provide two complete sets of "tank natures" in different calibers for use within the same subunit may be an acceptable expedient but is certainly far from ideal in economic and logistic terms. This is why, with gun feasibility proven by the DARPA/ARES project and mounting feasibility by the Marder/105-mm test vehicle, I would now favor what still looked unfeasible when I wrote *Tank Warfare* — a tank destroyer (TD) and a fire-support tank (FST) with the *same caliber* of gun and tube lengths matched to the respective mountings.

I believe I said enough in Chapter 10 to justify the choice of 105 mm, with a 70(+) L tube for the TD and the standard L51 tube for the FST. Maybe, though, I should reemphasize here the need for both mountings to be compatible with the German smoothbore 120-mm, again with tube lengths optimized for the two vehicles. The improvement in gun performance achieved by DARPA marches with the need to spread the jam rather more thinly over an extended frontal arc (Chapter 4) to suggest that 105-mm is enough — maybe in fact more than enough. But the 120-mm caliber just could prove necessary if the Soviets fielded a tank with advanced compound armor concentrated over the traditional frontal arc.

Once we abandon the concept of an MBT which as "queen of the battlefield" has absolute design priority, we need to think in terms of a family of vehicles in which design is optimized across two or more principal models. So at this point we must digress from the theme of antiarmor proper and consider the vehicle family for the main mechanized force as a whole. I want to leave the "attack/defense" argument over for the moment, but I think it fair to say here that a swing of opinion over hardware and grouping alike is taking place in much of NATO — most of all maybe in the Anglo-Saxon military mind. Traditionally one has tended to regard tanks as *off*ensive and mechanized infantry, antitank guns, tactical air defense systems and the like as mainly associated with the *def*ense. The German and Soviet view that these elements are in fact most needed to help gain and maintain the momentum of a mechanized attack or advance is not only becoming more and more prominent in these countries' own armies but taking root among the Americans and British as well.[1]

On a second general point, feedback is on the one hand one of the satisfactions of writing books like this one and its predecessors; on the other it demands a response if one is to be taken seriously. As I remarked above, the tide now seems to be flowing under the TD/FST thesis I put forward in *Tank Warfare*. More surprising maybe is the interest and positive comment evoked by the kites I flew there and in *Mechanized Infantry* on composite organizations and reduction of the maneuver squad to 1 + 6; some of the comments have even shown that 1 + 5 is enough by allocating a precise role to each man. Less favorably received was my support for the Merkava concept in the shape of a combined FST/IFV. Loss of flexibility and the avoidable risking of men by putting the maneuver squad and one of the key antiarmor

---

1 Cf. *Mechanized Infantry*, page 48.

TABLE 2 — *Summary of some World War II Soviet tank casualties (1943-5)*
(Extracted by Professor John Erickson, University of Edinburgh)

Operation	Army TA = tank army	Losses (as % of total losses) from				
		arty fire*	mines	air attack	bazookas	various
Oriel (1943)	2 TA	76	14	10	-	-
	4 TA	68.5	8	17.7	-	5.8
Kiev (1943)	3 Gds TA	94.8	2	.5	-	2.7
Lvov-Sandomierz (1944)	3 Gds TA	80	6	14	-	-
	4 TA	91.8	3	3.4	-	1.8
Vistula-Oder (1945)	3 Gds TA	88.5	2	9.5	-	-
	1 Gds TA	63.1	5.3	10.5	20	1.1
	2 Gds TA	79.5	2	1.5	-	17
	4 TA	78.5	9.5	1.0	6.2	4.8
Berlin (1945)	2 Gds TA	58.7	5.8	6.6	24	4.9
	3 Gds TA	67.1	6.6	10.3	16	-
Mean (RMS)		68.12	5.28	7.28	13.78	5.54

*By elimination this must include direct fire tank, assault (SU) and antitank guns.

weapon systems in the same vehicle was an important criticism and an entirely valid one.[2] I accept this but still regard the FST/IFV solution' as one possible tradeoff if one is faced with fielding the greatest possible number of KE antitank weapons under the dual constraints of combat manpower and cost ceilings.

By far the strongest criticisms were, surprisingly maybe, the exclusion of cannon and high-angle fire from the company combat team and — more surprisingly still — my abandonment of the notion of a "tank support vehicle (TSV)" at platoon level which I floated in *Tank Warfare*. In a broader setting, though, this might better be called a "command/support vehicle (CSV)". So while staying with a composite "tank/infantry" unit and subunit, we need to think in terms of a family with four primary members —

tank destroyer (TD) — fixed 105-mm/72 L, crew 3;

fire support tank (FST) — external 105-mm/L51, crew 3;

infantry fighting vehicle (IFV) — 9 men (*see below*);

command/support vehicle (CSV) — normally 6 men (*see below*).

These last two types, which are essentially minor variants on each other, are not strictly relevant to our theme; but I cannot leave them floating in the air. Both should mount — coaxially, stabilized and with a wide elevation arc — a 20-30-mm automatic cannon, a low-pressure 76-mm gun[3] and a 7.62-mm machinegun. The driver would need to be to one side to match his position in the TD and FST. A HSTV-L-like two-man turret (pl. 11) may be feasible, but I believe a better solution would be a two-man rotating command console to the driver's right. This would contain the overall/maneuver squad commander and the vehicle commander/gunner, who need to be physically together, along with all requisite "vision", sighting and fire-control elements. The armament would be in a slaved pod with on-mounting ready magazines located to the left behind the driver and surmounted by a sensor head common with that of the FST. The maneuver squad commander more than any other vehicle commander

---

2 This may be the reason for removing Sagger from squad BMPs, though I do not think so: *see also* footnote 4 to page 136.

3 e.g. the British gun on Saladin and CVR(T) Scorpion.

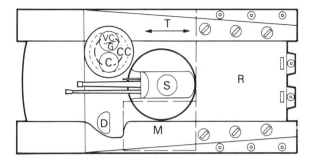

22. Schematic plan view of IFV/CSV vehicle
    C = overall/maneuver squad commander
    CC = command console, D = driver
    M = hull magazines (externally vented)
    R = rear compartment
    S = sensor head, T = access tunnel
    VC/G = vehicle commander/gunner
    Armaments, mounted coaxially in a stabilized, slaved pod with large elevation and
    depression arcs, are (*bottom to top in plan view*) 20-30-mm automatic cannon, low-
    pressure 76-mm gun, 7.62-mm MG

needs natural vision, specially to look at the ground before he dismounts; the same goes for platoon and company commanders. I therefore believe the armament/sensor pod should be semi-retractable to the point where its top was level with the optical heads of the command console. This would also allow manual reloading of the ready magazines from the rear compartment.

The rear compartment shell and rear doors would be common to both IFV and CSV versions, the IFV being provided with six seats, periscopes and weapon ports on the BMP pattern (with alternative side and rear periscopes and ports in the rear positions). In its primary role of platoon headquarters vehicle, the CSV would carry in its rear compartment a medical orderly, one or more reserve crewmen, two stretchers with folding brackets and packs containing human and materiel "survival kits". In CSVs of company, higher and specialized command posts the rear compartment would carry the additional staff officers, signalers and command/communications facilities required. Additionally all CSVs would mount on their front a hydraulically controlled male "docking type" recovery probe matching a female docking socket on the rear of the other variants.

One reason I felt justified in exploring the IFV/CSV concept in this amount of detail was to put forward the idea of a two-man command console with a fully slaved armament mounting as an alternative to the stabilized commander's cupola and one-man turret proposed in the Swedish project (pl. 2). As I remarked earlier, the time has come to go for slaving, though not yet maybe — as some suggest — for putting the whole crew in comparative safety at the rear of the vehicle, thus removing all possibility of "natural" vision through optical heads or unbuttoned. This approach could provide very high commonality between the FST, IFV and CSV. In the FST the mounting would of course be fully external. The rear compartment would be bulkheaded off and given over to jettisonable magazines and an autoloader; and the space immediately behind the driver and the command console would be used for electrical/electronic/optronic packs. Here the direct-vision arrangements on the command console would come into play when the sensor head on the gun mounting was damaged — a backup system that is needed with this concept anyway.

In *Tank Warfare,* when I was using combat manpower as a resource parameter, I was insistent on keeping the crew of the fixed gun TD (S Tank derivative) to two. But the Swedes are very sparing with manpower, do their homework thoroughly and repeatedly insist on a three man crew — "the one man tank with a crew of three". With NATO's manpower situation going the way it is (page 1), the acute need to reduce acquisition time in face of enhanced mobility (page 36) and the chance of maintaining commonality over all four key vehicles, I am now inclined to stand on my head and suggest keeping the same crew layout and command console for the TD. My ballpark figuring indicates that this would leave sufficient clearance on the driver's right for the fixed gun. This version would have hull machineguns as "coax equivalents" (like the S Tank) and could have a traversing machinegun externally mounted on or slaved to the command console. (In *Tank Warfare* I suggested a slaved cannon/MG mounting for this vehicle; user comment wanted the cannon (*see above*), but not on the TD.)

In previous discussions I put vehicles like these at 40(-) t, around the S Tank's weight. But looking at the HIMAG and HSTV-L work, I feel there may now be a solution at MLC40 (36 (+) t) and very possibly at 30 t — the Bundeswehr's very long, hard and wisely sought target weight. I guess the trick has to lie in slaving, despite the added complexity of this approach. With the HIMAG[4] or Leopard 2 power train we are looking at a

---

4 Continental AVCR-1360-2 (1500 bhp) and Allison X300-4A, the power train rejected for XM1 in favor of the Lycoming gas turbine.

power-weight ratio of 40-50 bhp/t — interesting enough, though
I still go with the German long-term target of 60 bhp/t.[5] At this
kind of weight, the hull becomes economically attractive not only
as an IFV but also as a weapon platform for surface-to-surface
and air defense artillery, above all for a tactical air defense
vehicle (ADV). A matching armored vehicle launched bridge
(AVLB) would evidently be needed; and since there would be no
further requirement for routes above MLC40, a compatible
armored recovery/armored engineeer vehicle (ARV/AEV) would
also have to be phased in. For these secondary roles the superficial
elements of compound armor could be dispensed with to make
more weight and space available for payload.

In broad terms of logistic and engineer effort, limiting weight
to MLC40 would reap a saving of around 70% (*cf.* fig. 2, page
25). With widespread commonality of automated subsystems,
one might even ballpark this saving at 75% (for a given number
of vehicles). Along with the benefits of long production runs, this
gain should more than offset in real terms added production and
logistic costs arising from the complexity of the hull and its
automotive subsystems. More narrowly, a very high degree of
commonality throughout the major vehicles of the maneuver
force would bring logistic savings and simplification in the
combat zone, where these matter most.

By contrast ammunition replenishment of composite units is
going to be complex. It may be worth listing the requirements of a
composite company, even maybe of a platoon. Table 3 makes the
problem look appalling. Fact is it is only one degree worse than
the requirements of any typical tank-infantry combat team; and
the difficulty of the extra caliber is likely to be more than
outweighed by the fact that we now have just one set of supply
vehicles working to one organic subunit. By the same token the
"muddy wood on a dark wet night" scenario does not add up
to one of twentieth-century soldiering's more distinguished
achievements. I have often seen it being acted out with about the
same measure of chaos in BAOR, the Bundeswehr and 7 (US)
Army — and I have equally often envisioned exactly the same
chaos, accompanied by an equally rich flow of language, going
on the other side of the Elbe. Maybe by the nineties somebody will
have gotten around to putting the show into modern dress.

In the setup depicted in Table 3, the worst case is the IFV, with
the CSV not too far behind. With the rear compartment of these

5 Now the Germans have achieved 1850 hp from the compact MT880 diesel, one can
better 50 bhp/t at MLC40 and 60 bhp/t at 30 t.

vehicles allocated to personnel, fittings or stores, the magazine, although externally vented and sealed off when not in use, has to be physically inside the hull — probably with the gun mounting (or in other possible layouts some other equally substantial subsystem) above it. So there is no real alternative to bombing up by hand in the conventional way. I reckon we are stuck with "IFV/CSV loaded" trucks, which will also serve any scout vehicles and the like. Luckily the IFV has plenty of manpower and the CSV may often require only minor topping up with ammunition.

It must always be possible to bomb up TDs and FSTs by hand in emergency; but these vehicles will have external magazines that are jettisonable and can therefore be made exchangeable. Evidently the magazine proper must be surrounded by a fixed shell of armor with a hinged back flap which is either blown open (in the case of an ammunition fire) or opened manually for replenishment. Within this shell the magazine units could ride on short rails which could be married up with matching rails on the drop side or lifting platform of a dedicated ammunition supply vehicle and/or on the fork of a forklift. A wholly or partly expended magazine would be withdrawn, with mechanical assistance from the supply vehicle, and replaced by a full one. I believe the trick is to include in the magazine unit stowage compartments for all secondary natures. A replenishment unit would then provide a refill of one 105-mm nature and 50% of each secondary nature. A jettisoned magazine would simply be replaced as soon as any necessary repairs and cleaning had been completed. As mentioned earlier (page 131), the problem of 105-mm smoke requires further consideration; but with this exception I can see no objection from the tank end to this bulk system. Spent or part-used magazines would be refilled by the service platoon/company or, if forward supply was in operation, by the logistic unit at which bulk was broken. It would simplify matters greatly if magazine units could be common to TD and FST; at first sight there is no reason why they should not be.

A transfer of this kind would require a road surface or hardstand, if only to get the tank and supply vehicle aligned and level. Fact is, with most fuel in tankers and any kind of mechanized handling of ammunition, the "muddy wood" scenario is not too realistic any more. Apart from minor topping up with fuel in waiting areas and hides, the system sometimes known as "running replenishment" and long favored by the US Army needs to become standard practice. The service company and/or logistic unit sets up a roadside replenishment point either

TABLE 3 — *Organic ammunition requirements of a composite subunit*

Caliber (mm)	Natures	Vehicles
105	APDSFS, AP/HE (*or* HEAT/FS), SMK	TD, FST
76	HE/HEP, SMK	IFV, CSV
20-30 (i.e. cannon)	AP/HE (*or* HEDP), HE	IFV, CSV
7.62-mm belt	normal	all
7.62-mm box/clip	ball	all
9 mm	ball	all
Manportable/crew served antiarmor systems		
ATGM	1 nature	(*some*) IFVs
Rockets	1 nature	IFV
Antitank grenades	1 nature	IFV (plus)
Limpet mines	1 nature	IFV (plus)
Grenades (* = plus cartridges)		
(4/28) Anti-ATGM*	(1 nature, *see* page 72)	TD, FST, IFV, CSV
SMK*	(for conventional cups)	all
Hand	HE/FRAG	all
Flares (*see* Chapter 11)		
Cartridges signal/ illuminating	various, at least 4 types	all

along a route or at the entrance to a dispersal or deployment area. The armored vehicles pass through this, take on in succession fuel, ammunition and rations/water, and then move on. Running replenishment does entail some tactical risk, specially in an adverse air situation; but if properly organized it gets a subunit replenished very rapidly. In reality it is probably a more secure procedure than the "muddy wood" act, which is apt to drag on into the small hours with an obligato of revving truck engines and folksy dialog.

Maybe the reader will feel he has been robbed of the argument the title of this chapter made him want to have. There are really two fundamental issues which are interlocked and paradoxical though not contradictory. The tank is its own worst enemy. No matter whether you are an aggressor shopping around for a "tank" or a politically virtuous defender in the market for a "primary gun-based antiarmor weapon system" you are going to buy much the same product. In either case, the salesman is now likely to offer you a similar choice. You can have a conventional main battle tank which wraps the whole package up in one at the cost of a weight around 55 t and the need to expose an uncomfortably large turret when firing. Or you can have a fire-support tank which does most all the MBT can, trading off a reserve of antiarmor fire power for 20 t or so in weight and the ability to fire without exposing a direct-fire target, backed up by a tank destroyer which gives you the ultimate punch, weighs the same as its partner and likewise presents a very small, notably a very low target when firing. If you go this way, you can make up your combat team with vehicles that have automotive identity with the TD/FST pair and complementary firepower from subsystems which have high commonality with that pair. If the Americans with HIMAG and the Swedes with their S Tank successor options have got their homework somewhere near right, there's no argument to be had any more.

16

Helicopters

How and how much helicopters participate in the land battle, mechanized and otherwise, is one of the leading military questions of the next few decades. Here it is not much use just to put on a cozy pair of blinders and concern ourselves only with hurling missiles at hard targets. The name of the game is the defeat of a hostile mechanized force, and the issue of a mechanized battle is just as likely to be decided in the Treasury, on the drawing board or in the air as on the battlefield. So we have to examine the various ways in which helicopters and mechanized forces may interact.

Likewise we need to address the problem with technical boldness. The fact that a mixture of financial stringency and indecision has left the West with a serious lag in the rotary-wing field does not mean that helicopter forces comparable in every way to mechanized forces are in the realm of scifi. The Soviets — and less obviously maybe the Americans — have all the hardware needed in their inventory. After months of bumbling around Afghanistan with doctrines and hardware designed for the steppes and learning a lot of lessons the hard way, it would be surprising if the Soviets are not putting the requisite doctrines and organizations together too.

Within a wide, seemingly almost continuous spectrum of national philosophies on combat helicopters one can maybe distinguish four roles or levels of activity —

> reconnaissance with occasional attack (armed scout helicopters);
>
> covering force, screen and economy of force operations (scout *plus* attack helicopters);
>
> tactical support of the main mechanized force (scout *plus* attack helicopters);

intervention at operational level (balanced, self-contained
helicopter force).

Broadly speaking European NATO members are into or
moving into the second of these. The US Army is established in
the second and well into the third. The Soviets look to be
established in the third and poised to move, or at least
technologically capable of moving, into the fourth.

Since the cost of this fourth stage could be mind-blowing even
by aerospace standards, one can only envision it as a replacement
for another function — like a dedicated armored reconnaissance
force or a parachute/airborne capability. Fact is World War II
parachute forces on both sides chalked up a splendid history of
heroic exploits but relatively little in the way of solid gains. Also,
they were used in their proper role far less frequently and less
boldly than might have been expected. This is maybe even truer
of glider-borne forces both in the *coup de main* role and *en
masse*. As a tanker I am very hesitant to express a view on this
question, but it strikes me that parachute troops have too long a
period of weakness from the moment they start to drop and lose
surprise to the time they concentrate and organize themselves as
an effective fighting force. Gliders put men in faster but have
always had an appalling casualty rate and, once again, scatter
troops too widely for speedy effect. By contrast, a dedicated,
balanced helicopter force, backed up if necessary by heliborne or
airlanded forces, can act with the transit speed of transport
aircraft, the precision and concentration of a mechanized force
— and a tactical tempo an order of magnitude greater. Whether
an army can afford a helicopter force at all, and if so whether it
represents the most effective use of a large slice of resources, are
political decisions. But the possibility is one we need to examine
in this chapter and again more broadly in Part 5.

Meanwhile we should explore another important national
difference — that of flying techniques, or better maybe flying
tactics. The two factors here are density, or the size of the fire
unit, and height. On the American definition, now generally
accepted, *terrain flying* breaks down into —

low-level flying,

contour flying,

nap-of-the-earth (NOE) flying.

Low-level flying maintains a cruising kind of flight profile with reasonably constant heading and altitude, while making use of terrain cover most of the time. In this mode, for instance, the pilot maintains altitude when crossing narrow valleys but observes a 60-m operational ceiling. *Contour flying* is exactly what its name suggests; the pilot follows the straightest course he can while maintaining a constant vertical or slant distance from the ground. *NOE flying* is quite simply "rotary-wing fieldcraft". Cover takes precedence over direction and time; dashes across open space are made only when they have to be. NOE flying demands extremely high pilot skill, meticulous preparation — like 2 hours briefing for a 15 km mission — and rigorous discipline of every kind. In this mode unmasking is limited to acquisition and engagement of target. To minimize signature and improve endurance, machines often touch down and wait in cover at "flight idle".

An additional factor which lends great tactical importance to stealthy operation is the likelihood that the Soviet AD system has a gap — or at least an area of relative weakness — 3-4 km behind the line of contact. Presumably this arises because the ZSU23/4s deployed around 1 km behind the leading troops start lacking the range to fire effectively "over their shoulders"; and SA7s[1] are unlikely to acquire low-level targets because there is often a lack of troops on the ground at the back of the direct-fire zone. In any event a helicopter fitted with "black hole" (IR-suppressing) exhausts and lurking behind cover is not a particularly suitable target for the heat-seeking missile SA7 or SA9[2]; and it should be able to stay below the horizon of the forward SA6 (GAINFUL) radars. Since so far as I know no other advanced army yet has a comprehensive tactical AD setup developed and deployed, it is hard to tell how far this gap is associated with Soviet state of the art and deployment and how far it is characteristic of any tactical AD system. But the combat value of helicopters which have worked their way into this gap is enormous. They can pass exactly the information the defending tactical commander needs; they can greatly extend the depth of observed artillery fire; and with their own firepower they can wreak havoc with the tactical reserve or the follow-up wave.

At one end of the spectrum comes Britain with no dedicated gunships or antiarmor helicopters, just armed adaptations of the

---

1 The company weapon, shoulder-launched; range 3500 m, maybe 4700 m.

2 Either mounted (as formerly) on BTR40P (GASKIN) and colocated with ZSU 23/4 to make use of its radar outputs; or maybe now mounted on the ZSU 23/4 turret itself.

utility model Gazelle (SA341) and Lynx. I am not convinced that British thinking has really moved beyond the second stage (covering force, etc). Certainly they favor stealth and the use of machines singly or in pairs. My feel is that, after 25 years or so of biting financial stringency, the British Army reckons that choppers are too rare and expensive to risk — and physically lacks operational reserves of them. The specification of the SA342M Gazelle makes the French look like the ultimate proponents of stealth. Two missiles out of a possible eight have been sacrificed to maintain endurance and mount defensive avionics, NOE flying aids and ECCM; intake and exhaust suppression is extreme; low-frequency noise is restricted; and special paint is used. One assumes these machines too will be used singly or in pairs.

Next come the apostles of group stealth. After its usual exhaustive analyses and trials — in this instance extremely successful — the Bundeswehr organized its PAH1s into flights (*Schwärme*) of seven, six armed machines and an unarmed VBH in the command/scout role. The PAH1 is a relatively light helicopter, but it may be worth noting that the German-French PAH2/HAC[3] is just double the gross weight of Gazelle SA342M. Also in this group and much more importantly comes the US Army with its "five by three" teams of five Cobras and three OHS8 Kiowa scouts. We will discuss the Huey Cobra AH1S's armament a little later. Enough for the moment to note that its gross weight is almost twice that of PAH1, with the successor AH64 half as heavy again.

At over twice the weight of the Cobra and with much more extensive direct protection, the Soviet Hind D is aptly described as a "flying tank" or "battle cruiser". On the figures I have, Hind D's rotor diameter is significantly smaller than Hind A's and a little below that of the utility version of Blackhawk. But despite a retractable undercarriage and other features associated with high performance, Hind is rather short of puff by modern Western standards. It is very hard to envision a Soviet pilot using this machine to crawl around under the trees the way the Americans do with Cobra. There is considerably stronger evidence that the Soviets favor bold tactics, flying a kind of "top cover" for their leading armor. Although the Hind series, specially the dedicated D and E models, are said to have considerable direct protection, I cannot believe that the Soviets would risk them in the open in face of a tactical AD layout like their own. More probably the Soviet assessment of the likely tactical air situation combined with their

---

3 i.e. *Panzerabwehrhubschrauber 2/hélicoptère anti-chars.*

knowledge of the virtual absence of forward AD in the NATO armies led them to rate the risk of attack as low. As a layman in helicopter matters with some understanding of Soviet equipment policy in other fields, I believe, though, that the Hind series is — or was and may be again — intended for a role quite different than killing tanks.

At this point it may be worth summarizing available information on numbers of purpose-built and adapted attack helicopters.[4]

TABLE 4 — *Numbers of attack helicopters*

Country	Attack helicopters — type/number		Utility/heavy lift helicopter capability
UK	Gazelle Lynx	(*no numbers available*)	limited
France	Gazelle SA342M Gazelle SA341 (HOT) Alouette 3 (SS11)	120-160 ?80-90* 70*	qualitatively good
FRG	PAH1 B0105P (*plus* 227 × VBH convertible to PAH1)	212	fair — mainly imported technology
USA — Army Marines	Cobra AH1S AH1T	986 120(?+)	was outstanding, now adequate for most purposes
USSR	Hind A-D (*plus* Hind Es and Fs)	650	formidable

*Presumably to be replaced by PAH2/HAC.

We have already discussed the ATGMSs concerned, but the other armaments of United States and Soviet helicopters are of considerable importance to the antiarmor picture as a whole. The latest *FFAR rockets* are far from being the rather simple area fire weapons one might suppose. They will fly up to 5500 m. In addition to HE and WP (smoke/incendiary) warheads with fuzing options, they include HEP, a carrier with five submunitions and a flare. On AH1S and AH64 the pods are selectively loaded and fired, the crew having three sets of fuzing and warhead options immediately under their hand.

The grenade launcher when fitted fires at a cyclic rate of over 400 rds/min to an effective range of 1300 m; and the *Minigun* rounds trace out to around 3000 m. However, these two options are unlikely to be used when operating with mechanized forces in the sophisticated combat environment. More serious contenders

4 Early 1979 published figures, including future budget provision.

for the chin turret are a three-tubed 20-mm Gatling gun firing 750 rds/min, for which an APDS round has been developed (*see* Table 5); or the 30-mm chain gun; again three-tubed, which fires standard NATO AP and HE rounds, or the new XM789 HEDP (high-explosive dual purpose) round specially developed for it.

Little information is available on Soviet helicopter-launched rockets, but they are of around the same caliber as the FFAR — at a guess 73 mm — and probably have much the same capabilities. Hind A has only a single-tubed 12.7-mm heavy machinegun in a fairly elementary chin mounting. By contrast Hind D has a chin turret carrying a 4 × 12.7-mm Gatling gun or a single-tube 23-mm cannon along with sophisticated sensors and sighting systems. To sum up, both the American and the Soviet chin turret armament has a very significant antiarmor capability — specially when one considers the multistrike effect of high cyclic rate fire (page 107).

Before reaching any conclusions on the helicopters in the family of antiarmor weapon systems, I want to digress a little (rather as I did in the previous chapter), explore the thinking that appears to underlie the Soviet Hind concept and see where it leads. We know the Soviet Army has long favored helicopters for a wide variety of roles and that the Soviet Union probably moved into a world lead in many categories of rotary-wing machines while the West argued in circles or tightened the purse strings at the wrong moment. Likewise we know that way back in the early sixties the Soviets saw a tactical role for heliborne operations aimed at maintaining or regaining momentum when crossing major obstacles.

This was quite different from the conventional bridgehead concept, more a kind of tactical heave to get the armor out of the river and rolling free. They developed SOPs for these operations and trained in them.[5] Fact is, though, this was a straightforward *heliborne* operation, using transport helicopters and infantry trained only in squadding, loading/mounting and dismounting/ unloading. The machines carried some defensive armament, maybe an *ad hoc* modification. But the supporting fire came entirely from artillery and low-level fixed-wing support flown under close fighter cover.

Again we know that the Soviets favor strategic airborne operations in the classical mold and are excellently trained and equipped for them. (As I write this they have just demonstrated

5 As evidenced by an early/mid-sixties recruiting film, featuring a snorkel crossing on a wide front, probably of the Elbe.

the Warpac capability with a major exercise, matched within a week by a similar NATO drop.) As I mentioned earlier, I am singularly unsanguine about this particular type of offensive operation if there is any risk of organized opposition. But if the Soviets really let their armor cut loose and "go West", a backup airborne operation into a secured dropping/landing zone could well be a very good way of quickly reinforcing operational success.

Between these two extremes there has long been talk of Soviet *helicopter operations* at depths of 200-300 km, either with specific operational objectives like bridges or key installations or aimed at securing, say, a logistic support area for roving spearheads. These operations would be carried out by a force, small in numerical terms, of specialized troops with dedicated hardware. We can think in terms of Hind A and Hind D (the models on which I at least have most information), bearing in mind the later models. Figures about the troop-carrying capacity of Hind conflict, but it looks like Hind A can carry not the "two squads" sometimes credited to it but at least ten fully equipped men (using two of the four crew positions). The machine is well described as an "assault helicopter" — in effect a kind of "flying IFV". Again one does not know just what tradeoffs have to be made to maintain flight characteristics, but on the face of it Hind D, with its crew of two, can carry a full armament load *and* a maneuver squad of a commander and seven men. With an armament makeup which is mixed and fairly inflexible, this machine fills both antiarmor and fire-support roles — not just a "flying tank" but the aerial equivalent of Merkava. Evidently the Hind force would require backup from utility and heavy-lift helicopters, maybe from other types of rotary-wing weapon platform and certainly from fixed-wing aircraft.

The value of this kind of operation in support of a fast-moving offensive needs no stressing. This is carrying to extremes the concepts of moment and momentum, or shock effect, that underlie the philosophy of the movement of masses. Just as the high mass of the full-bore solid shot was succeeded by the smaller mass and higher velocity of the long rod penetrator, so the relatively large mass of a mechanized ground force is supplanted, or at least complemented by the smaller mass of a helicopter force moving an order of magnitude faster. In his Introduction to *Tank Warfare* General von Senger und Etterlin emphasized the concept that underlay the Wehrmacht's Panzertruppen — a fast-moving mechanized army within a larger slow-moving dismounted army. "As a result [of universal mechanization]", he continues, "the commander in the field no longer has an element of his force which, although not large in terms of numbers, stands out from the rest in mobility and fighting power... This situation adds weight to any effort to use technological advance to restore superior mobility to at least parts of the army."

I suspect the real significance of the assault and attack helicopter may be just this. Back in the sixties the Bundeswehr were looking very hard at the possibility of "flying tanks" to enhance shock effect and plug the time-space gaps in fluid operations.[6] The expectation of compound armors resistant to shaped charge gave this concept a nasty knock; and the hopes of trading off performance out of ground effect to get relatively cheap and easy-to-fly rotary-wing machines have, so far at least, remained unrealized. But as a firm adherent of the German and Soviet doctrine of movement of masses and shock effect, if not an apostle at least a disciple of mobility, I reckon that this is what Hind is about.

We need then to address two further questions — whether, as the Bundeswehr feels, this concept applies equally to the defense; and whether Hind is the right kind of machine for it. Even if the US Army and the Bundeswehr succeed by the nineties in improving battlefield mobility by a factor of 3 and doubling operational mobility — the thing that matters here — there is no reason to suppose that the Soviets will not, or at least could not, do the same. Likewise it is hard to envision a defensive tactic which could prevent fast-moving breakthrough forces acquiring as they advance the advantage of interior lines at higher tactical and operational levels. The measure of this advantage increases not only with depth but directly and indirectly with speed. So speed matters to attacker and defender alike; but the *margin of speed* over the opposition matters most to the defender. Helicopters have the speed to plug the time-space gap until the armor can get there; they have some of the firepower. But as presently organized in Western armies they lack combat manpower and fire support.[7]

Harassment of advancing spearheads is certainly an important role for attack helicopters but is not of itself enough; it thins the armor out rather than slowing it down or containing it. Likewise attack helicopters can provide the hammer of a hasty hammer and anvil defense; but not the anvil or pivot of maneuver. Because of the tempo and scope of aerial maneuver and because

---

6 See *Tank Warfare,* Chapter 16.

7 The organization that comes nearest to this requirement is the US Army's proposed air cavalry attack troop (ACAT): *see* Bibliography (Sayre) and Chapter 23.

the operation is essentially a stopgap until a mechanized maneuver force arrives, the anvil can be a lightweight one. But I guess it has to be there and has to be solid enough to force the enemy to do something about it. This means putting men and materiel on the ground, hopefully into secure or unheld areas but occasionally against light opposition. In the absence of a crew served weapon system capable of taking tanks on frontally, it means dedicated and general artillery support too.

It may help here to establish one or two basic parameters. As in ground operations, the anvil or pivot has to be centered on some terrain feature, in this case some kind of defile. This could be a topographical defile, a neck between forests, marsh or patches of urban terrain, or an easily crossable stretch of a river (like the Weser ford at Holzminden). But it has to be some feature that either channels the attacker or makes him pay a heavy time penalty for not being channeled. "Good defensive ground" in the conventional sense is irrelevant, because there is no chance of deploying the kind of force that might "hold" it. The need is for a combination of defile and convergent fires, an extension by a level or so of the American dispersed strongpoint concept.

A helicopter force can be held at instant readiness but cannot be launched onto a given objective until the operational commander is reasonably certain the enemy will go that way. My knowledge of West German terrain suggests that this will normally be when he is 20-30 km short of it.[8] We can assume a target rate of advance of 200 km/24 hr, an average of 8 km/hr, and double this if the enemy has cut loose and is "motoring".[9] So we are looking at a period of around 1½ hours from the order to go to the arrival of the enemy. Suppose the nearest element of the mechanized operational reserve to be upward of 100 km from the point chosen for the helicopter operation or another blocking position in depth behind it. Suppose this reserve force to be at 15 minutes' notice; and to have a real movement speed of 50 kph and a low-density time length of 1 hour on the available routes. This means the mechanized force can become effective in 3½-4 hours. So if containment is to be achieved the helicopter force needs somehow or other to impose a total of around 2 hours' delay.

It may be worth stressing that this concept is quite different than a screening or economy of force operation to which the US

---

8 I could support this statement with numerous examples, but many readers will be as familiar with them as I am.

9 *Cf.* page 17.

Air Cavalry, for instance, is already geared. Success here is not a
bonus but essential to the conduct of the antiarmor defense as a
whole. One can maybe identify six phases, some of them
overlapping or simultaneous —

reconnaissance update (assuming preplanning);

helicopter deployment of artillery and logistic support
(FARRP[10]), which could well be colocated to minimize
security effort;

deployment of scout/attack teams forward for close reconnaissance and harassment by minelets, their own fires and
observed artillery fire;

deployment of the pivot force, which might consist of a
scout/attack team for close cover during organization,
minelet-scattering helicopters, a team of engineers with
appropriate stores, one or more artillery forward observer
teams and an "infantry" element of around company
strength with manportable support weapons and a boosted
scale of short-range antiarmor weapons;

deployment to immediate readiness positions of the scout/
attack helicopter teams forming the hammer;

securing of a collecting/pickup point for dismounted elements.

The course of the battle needs no explanation, I guess, except
maybe for one remark. If the opposition mounts an attack with
artillery preparation and/or motor rifle elements on their feet,
the goal will have been achieved and the pivot force must pull out
rather than attempt to oppose this attack. Helicopter general
support and air-observed artillery fires can evidently be maintained to cover displacement of the dismounted force and to
impose further casualties and delay.

If this bears too close a resemblance to projected Air Cavalry
operations to be worth discussing, I apologize. But I believe it
extends the concepts I am aware of in three respects — the use of
combat engineers for obstacle/defile improvement; the use of
men on their feet in a *tactical* as opposed to a purely defensive or
security role; and the use of specially deployed artillery. The key
point is maybe the last of these. To some extent it is an expedient
forced on the defender as a consequence of compound armor.

---

10 Forward area rearming and refueling point.

But more importantly the concentrated use of attack helicopters combined with artillery could produce a pattern of defensive fires at once similar enough to that of the mechanized defense to leave the opposing commander guessing what he has hit; and damaging enough to make him at least attack off the line of march and hopefully deploy his tactical reserve. Once one starts thinking along these lines, he is tempted to suggest using medium- or heavy-lift helicopters to drop in light armored vehicles. But I am fairly sure these would give the game away and become hostages to fortune. In the kind of bottleneck needed for an operation like this, it is far easier to get away on foot.

The key conclusion to be carried forward into the next chapter is that some or all dedicated antiarmor artillery units must be readily and economically heliportable and must have a secondary general support capability.

As to helicopters, one can see exactly how reasoning along these lines might have led the Soviets to the concept of a helicopter assault team and thus to the Hind. By contrast it is hard to see what real advantage lies in using one machine to carry offensive weapons and troops — specially when this results in large choppers with a lack of flexibility in their armament. The job can surely be done better by the range of helicopters now in service with or proposed for the US Air Cavalry. Sure, there are two distinct roles for attack helicopters — antiarmor, and the maybe more traditional "gunship" role of fire support — but the armament options available on Cobra AH1S provide just this flexibility. Utility helicopters used for carrying assault troops need light armament like machineguns for defensive and short-range suppressive fires. But at least I cannot see any validity in the "flying IFV" concept. With direct protection limited in strength and aspect, surely the need is to get the troop carriers in fast under close cover (and if necessary intense suppressive fires) from gunships, get the men and stores out even faster and get the machines out of it faster still.

There are, however, two questions which seem worth raising about the US Army's current helicopter inventory and program. The first I mention with some diffidence as a "helicopter layman". For very good reasons, most Air Cavalry TOEs contain rather more scout than attack machines. SA342M, France's primary antiarmor helicopter, weighs only 25-30% more than typical scout machines and has a rotor diameter only 1(+) m greater. One wonders whether it would not greatly increase cost-effectiveness to go for a Gazelle-sized machine as a scout and arm

TABLE 5 — Typical combat helicopters

(*Note.* It is extremely difficult to find data on helicopters which are accurate, consistent and comparable. The figures in this table have been taken from a number of sources and should be treated as a guide only, with my apologies for any substantial errors.)

Type	Origin	Gross weight (kg)	Endurance (min)	Normal range nm (km)	Max. speed kt (kph)	Power (shp)	Rotor dia. (m)	Armament AT	Armament FS	Armor
Hughes Defender 500 MD	USA	1310	?70-90	?130(243)	121(222)	420	7.92	4×TOW	or 30-mm chain gun (HEDP) or MGs	Partial v. 7.62 mm
Gazelle SA342M	France	1792	150	197(360)	170(310)	?600	10.50	4×HOT	?	No
PAH1 B0105P	FRG	2300	210	314(575)	148(270)	840	9.82	6×HOT	+ 20-mm cannon, MGs	No
PAH2/HAC	FRG/ France	3620	?	?	?	1000	?	6(?8)×HOT	?	?
Huey Cobra	USA	4309	120-150	383(700)	170(310)	1800	13.41	8×TOW	+ 2×19×FFAR 30-mm chain gun (HEDP) or 12.7/20-mm APDS (1372 m/sec)	Yes

	Country									Survival
Advanced attack helicopter Hughes AH64	USA	c.6150	108 156	267(489) 380(695)	204(373)	3200	14.63	8-16× Hellfire (?Maverick)	(+) 2×FFAR pods 30-mm chain gun (HEDP)	Yes (30 min survival from 23 and 30 mm)
Sikorsky S67A Blackhawk (utility version)	USA	10 000	115	339(620)	?196(369)	3000	18.90	? (attack version possible alternate to AH64)	?	?
HIND A (also 8-12 troops)	USSR	11 100	?120	232(425)	137(250)	3000	21.29	4×Sagger + 4×32× rockets 1×12.7-mm MG		Yes
HIND D (also 8 troops)	USSR	9955	?120	?259(473)	150 + (275 +)	3000	17.07	4×Sagger + (?2×Spiral as retrofit, cf. Hind E)	4×32× rockets Gatling gun (4×12.7-mm) or 1×23-mm cannon	Yes

it with four ATGMs (or even just two larger missiles). This would allow scout choppers to take on opportunity targets and would make it possible to fly antiarmor missions maintaining NOE cover in terrain which Cobras could not traverse in this way.

The second question is fundamental both to helicopter participation in the mechanized force defense and to independent helicopter operations. It is whether attack helicopters should always engage on the wing or should take up fire positions in rotor defilade and remain at flight idle while firing. Technically the implications of this are comparatively simple. Target acquisition and guidance requires either a dismounted sight (like Swingfire) or a forward observer (on the ground or in a scout helicopter) in conjunction with a TV-headed missile. Launch needs rails capable of being elevated (which AH1S already has for TOW) and could require the heavier missiles of the future to have a larger boost motor than they need for in-flight launch. But the question comes down to one of security and endurance. Most agree that somebody on the other side is frequently going to track an ATGM back to its launch point and put down fire on this. So to maintain survivability the helicopter, like the tank, needs to displace after each shot — and unlike the tank may not have time to. Much as ground commanders would like to have attack helicopters in fixed fire positions, it looks like the policy of sitting at flight idle under cover and in relative safety and unmasking to fire on the wing is preferable.

I believe then we should carry two types of attack helicopter into the family of antiarmor weapon systems. Neither of these need or even should be a strictly dedicated antiarmor machine. One is the scout/light attack helicopter similar to SA342M. The other is an attack helicopter excellently represented by Cobra AH1S. This machine must have flexibility of armament to suit it for the antiarmor or fire support roles, or a tanklike combination of these. We must not become so obsessed with killing tanks as to forget the importance of direct general support fire in the mechanized battle. This attack helicopter may have to go up in size to accommodate a reasonable load of the larger ATGMSs which will be needed in future. But a heavier machine with a larger rotor should not be adopted just for the sake of carrying more missiles — there seems to be a real danger of the helicopter going the same way as the tank! Additionally we need to assume the availability of communications, utility and heavy-lift helicopters to the extent this now exists in most advanced armies.

17

Indirect-fire systems

Around 1970 the importance of surface-to-surface artillery in the armored battle reached a low. Outside of nuclear capability and an offensive chemical capability, should NATO opt for one, the artillery's main task seemed to be an exchange of counterbattery fires of doubtful significance to the main battle. This state of affairs is perhaps exemplified by the fact that, although historically the Russian Army had shared a world lead in artillery with the French, the Soviet Army was the last major one to field a self-propelled force of tubed artillery. No way, it seemed, could artillery compete with the family of direct-fire antiarmor weapons — high-pressure guns, line-of-sight ATGMSs and rocket launchers.

Probably the factors that reversed the swing were not so much the increasingly certain advent of compound armor as the progressive shift in the balance of conventional power in favor of the Warsaw Pact and against NATO, along with the Bundeswehr's preaching of its doctrine of mobile defense. Everything that might add to the weight of defensive fires was justified; and the available barrier resources needed to be used at successive depths in front of the actual enemy rather than spread out in a line where most of them would make no contribution to the battle. Technologically the laser target marker opened the way to the guided shell and seemingly to the fire-and-forget missile. The size and the effectiveness against armor of submunitions, bomblets and minelets alike, began to converge on a point where they could be delivered in useful numbers by medium artillery. And the Soviets increasingly showed the way to the use of rocket artillery, free-flight and guided alike.

Looking ahead from 1980, with compound armor forcing the ATGMS out of the middle ground where handiness and effectiveness were combined, we see artillery starting to regain the importance it had in World War I, when men in the open and in earthworks were its target. On the Soviet side it has literally moved back into the direct-fire conflict. Within NATO by contrast a separatist trend, stemming maybe from the tactical nuclear heyday of the fifties when artillery ruled, seems still to prevail. Sure, the artillery will play a large part in the antiarmor battle; but it will do this mainly by counterbattery fires and by intervening with immediate and delayed effect submunitions in places where the maneuver force is not — in effect an economy of force mission.

This is undoubtedly an important role. Harassment in depth will be invaluable too, specially in air situations near the less optimistic end of the spectrum of prognostications. Likewise there will be instances, maybe all too many, when nothing except fire can be put in front of a breakthrough force. Yet again, counterbattery fires will increase in importance with the effectiveness and bold handling of the other side's artillery. But I believe I have shown in earlier chapters that the maneuver force and the artillery need each other desperately. The maneuver force needs the artillery to crash down with neutralizing fire on an attack, setting the opposing armor up for the direct-fire weapons; and to thicken up its own lethal fires by getting at the relatively weak roofs of the attacking vehicles. The artillery needs the maneuver force, on tracks and in helicopters, because indirect antiarmor fire must be observed if it is to be effective and observers need protection; and because the lethality of attack with submunitions is at best questionable. These specific factors apart, the name of the game has to be *maximizing the concentration of firepower in time and space for optimum shock effect.*

We have in fact developed in earlier chapters a rather clear picture of artillery in the antiarmor battle, so it will suffice to résumé this. In the longer term pinpoint fire needs to be independent of target marking; there seem to be great attractions in going indirect with terminal active homing for the primary surface-to-surface ATGMS, and this adds up to dedicated antiarmor artillery units. Active homing would be equally desirable for a guided shell, Copperhead successor. There may be a case for a neutralizing weapon with true area effect as opposed to discrete scatter, for instance to black out vision and sight heads. But even if feasible this mode of attack could be shut out by more lethal munitions. In submunition attack numbers are what matter. Because their effectiveness is extended in time, minelets have a greater chance of success than bomblets, specially if they are laid just in front of an advancing enemy; and if it means more of them the minimal track-cutting minelet will do.

Artillery must have an alternate communications system, and this must link to all arms, notably helicopters. One solution here is the use of flares, signal cartridges and indicator shell (fired direct) or tracer in conjunction with a "rear observer" linked to the guns by line. By the same token the electronic warfare problem could be one argument for moving some guns up to fire direct. General support artillery units evidently require a secondary antiarmor capability. At least a proportion of or elements of dedicated units must be heliportable; and some general support capability is needed to go with this.

Maybe the first point to tackle is munitions — how their natures can be held to a manageable number, bearing in mind that general support units have to handle nuclear and probably in future chemical munitions as well. HE and smoke are evidently essential. Then there have to be a guided warhead and shell for pinpoint attack. Bomblet attack looks attractive for counter-battery fires against armored self-propelled artillery and for harassment in depth. By contrast minelets seem best for support of the maneuver force battle. For starters one might try a pattern something like this.

General support tubed artillery			Close-support antiarmor artillery
Medium		Heavy	
...	nuclear	...	guided warhead
...	(?) chemical	...	minelet warhead
...	HE	...	bomblet warhead
smoke		bomblet shell	
guided shell			(*plus* some form of general support
minelet shell			capability)

This leaves medium tubed artillery with an alarming six natures and heavy with four. Evidently some specialization of medium batteries might be needed to ease the problems of ammunition handling and supply. Additionally, if concepts like Assault Breaker come to fruition, there will be a need for heavy missiles (presumably with full trajectory guidance) and aircraft bombs with a load of minimissiles or "smart" bomblets. These requirements correlate to the corps, army and tactical air force nuclear delivery systems.

As will not have escaped the reader, I have just slipped in an assumption that the main antiarmor artillery system will be rocket (and tactical general-support systems tubed). When considering the characteristics of the guided warhead/missile we postulated a range of around 10 km for support of the maneuver force, with a range bonus (to be optimized on technical grounds) for harassing fire and the massing of fire. For these tasks where direct fire is absent a combination of bomblet and minelet attack may be needed as a backup to the pinpoint fires. And helicopter operations should have some kind of general fire support.

The ATGMS weapon platform and its "limber" should have matching mobility. Command, command post, signals and some observation-post vehicles need a speed margin of at least 33% if the mobility of the launchers is to be fully exploited. The cross-country truck type of running gear would not be adequate, and close-coupled wheeled running gears are increasingly being shut out by cost. So the launcher and missile transporter need to be fully tracked. Following the normal convention for this category of vehicle, they should offer the detachment basic all-round protection along with collective NBC protection when not in action.

The going weight for roughly comparable systems looks like 12-15 t, but this may stem from the characteristics of various armies' workhorses rather than from the parameters of the weapon system. This vehicle really needs to be carried as an underslung load by helicopters of the Chinook class, around 10 t that is. At an informed guess it should be possible to field a twin launcher and a four-missile transporter at this weight by using light alloy construction and a lightweight set of automotive subsystems like those of the United States M667 (Lance launcher) or the British CVR(T) family. If this is so the command vehicle of that family, Sultan, with a 2 t weight advantage over the launcher and limber, would team up fine. Forward observers must be able to work on their feet and from helicopters. Additionally they will need a proportion of "main force" vehicles — in the family we are working on the CSV (Chapter 15).

If the ATGMS unit or subunit can be made readily heliportable, there is a need to provide some kind of general support fire with the same operational mobility, both helilifted and on tracks. Multitube rocket launchers (of the "Stalin organ" type) would be ideal both for neutralizing antiarmor support of a helicopter blocking operation (Chapter 16) and for the "crash" defensive fires envisioned in the main battle (Chapter 9). But there looks to be no way of getting a useful multitube launch pack onto a 10-t armored vehicle. Anyways this type of weapon system lacks the flexibility and versatility that a helicopter operation outside the reach of medium tubed artillery would need; and it expends massive amounts of ammunition.

Thinking of high rates of fire from simple equipment, one next turns to mortars. Like missile launchers, normal "armored mortar" vehicles with heavy mortars (120-mm, 8000-9000 m) run out at 12-15 t. But again this is due in some measure to the size and weight of the workhorse hull and subsystems. Additionally, in the mechanized infantry scenario, the mortar is customarily fired with the detachment under armor; and the same vehicle carries all the "on gun" ammunition. On the same principles as we applied to the ATGMS — a detachment unprotected when in action and a separate launcher vehicle — a 120-mm mortar on an 8-10 t vehicle is a certain starter. Alternatively, to maximize rate of fire and minimize the effect of losing a vehicle, it might pay to mount a mortar on both vehicles of a pair and carry a limited amount of ammunition on each. This mortar would fire standard HE and smoke rounds plus an overweight rocket-assisted minelet carrier.[1]

I do not want to get overly committed to organizations at this stage, but a picture is emerging of a heliportable antiarmor artillery battalion, self-propelled on tracks on a 10-t (MLC 12) basis. This unit would have a number of missile batteries, and a "light" (mortar) battery capable either of operating as a fire unit or of hiving off a platoon or section to each missile battery. I see this essentially as a unit to be handled well forward using "shoot'n' scoot" techniques. The missile battery will need precise survey, but "instant survey" no longer poses too much of a problem.

Having already probed dangerously into gunner territory, I should like to close by addressing three broader points. Gunner logic probably requires the suggested mortar batteries to be organized into light battalions. But as a maneuver combat team commander or the staff officer planning a helicopter operation I would need to be absolutely sure of getting the mortars along with the missiles, not finding they had already been allocated to some arcane task unconnected with my needs. So I reckon the mortars belong in the antiarmor battalion as a complement to the

---

1 I believe a project for a medium mortar on Spartan (the APC of the British CVR(T) family) was taken to prototype stage; but there the mortar was mounted under armor.

ATGMS — a point clinched by the requirements of support for helicopter operations.

Maybe I am paranoid about not getting artillery support, but I have so often been told, and seen others told, on exercises that it was urgently required elsewhere that I suspect this could be the way the thing might go for real — whence my mention above of the maneuver combat team commander. Given the latest known Soviet thinking on the use of artillery to support the break-in battle, there is evidently going to be one hell of a clash over the defender's use of his general support artillery. I would like to invite the reader to pause a moment, envision the attack rolling in, and set a general order of priority on counterbattery missions, harassment in depth, and defensive fires.

I guess harassing fires have to step down or be left to the "heavy" systems once the direct fire battle is joined; the maneuver team commander must have the fullest and closest possible support as the crunch point approaches. The problem is just where *his* greatest need lies. Unless the opposing artillery is suppressed, he cannot maneuver freely — or even see to move and fire. Contrariwise he must have "crash" defensive fires to turn the battle his way — to give his direct-fire weapon systems time to cope with the target density.

The answer seems to lie in a very careful distinction in time. Up to the moment the first main wave of armor enters the optimum target zone for his direct fire weapons,[2] the defender needs to be preserved and left free to observe by maximizing counterbattery fires. Then comes the call for *a crash concentration of direct and indirect firepower in time,* the maximum shock effect. Here it is defensive fires that matter. Once this tactical crunch point, which may last only 2 or 3 minutes, is past, the defender will hopefully be able to maintain control with only dedicated artillery support close in. But once again he needs the attacker's artillery kept off his back.

These apparently simple switches from counterbattery fires to close-in defensive fires and back again present a number of technical problems, mainly associated with the different natures of munitions and the different charges required for each. Guns will be silent — briefly, but just when they are most needed. The point is worth stressing because the changeovers come at the tactically critical moment of the encounter. Almost certainly

---

2 I am deliberately avoiding the phrase "killing area" or "killing pocket" since these terms are associated with particular tactical doctrines.

special fire planning techniques and SOPs on the gun positions can do a lot to minimize these gaps.

My last point is a frank plea. Even with one of the two main surface-to-surface antiarmor weapon systems *and* the minelet capability assigned to the artillery, *by far the most important artillery role in the maneuver battle remains air defense.* In *Tank Warfare* I rather desperately made the forward air defense weapon systems organic to the composite "tank/infantry" battalion in the hope that they would at least be around when needed. Having since studied the Soviet tactical air defense in more depth, I doubt this solution is technically practicable — at least without gaps and/or considerable loss of effectiveness.

Problem is the fundamental clash of philosophies about tactical air defense. The maneuver force reckons it is there to stop them getting pinned down and protect them. The gunners are convinced they are there to shoot down aircraft and help gain local air superiority. These goals often conflict. If NATO fails to field a coherent tactical air defense, its maneuver forces will be paralyzed. But if human and material resources are to be deflected from the maneuver force into tactical air defense — as they increasingly must be — somebody at the highest level needs to lay down a clear-cut distinction. The goal of the aerial elements and strategic/operational ground elements of air defense is to gain air superiority, at least temporary and local. *The goal of tactical air defense is to gain and maintain freedom of movement for the maneuver force.*

The changeover point can best be seen in the Soviet system. ZSU23/4 (with GUNDISH) and SA9 (GASKIN) are tactical weapon systems, making up the air defense batteries at regiment (brigade) level. SA5 (GANEF/PAT HAND) is an operational system handled at army level. SA6 (GAINFUL/STRAIGHT FLUSH) units are also army troops but often seem to be assigned to division and deployed 30-35 km behind the line of contact. This is the bridging fire-control and weapon system which from its position and nature can act at either tactical or operational level. Some will argue that this distinction was none too evident in the early stages of the Yom Kippur War; but it looks like the boldness, persisting to the point of foolhardiness, of the Israeli Air Force allowed SA6 to do both jobs very nicely at the same time.

18

Fixed-wing aircraft

There is no technical difficulty in providing strike and other fixed-wing aircraft with a formidable antiarmor capability. The problem is one of availability. Assessments of the air situation within the NATO center scenario vary widely; and because the opposition would be on central lines, the initial air situation is likely to be very unfavorable in any NATO v Warpac flare-up in the Middle East. On at least one authoritative view, the power and complexity of the Warpac air defense system is such that the Pact probably could not, even if it wished, fly combat alert patrol (CAP) fighter cover over their part of the combat zone. So the air situation may not be directly relevant to NATO's ability to operate in that airspace.

One can argue about priorities of artillery missions; but for fixed-wing aircraft the name of the game just has to be gaining control of the relevant airspace. If the air situation is bad, ground attack aircraft will have to be directed initially against priority counter-air targets — the hostile air force's and/or air defense's forward ground installations. Nonetheless, if the situation on the ground starts to get out of control, these aircraft could fly battlefield interdiction missions against choke points like crossings of the Elbe or other major obstacles; or maybe, less dangerously and more effectively, against the logistic backup for both the maneuver force and its supporting artillery. The latest Soviet doctrine seems to call for the expenditure of artillery ammunition on a near World War I scale; I myself and others are not entirely convinced, but just a few grains of truth in this would suffice to create a prime interdiction target. The risk to strike aircraft attacking choke points in face of the full AD system depends on many variables such as terrain, but largely on how much NATO air forces are prepared to spend on ECCM packs for these aircraft. Technologically, as usual, the "countermeasures to the nth" game is likely to remain a fairly even one.

A second question mark which hangs over antiarmor missions by strike aircraft is weather — not so much foul weather in the normal sense as poor low-level visibility. Those misty fall mornings on the North German Plain, in the Einbeck basin, along the Fulda valley or wherever send two separate kinds of shiver down the spine of NATO commanders on maneuvers — one of physical chill, the other of apprehension at the helplessness of the defense in face of advancing armor. Nobody who has not been there is going to allow there are chilly, misty fall mornings in the desert too; but sandstorms, haze and inversion effects frequently impair surface-to-surface and low-level visibility.

At the moment mist and even dark nights set a limit on terrain flying by fast jets and may force them up to dangerous heights. By contrast the nineties state of the art should allow them to maintain their normal terrain mode in all weathers. Likewise by the nineties a suitable mix of forward-looking sensors should permit *detection* of individual armored vehicle targets in all weathers; but *acquisition and instrument engagement* of anything less than, say, a company concentration of tanks or IFVs may be marginal. Assuming full use is made of predictable technology, both fixed- and rotary-wing aircraft should by then have an edge on the ground troops they are supporting in poor visibility. Evidently, though, much will depend on the way the opposition behaves. If he bunches or even maintains normal densities, he is likely to run into trouble. If navigational skill and boldness allow him to thin out, he will still be likely to slip through.

Anyways desert terrain, while often full of folds which vehicles and light or medium helicopters use for cover, offers little opportunity of concealment to large high-performance fixed-wing aircraft. So terrain flying over desert is problematical for fixed- and rotary-wing aircraft alike — the first because of exposure and the second because of downwash and dust or sand (page 21).

The strategic importance of the armored battle in the NATO center and the relatively high probability of its happening mean, in my view at least, that resources have to be committed to those weapon systems least likely to be hampered or made inoperable by across-the-board enemy action like electronic, chemical or nuclear warfare, or by weather conditions and their consequences. This is why I opted in earlier chapters for systems which are invulnerable to the EW threat or could be made so. These factors weigh both for and against ground attack by fixed-wing aircraft. Yet successful air strikes in depth could destroy the momentum of the enemy's advance and weaken the power of his punch. Additionally, as I remarked above, a point may well be reached at which medium and deep battlefield interdiction offers the only hope of maintaining or regaining control of the situation on the ground.

Maybe the key terms in this difficult equation are the way a strike by a modern fast jet represents an extreme concentration in time and space of a massive *weight of fire* — in the literal sense; the way this can be very rapidly applied to *any desired point* in or behind the combat zone; and the fact that, within his brief, a pilot, like a forward observer, can *intelligently select* his target once he sees what is actually going on in the target area.

At first sight the way to balance resource expenditure seems to be the development for fixed-wing aircraft of antiarmor systems which make extensive use of subsystems developed for key surface-to-surface or helicopter-delivered weapons. But the history of attempts to design weapon systems or even subsystems compatible with fixed- and rotary-wing machines, or with either and armored vehicles — let alone with all three — is one which most of the few who know some of it would prefer to forget. The same goes for adapting systems designed for any one of these means of delivery to another. Sure, there are exceptions; and the more recent instalments of this saga are slightly less horror-packed than the earlier ones. But these success stories usually concern adaptations of weapon systems which have been estabished and thoroughly debugged in one field and are comfortably within the state of the art when they come to be applied to a second. So anybody seeking to economize on resources by this particular kind of commonality needs a specially skeptical eye and sensitive hackles.

With this warning note struck, we can address the problem of techniques and armament options. In face of the Soviet AD threat a lo-lo-lo profile is a must. The only deviation from the fast jet NOE mode which might be acceptable is toss bombing. Even here the risk entailed is scarcely justified except for nuclear weapon delivery. Anyways, the accuracy of this technique is currently inadequate for any form of antiarmor attack, even with submunitions, and may be no better than marginal by the nineties. So we have an aircraft maintaining an optimum height over the ground of under 30 m with an operational ceiling of 60 m; this machine is traveling at supersonic speed, probably slowing to high subsonic on the run-in to the target area.[1] Even if the FFAR size of rocket (page 191) and 30-mm multitube cannon attack were lethal against compound armor at the angles of descent involved, aimed direct fire at pinpoint targets is unfeasible.

So the realistic options, both using virtually horizontal attack, are laydown bombing with cluster munitions and submunitions or standoff attack with salvos of ATGMs. The problem about cluster *bombs* is the limited space and time the bomb has to arm and fire and the submunitions have to deploy. One very simple and effective technique would look to be the *controlled release of a stream of minelets.* Ballpark figuring based on current United States hardware and developments suggests that a suitable combination of spoilers and directional fins would make shaped charge minelets of the "mini-javelin" type (page 83) feasible in this application. We are talking here about at least 1000 lethal minelets with influence fuzes and antilift devices *plus* a suitable mixture of track-cutting and antipersonnel types per aircraft load.

The second possibility is a salvo of *cluster rockets* fired at a slight positive launch angle and designed and fuzed to burst at the range and height to deploy their submunitions correctly over the target area. The main submunition used here would presumably be *"smart" bomblets,* with a nuisance mixture of minelets. This technique would give the aircraft a measure of standoff. If however one is going to use up space, weight and money on a primary projectile, the cluster/submunition principle may not be the best approach and should certainly not be the only one.

Fact is a salvo of ATGMs like Maverick or the French Sabre looks very much more to the point. The terminal active homing head of the ATGMS proposed for artillery use might be a good starting point. The difference in terminal velocity between aircraft *plus* cruise missile and ballistic missile could probably be accommodated. Launched from a platform traveling at, say, Mach 1.25, this missile would have a ground speed around Mach 2.15, so that the time of flight to 6000 m would be well under 10 seconds. Thus the "terminal" guidance of the warhead in the

---

1 This being so, I do not think the notion of cheap, piston-engined, subsonic "tank busters", widely aired in the British *Daily Telegraph* a while back, merits discussion here. Being (in the terms postulated) incapable of NOE flying, they would be a piece of cake the moment they entered the defended area. Even if their high turn rate allowed them to duck the missiles, they would be what one might call a custom-built gâteau for ZSU23/4.

artillery mode could serve as full trajectory guidance in the air-to-surface mode without fear of spoiling by active protection systems. Taking account of real system costs, though, it would probably be cost-effective to provide this missile with multiple sensors — as indeed it might prove to be in the artillery role.

A nineties strike aircraft could be expected to carry around eight missiles of this type, maybe more. Against a concentrated enemy — one of the prerequisites for justifying an air strike — the success chance should be very high. Equally important, the standoff of several kilometers, although sometimes limited by terrain, would greatly enhance the aircraft's survivability.

The future use of ground-attack aircraft in support of the land battle rather than in the counter-air role poses two paradoxes. Counter-air must come first — in priority and time alike — but battlefield interdiction may become indispensable as the land battle develops. If these fast jets are to have any reasonable hope of reaching the target area, let alone surviving the mission, they must stick to NOE flying; this severely limits the choice of armaments and attack modes. In the event these two paradoxes combine to offer a mutual solution — you have to win some! Chasing after "bus" bombs or rockets with immediate effect submunitions once again looks to be "a technologists' ball on thin ice" (*cf.* page 158). The needs are first, a directional shaped-charge minelet which could probably be a variant of the existing (helicopter-delivered) M56, along with a dispensing system compatible with a fast jet's "NOE" height and target-area speed; second, an effectively autonomous air-to-surface ATGMS. The parameters for this ATGMS are quite different from the helicopter system, but have much in common with existing air-to-air and air-to-surface missiles and with the proposed artillery antiarmor warhead.

19

Antiarmor capability in light mechanized and dismounted forces

For at least a decade line-of-sight ATGMSs with small shaped charge warheads have conferred a substantial antiarmor capability on airportable and other light mechanized forces. By their nature such troops could never muster the fighting power to face squarely up to a full-scale tank punch. But the combination of an ATGMS, a hand-held rocket launcher and a low-pressure gun capable of defeating light armored vehicles put them in a position both to look after themselves and to shape up a useful fist in support of dismounted infantry. Likewise infantry itself possessed the two most important of these capabilities. So the likelihood that this category of missile or rocket will be unable to defeat the frontal arc of tanks with compound armor adds up to a serious loss of combat value.

We need then to bracket in on this gap and identify its edges. We saw in Chapter 12 that, given suitable tactics, crew served and hand-held antiarmor weapon systems still had a very important part to play by attacking the sides, rear and roof of tanks. We noted, though, that for these tactics a lightweight rocket launcher like RPG7V was much preferable to a more cumbersome weapon like Carl-Gustav, despite the latter's greater range and versatility. Likewise, in spite of the alleged drawbacks of manual command link guidance, a really handy ATGMS like improved Sagger would show up well against more cumbersome systems like TOW or even MILAN, whose large indivisible loads are little suited to being manpacked into ambushlike positions across country and through forests or scrub. Extending this argument one stage further, vehicle-mounted systems like Swingfire will be of little value despite their range because of the problem of working them discreetly into ambush and enfilade positions — and even more of getting them out again.

At the other extreme come attack helicopters (Chapter 16) and the heliportable antiarmor artillery battalion with its secondary general support capability (Chapter 17). I designed this battalion the way I did to make it capable of supporting independent operations by helicopters; but with a maximum indivisible load around 10 t it is even more readily airportable in transport aircraft and is inherently well suited to difficult terrain.

So there is no problem — aside from the evident logistic one — about deploying attack helicopter units and a long-range surface-to-surface ATGMS at the end of air lines of communication.

Thus the gap, as one might expect, is precisely that filled in the main maneuver force by the tank — or rather by the TD/FST pair (Chapter 15). Question is whether this gap is worth plugging in the light force situation; but let us suppose for the moment that it is. I guess we should not get too involved here about the whole span of vehicles which armored reconnaissance and light mechanized forces need. We are looking specifically for some equivalent to the tank destroyer.

Using the British CVR(T) family as a point of departure, we postulated four variants[1] for the antiarmor artillery battalion; we should now note that a fifth is needed — a light armored recovery vehicle (ARV).[2] Again we do not need to explore the point in detail here, but standard infantry battalions (as opposed to mechanized battalions or whatever) need a light, basic squad APC.[3] An extended version of the light armored vehicle hull looks to be a good starter for this role.[4] So the addition of one more variant would not be too serious, specially when this might provide dismounted infantry with a direct-fire support capability as well.

In Chapter 10 we moved away from the DARPA/ARES 75-mm gun (as on HIMAG and HSTV-L; pls. 10 and 11, page 36) or a possible 90-mm option because of the many and great advantages of staying with 105-mm as the caliber for the main maneuver force's high-pressure gun. But accepting for the moment DARPA's contention that 75-mm is adequate for the antitank role *per se,* we can look at the possibilities of getting the 75-mm/72 L

---

1 Excluding the numerous subvariants of the command vehicle.
2 Samson in the CVR(T) family.
3 See *Mechanized Infantry,* Chapter 9.
4 Like FV4333, "extended Spartan", in the British CVR(T) family.

gun[5] onto a vehicle of 10 t or at most 10.85 t (MLC12). HSTV-L is one size too big, but we can take Scorpion, the parent vehicle of the British CVR(T) family (pl. 29), as a model. Scorpion weighs a shade under 8 t and has very high mobility; with a mobility tradeoff matching the tank-destroyer role in a dismounted battle, it could certainly be raised to MLC12 and extended by one roadwheel station if necessary. Likewise a hydropneumatic suspension system for the CVR(T) family was taken to an advanced stage of development and is now entirely within the state of the art. So a fixed-gun vehicle looks feasible.

Recoil forces and stability apart, this long 75-mm gun in a turret mounting on Scorpion would be patently out of scale. In a "mini-S Tank" configuration, though, the gun would go on the existing length of hull with an overhang of only 1-1.25 m, equivalating to an angle of attack around 35° with the gun horizontal. A 90-mm/72 L gun on a hull lengthened by one roadwheel station gives almost the same figures; but the vehicle would then have to be widened to maintain slew characteristics good enough for laying the gun. Ballpark figuring on weight gives a span from 10.5 t to 12 t for this larger vehicle, so we are getting into a very questionable area. If, as in the family of weapons postulated in this book, this is the only requirement for a high-pressure gun in the 75-90-mm caliber range, it would be possible to go for a compromise caliber around 83-85-mm. Conversely it would be very hard to justify development of a gun-ammunition system for this requirement alone.

It seems far more sensible to take the 75-mm system already developed and settle if needs be for a maximum effective range of 2500-3000 m. On conservative figures this should suffice for around 85% of the targets offered to this type of weapon system in European terrain and 60-65% in flat desert terrain.[6] My own judgment is that the weapon system would be justified in a European scenario in which both medium armored recon-naissance and dismounted infantry in positional defense figured large; but *not* in the eighties/nineties European setting or a Mideast scenario. The resources could be better used for addi-tional antiarmor artillery battalions. By contrast, for reasons discussed in Chapter 14, I would prefer this system to the STAFF approach of using a low-pressure gun of similar caliber to

---

5 My rough scaling from published diagrams puts this gun at 70-75 L.

6 As in my previous books and earlier chapters, I am staying well within the percentages determined by operational analysis, since many users regard these as controversial.

detonate downward-looking self-formed fragment projectiles at a
given standoff above the target. For reasons I set out in that
chapter I see this only as a possible backup warhead for ATGMSs
like Sagger, MILAN or TOW.

So we end up with the gap we defined left unfilled and a virtual
standstill — at best slow evolution — in antiarmor weapon
systems for light mechanized and dismounted forces. This is an
unhealthy situation in any language, probably an unacceptable
one in American. Yet it raises a point of the utmost general
importance and interest. At any given moment some fields —
currently microelectronics for instance — are moving so fast and
to such radical effect that even the telling can scarcely keep pace
and hardware is obsolete before it is produced. Contrariwise other
fields are virtually standing still. Commercial factors dictate
innovation where it bites hardest, likewise conservatism where the
status quo obstinately persists. If this approach makes most
money, it has to stand for some kind of optimum effectiveness
too. Oddly enough, despite the known horrors of Russian Marxist
bureaucracy, the Soviets achieve much the same in fields where
they think it matters like aerospace and defense. Entrepreneurs
and Soviet equipment planners seem equally content to abstain
from attempting a quantum jump until they have a strong, well-
secured springboard under them.

By contrast Western defense procurement is apt to move slowly
in directions where success is waiting to be exploited and to bang
its expensive head hard against brick walls or to go tilting at
windmills where technology is stagnant. Many of the folks in these
systems, serving and civilian alike, are intelligent and dedicated
men with good track records of exploiting success in war or in
industry. So the reason for their persistent reinforcement of
failure has to lie in the constraints under which they operate.

Once a system goes into production it needs a service life of at
least 10 years (a "half generation") to justify its cost and to match
the pace at which the *physical* inertia of a large organization
allows the "pipeline" processes of training, issue, modification,
withdrawal and replacement to proceed. There is in effect a limit
on the pace of progress attainable for real; and this limit is wholly
unrelated to the pace of technological advance. In fast-moving
fields this makes the decision on when to produce so difficult that
most folks inevitably get it wrong most of the time.

Two other constraints, though, are wholly avoidable, stemming from the *psychological* inertia of large organizations. For
reasons touched on earlier and summed by the tag "Armies

equip men; navies and air forces man equipment" armies suffer
far more than most from this inertia.[7] *Users, most of all the
combat arms, are equally reluctant to adapt force structure to
exploit new technology and to adapt tactics to apply existing
technology in a new situation.*

These linked attitudes at once create the brick walls and the
windmills and invite the designer to bang his head against them
or tilt at them. If he is a man with a high sense of duty, he feels
that by doing so he may somehow succeed in improving the lot of
the combat soldier. If cynical, he reckons that if he declines to
play somebody else will. Since most intelligent folks are a bit of
both, they are very strongly motivated to reinforce failure or at
least to nourish obstinacy with unfounded expectations.

The gap discussed in this chapter is a textbook example. On
the one hand technology is available to plug it with an indirect
fire ATGMS. But that means a transfer of function from armor
and/or infantry to artillery, whence a transfer of manpower. And
the amount of manpower controlled looks to be the touchstone of
power in any large organization. On the other hand, existing
weapon systems can be used to excellent effect by tactics based on
cunning rather than confrontation — a back play rather than a
forward play. The user would be delighted to make this change if
he had thought of it — as he did in the case of the dispersed
strongpoint. But rather than make a change forced on him by the
lack of a new toy, he will call the honest technologist a fool, clutch
at any straw he can find and thus divert resources from the fast-
moving fields which could use them to best effect. Doubtless Dr
Spock has a word for it; I seem to recall the bionic Mr Spock of
Star Trek has too!

7 *Cf.* Stanhope, *The Soldiers: see* Bibliography.

20

The family of antiarmor weapons

The Appendix sets out one possible family of antiarmor weapons derived from the arguments deployed so far in this book. The next stage in the approach I am using is to recycle this family through an examination of operational doctrine, tactics and force structure. First, though, it may be worth highlighting some of the differences between this family and currently accepted ideas, and the reasons for these. Then we might venture on a glimpse into the beyond three half-generations ahead, the period in which innovations now coming up in research might materialize as serviceable weapon systems.

For me, unexpectedly I have to admit, the electronic warfare threat, including the possibility of active protection systems for armored vehicles, has proved to be the most important single issue. This is because the effort, always intense and sometimes desperate, to gain a lead or pull back an opposition lead brings mounting sophistication in every field. And sophistication seems frequently to entail vulnerability to the EW threat. Evidently there are some fields which by their nature or their importance require both sides to play the "countermeasures to the nth" game. Outside these, it looks like the threat has been ignored or pushed aside in favor of other issues.

The most striking example is readiness to use radio links both within fire-control systems and in the associated organs of command. Artillery just could not function with its radio nets out. Again the West makes use of electromagnetic radiation for target acquisition, indication and marking with utter disregard of the opportunity this gives the target to react offensively or by evasion. All these sources of radiation, from long wave RT transmitters to visible light lasers, bring with them great advances in capability. Nobody would suggest dispensing with them, at least until better techniques can be found. The need is for an alternate system to fall back on when countermeasures are in operation.

By contrast it is hard to find any justification for the way some Western armies go to great cost and complexity and forgo many real advantages just to ease their selection and training problems. This is most conspicuous in the antitank guided-missile field. The Soviets have accepted the personnel problem and stayed firmly with a countermeasure-proof system. I believe I have been able to indicate how adaptation of a TV head from guided bombs and acceptance of manual control could provide a countermeasure-proof system with all the advantages of an autonomous missile bar rate of fire.

Compound armor has to be a major factor for the next decade or two. The big question, on which one can only wait and see, is whether the user will in fact accept the penalties of compound arrays capable of defeating the shaped charge warheads of existing crew served and hand-held weapon systems. For vehicle- and helicopter-mounted ATGMSs, line-of-sight and otherwise, the penalty imposed by compound armor on warhead weight, thence on missile weight and size, can be accommodated by a radical response. An indirect effect of compound armor in conjunction with other at first sight unrelated advances will undoubtedly be to extend the heavily protected frontal arc in both planes. This will inevitably lead to some weakening, or at least little strengthening, of protection over the traditional frontal arc.

This probability, linked with advances in KE penetrators, opens the option of staying with the 105-mm rifled tube for KE antiarmor weapon systems and boosting performance still further by lengthening the tube of the primary system. This possibility, linked with the operational and battlefield mobility now known to be available at around MLC40 (36.2 t), will with any luck give even the more conservative tankers and the vested interests which provide them with hardware a sharp enough kick in the pants to divorce them from their dinosaurs in favor of a hi-lo profile — tank destroyer and fire-support tank.

My guess is that the mobility on offer linked to the eighties state of the art in the fields of control engineering and sensor techniques may likewise swing even these diehards away from passive direct protection towards indirect and active protection. Problem is there are not one but two psychological blocks to be overcome here. The lesser one is the American/Rugby football forward mentality of most Anglo-Saxon officers. The greater one, shared maybe by all NATO armies, is an unshakable faith in technology linked to a refusal to face up to difficult training problems. We just noted one effect of this outlook. But the tempo now attainable in the land battle calls for a whole new set of attitudes, SOPs and training techniques for commanders at all levels, staffs and crew alike. It would surely be a pity to forgo the advantages this tempo offers to armor when it will be forced on armies by the helicopter anyways.

We will be addressing in the next chapter the question of whether the time is yet ripe for independent helicopter operations within the framework of the antiarmor defense. But the trend is in no doubt. Even when armor achieves the predictable twofold increase of operational mobility and threefold improvement in battlefield mobility, air cavalry will remain the *"Panzertruppen"* of the future — the small part of an army that enjoys mobility greater by an order of magnitude than the rest. This is not to say that air cavalry could supplant armor in the near future. By contrast one might expect to see the pendulum go onto its backswing as the operational significance of the helicopter mounts.

Like I remarked in Chapter 16, the helicopter still operates in a kind of *demi-monde* between ground and air forces. Given NOE or even contour flying, it is rarely detected by fighter aircraft; and then it can usually evade them. There are a number of weapon systems on the battlefield which can throw metal in its general direction. But the only surface-to-air weapon systems with any real antihelicopter capability are ZSU23/4, and shoulder-launched missiles like Blowpipe, Redeye and SA7 — all of them marginal on overall engagement time.

Despite its proven development potential, ZSU23/4 is no longer among the youngest of systems; dedicated antihelicopter air defense systems will inevitably emerge in both the Soviet and advanced Western armies. More importantly and no less inevitably, the already evident trend towards giving combat helicopters an antihelicopter capability will continue; and the appearance of a dedicated antihelicopter helicopter or rotary-wing fighter cannot be too far off. Initially, like fixed-wing fighters up to the Battle of Britain era, these are likely to be small, highly maneuverable and essentially defensive machines. Then, on the analogy of the pursuit fighter, larger and more heavily armed helicopters will go out in force and in depth to get every other kind of helicopter. In the long haul one can envision a balanced, self-contained helicopter force analogous to a modern air force.

We shall then have, in terms of altitude, a club sandwich land battle (fixed wing, rotary wing, ground force). In military terms it will be a four-tier one — fixed wing, rotary wing (cavalry), armor, infantry — each tier having mobility superior by an order of magnitude to the next. At one extreme the ability of fixed-wing aircraft to participate in the land battle and their availability to do so will be dictated in theory by their relationship to the rest of the air force and in practice by the air situation. At the other there is no indication whatever that the requirement for large numbers of men on their feet will diminish. In fact the whole broadening spectrum of revolutionary warfare, the increasing proportion of urban terrain and the need for positional and/or quasi-guerrilla operations within the mechanized battle[1] as the pace and scope of maneuver grow, all add up to an open-ended requirement for infantry.

The tradeoffs have to come between cavalry (by then all air cavalry) and armor, who will together, as they do now, fight the mechanized or maneuver battle over a battlefield of progressively larger dimensions. Infantry can easily be moved by vehicle, helicopter or transport aircraft as long as they do not have to fight on the way. Additionally they will acquire a basic armored personnel carrier for use in most of their nonmechanized roles just as inevitably as they once acquired trucks. With another few step advances in rotary-wing technology we shall reach a point when it will become *cheaper in real terms* to move a force of given combat value *above* unprepared terrain surfaces than *across* them. Since the military advantage of going an order of magnitude faster is beyond question, the point when this switch becomes *cost-effective* may not be too far beyond the turn of the century. By contrast it takes two to play any game; one power bloc cannot abandon armor unless and until the opposition looks like going the same way.

Many would interpret a reversal of the weight growth of armored vehicles as signifying that mechanization itself was on the downturn. Give or take a few swings of the pendulum, the shift away from armored vehicles towards helicopters and artillery which I have tried to depict in this book could mark the beginning of a trend which, like mechanization, will take a good half century to reach its peak.

1 Cf. *Mechanized Infantry,* Chapter 6.

PART 5

Operational Concept

21

The nature of the mechanized battle

I noted with amusement that a Soviet book on antitank warfare published as late as 1972[1] includes the immortal message that "the struggle against tanks ... calls for the appointment of an all arms commander". I first heard this as an officer cadet on a windy heath near Aldershot in winter 1940 — and in 30 years of soldiering I never once saw it respected. For even in a positional defense with tanks around on both sides, he who commands the antitank defense commands the defense period. In a contest between modern mechanized forces the antiarmor defense is the defense just as surely as the armored thrust is the offense. So in wrapping an operational concept and a force structure around the family of antiarmor weapons we need to consider mechanized warfare as a whole.

Even the superficial likeness of defensive behavior imposed by the circumstances of the seventies on the main NATO armies does not seem to have survived the turn of the decade and an infantry-inspired backswing of the pendulum of United States opinion. Anyways I doubt whether the US Army ever shifted far from its "fire base" doctrine any more than the Bundeswehr did from its belief in movement of masses and shock effect — or the British Army from its liking for positional concepts. But the recent thinking of these three armies, likewise of the Soviets, throws up a number of interesting and difficult questions at the level between what one might call the Anglo-Saxon rock and the Soviet-German roll on the one hand and a definitive concept of operations on the other. These questions we now need to address.

---

1 In this instance in English for the benefit of the USSR's Third World protégés: *see* Bibliography.

Like v. like

I have always seen the mechanized battle as an indivisible whole in which the maneuver force combines with supporting artillery and air to achieve maximum concentration of force. So I have to confess to some puzzlement and intellectual shock when I hear distinguished soldiers and eminent analysts joining forces to preach the doctrine of "like fights like". This thinking looks to stem on the military side from the desire for dedicated weapon systems and the trading off of organizational versatility for efficiency in a single role. Along with these go easement of the training problem, specially for conscripts, by focusing on a narrowly prescribed role, and a clear-cut, simple doctrine on how that role should be executed.

On the analytical side the underlying reasons seem more complex. One is an objection at both ethical and practical levels to pitting men against machines which are stronger than they are. Again "like v like" is far easier to analyze than "Category A v Category B and/or C and/or D...". Yet again my experience suggests that the user can most easily specify and the technologist most readily design, say, a tank in terms of outmatching another tank. Likewise it is relatively simple to establish the parameters of "Dedicated anti-A v A" — an ATGMS versus a tank or an AD system versus particular aircraft types and flight modes.

The "like v like" school of thought finds stronger support still in the fields of naval and air warfare. Conflicts in these fluid media, in which man is unable to compete without a machine and which are free of any variable of the importance and complexity of ground, are far more cut-and-dried than land warfare. They are fought between relatively large discrete units which can only be in one of a limited number of discrete states. All these factors make for a pairing off into "like v like" or "Dedicated anti-A v A".

Additionally certain phases of tactical and technological evolution have produced a "queen" — a weapon system of such power that the war is won or lost on the outcome of "queen v queen"; everybody and everything else is cast in supporting or character roles and serves only to set the scene for the main contest. But whether it is a knight in armor, a battleship or a nuclear-headed missile, a weapon system which has been and is acknowledged to have been "queened" is apt not to be used.[2] This line of thought always sparks in me two interesting and relevant

---

2 The best developed exposition of this argument is probably Mahan's "fleet in being" concept: *see* Bibliography.

conclusions. One is that presently a war is unlikely to go nuclear, even at tactical level. But space-based laser and particle beam weapon systems are now firmly in sight. These systems might well be used on a small scale in a direct or "sponsored" superpower conflict in the closing years of the century. They would then achieve "queen" status, unblocking the use of tactical nuclear weapons. The second and much narrower conclusion is that the tank was and is a dominant weapon system in the maneuver battle on land, but has never achieved "queen" status despite the efforts of its protagonists to "queen" it. The main battle tank, though, achieved a kind of "phony queen" or cult object status that has preserved it well into the stage of evolutionary decline and makes it hard to supplant.

Fact is all the "like v like" arguments contain a grain of truth and a deal of common sense. I believe though that they ignore the potential man contains within himself, specially when operating in his own medium — land. This potential operates at three levels. One is the "moral to the physical"; since I have never heard Napoleon's dictum challenged, no need to pursue it here. The second, which I referred to earlier (page 140), is man's ability to pull something out of the bag — to accomplish the theoretically impossible. The more man is encumbered with machinery and synthetic inputs, notably the more he is taken out of the primary control loop, the less he can exercise this divine spark. The third level at which human potential operates if permitted is versatility. In biological terms man is a nonspecialized species, and many schools of thought hold this to be the basic reason for his success. Technologists, however, and American technologists most of all, are apt to regard man as a slow-witted, cumbersome and unreliable bore. (In fact just like most of us regard our fellow men!) In their eyes dedicated is beautiful. These technologists are the sophisticated counterpart of the generals of satire who prepare meticulously for the last war.

Sure, a "capital intensive" force (a mechanized one, that is) is likely to defeat a "labor intensive" force (infantry) *on terrain suitable for both.* This is inevitable; quite simply, as I have shown elsewhere,[3] mechanization raises the fighting power of a combat soldier by a factor of around 3 as well as giving him new kinds of capability. By contrast military history, culminating in this instance in Vietnam and Afghanistan, is packed with examples of the containment or defeat of heavily equipped forces by light

---

3 *Mechanized Infantry,* page 69.

infantry and irregulars. "Like v like" certainly holds if it means "the fighting power of the opponents must be of the same order of magnitude unless terrain favors the weaker side". Equally "like v like" or "Dedicated anti-A v A" provides a useful guide to resolving conflicts of priorities — to frustrating attempts to overburden a tank with every kind of direct firepower, artillery with an unmanageable assortment of munitions or a unit with an unteachable clutter of roles.

Yet carried to extremes this doctrine reduces the land battle to a group of uncoordinated and unrelated exchanges. Tanks fight tanks, infantry somehow closes and fights infantry, artillery is confined to a counterbattery role, fixed-wing aircraft concern themselves exclusively with the air, and helicopters engage in a duel of a kind not so far seen. If there is a "queen" weapon system, then presumably the outcome is decided on "queen v queen" and the other subcontests might as well not have taken place. Without a "queen" it is hard to see how the across-the-board outcome can be envisioned, let alone decided in terms of a set of isolated subconflicts like this.

From a glance at the major technological innovations in air, land and sea warfare I incline to the view that "like v like" is an *accident of the state of the art.* The battleship and the tank (*cf.* Chapter 15) provide excellent examples of this. Generally speaking there seem to be three phases related to the growth and decline of the weapon system —

> growth — "A v A" *or* "Dedicated anti-A v A";
>
> peak — "A v A" (maybe at "queen" level);
>
> decline — "Dedicated, then versatile systems v A".

These phases add up to a low-frequency swing of the pendulum through a complete cycle. Within each of them higher-frequency swings, like the ATGMS/compound armor one, will take place. When a new form of "anti-A" appears and no counter to it can be found, system "A" becomes obsolete. This happened with the battleship. It may be happening with the main battle tank; but not so far with all the forms of protected, mobile firepower comprehended in the concept "tank".

In sum "like v like" represents a useful constraint on thinking but a sterile and dangerous doctrine. The need is rather *to concentrate all available effort, whatever its nature, in time and*

*space against the opposing element which is critical at that point
in time and space.*

Attack and defense

My hackles always rise when I find a word attracting, almost
compounding with an increasing range of qualifications. Once we
had a rather simple and very important concept known as
"leadership" — the ability to get others to cooperate in doing
things they would not otherwise choose to do. After World War II
the idea of imposing one's will on others became a shade
indecent. So the buzzwords took wing — enlightened leadership,
Christian leadership, moral leadership, *innere Führung*, you
name it. In the resulting confusion we found one day that
leadership had lost its original significance and come to mean
"encouraging somebody to become a virtuous, conformist
member of a community". So with defense. Once there was just
defense; now there is positional, static, linear, mobile, hasty,
elastic, active defense — once again you name it. Here, though,
the swarm of adjectives represents real evolution.

To probe a little deeper, attack and defense are each about two
things. One is common to both — the goal of swinging the
relative strengths of the two opposed forces in one's favor. Subject
to this, attack aims at territorial gain; defense is concerned to
prevent or at least restrict territorial gain. In positional warfare,
the difference between attack and defense is clear-cut at all levels.
The defense stays still and provides a rock against which the
attacker pounds himself. If part of the rock crumbles, the
defender restores it by counterattack. Finally either the attacking
tide washes the rock away, or it slackens and starts to turn as the
attacker's superiority diminishes.

In mechanized warfare the goals are evidently the same. But
within a theater whose dimensions are limited geographically
and/or politically, mobility reduces the *military* significance of
gaining or losing terrain. The North African campaign of World
War II was a good example of this, and a number of Mideast
scenarios provide others. So the importance of preventing the loss
of terrain becomes either political (like protecting the West
German population) or economic (like keeping control of the
Gulf's oilfields). Militarily there is little doubt that the trading
off of ground is an advantage. By the same token, given that
the terrain is basically suited to mechanized operations, the

traditional defensive value of high ground and other features is reduced. I believe it would be fair to say that the strength traditionally associated with the positional defense (and traditionally rated at a factor of 3) comes in mechanized warfare from *a combination of exploiting tactically useful features and of trading off ground for time and space.*

Luckily we do not need to go further into the various military doctrinal or politico-military disputes about how much ground must or should be traded off. Not even the British, I think, any longer dispute the need to give ground. Equally, any kind of defense has to be static at some level at some point in time. The moment maneuver at tactical level is accepted as an essential element in the mechanized defense, two additional major issues rear their heads.

First the tactical distinction between attack and defense becomes blurred to one of degree. Both come to invoke a combination of fire and maneuver in proportions that will depend on terrain, local relative strengths on the ground and in the air, equipment advantages and a host of other factors. In the attack, maneuver will consist basically of forward movement; in defense it will be mainly retrograde or gyratory (hammer and anvil). Both from first principles and from the facts of the NATO *v* Warpac scenario, the attacker's maneuver element is likely to operate at higher troop density, while the defender will seek to achieve a greater concentration of fire. But both sides are fighting in much the same way and engaging much the same types of target. And with the exception that one side is gaining ground and the other ceding it, both are operating within similar parameters of exchange rates — as they must to satisfy the primary goal of swinging the relative strengths in their favor.

Certainly the weight of authoritative opinion and evidence in East and West alike is coming to see mechanized attack and defense as requiring the same basic mixes of weapon systems, of machines to manpower and of maneuver elements to artillery and air support. And both sides have an equal need of tactical air defense to stay in the maneuver business at all. Since most major armies now favor the balanced combined arms combat team as the basic tool for all types of combat,[4] there is no need to take account of whether the strategic and operational postures are offensive or defensive in determining the weapons mix or force structure for the mechanized land battle. The points addressed below tend to bear out this hypothesis.

---

4 British: phases of war.

Prepared positions

The second question arising from acceptance of tactical maneuver as a major element in defense is the extent to which defensive positions can or should be prepared in advance. Nobody I think will dispute the need for a leg on the ground. The fundamental strength of the defense is the product of a force sitting tight on ground of the commander's choosing, to block or contain the enemy and force him to react. This anvil or pivot of maneuver is essential if the mobile element of the defense is to play its part without excessive retrograde movement.

Nor is there much doubt about the need for a prepared forward obstacle belt; in fact this should surely be in position in peacetime as a safeguard against surprise attack. The first role of such a belt is that of a psychological and military tripwire. Although it may quickly be penetrated by leading elements, it reduces the momentum of the enemy advance, canalizes him and with luck causes vulnerable traffic buildups on his approach routes. By deploying forward and keeping this belt under observation and fire, the covering force (of which more below) both increases the tactical value of the obstacle and regains for itself some of the strength it constitutionally lacks.

The problem then is whether and to what extent the planned main force positions should be strengthened by deliberate minefields, improvement of natural obstacles, dug-in positions, vehicle/weapon pits and the like. Associated with this question of physical preparation are the need for the detailed planning of the operation and for reconnaissance down to, say, company level. The arguments for all these measures are well known. Historically many successful defensive battles have been characterized by meticulous preparation, sometimes over a period of weeks. And with the concept of "active defense"[5] American thinking seems to be moving towards extensive preparation and towards planning as detailed and complex as that of plays in American football.

As long as antitank mines had to be laid, it was hard to uphold the case against preparation. Minelets scatterable by helicopter and "instant" minelaying by artillery fires add up to a whole new ballgame. The first plank in the case against preparation is security of information. In the NATO center at least, one may be certain that *any kind of preparation whatever* will disclose the position and plan to the Pact by the time they need to know it, if not months in advance. Operating in their own country, the

---

5 Livsey: *see* Bibliography.

Bundeswehr can probably carry out fairly large-scale recon-
naissances clandestinely. But I always found the sudden invasion
of a peaceful stretch of German countryside by a fleet of station
wagons with BAOR number plates, a horde of retrievers and
a bunch of guys carefully disguised as British officers off duty,
complete with shooting sticks, utterly farcical. More seriously
one can assume a steady flow of information eastwards both
before and during hostilities. Once the attacker knows the defensive plan, he can either avoid main positions or time and measure
his punches to suit.

A second factor, at once more subtle and more important, is
the extent to which the defending commander is shackled,
psychologically at least, by his own preparations. By committing
effort and materiel to a piece of real estate, he is committing
himself to make use of it. In a situation where his initiative is
limited at best, he is further restricting his freedom of action.
Whether or not one goes along with the "American football"
concept of planning, tactical and fire planning and reconnaissance even down to squad level present no problem to forces
stationed in the theater in peacetime. By reconnoitring and
planning everywhere, they reveal nothing. Given the right
priorities, there is no reason why every armored vehicle
commander in Germany should not get to know the whole of his
corps sector, from frontier to Rhine, like the back of his hand.

The crunch then lies in physical preparation of the position.
Our brief glance at the factors of security and "commitment" is
enough to show that positions prepared well in advance are
hostages to fortune twice over. The root problem is in fact one of
tempo. The time it takes to prepare a defensive position is
basically incompatible with the tempo of the mechanized battle
of the eighties and nineties. In my experience the pace of combat
engineer operations (and I have worked with the Bundeswehr and
the US Army engineers as well as British) was not even compatible
with the British sixties tempo based on Centurion and FV432.
The answer has to lie neither in abandoning the strength
imparted by physical preparation nor in forfeiting security and
freedom of action but *in gearing preparation to the tempo of the
battle and confining it to what can be achieved in this timeframe.*

Speed means that preparation has to be done by the combat
troops on the spot with stores and power tools carried on their
vehicles. This is one reason why I argued so strongly elsewhere[6]

---

6 *Mechanized Infantry,* pages 43-45 and 54.

for the dismountable element of a composite unit or the in-house infantry (*Hausinfanterie*) associated with an armored unit to be put through a goal-oriented training program omitting some aspects of infantry training and including certain basic combat engineering (and other) tasks. I am convinced these men can do enough in a very short time to bridge the gap between the natural strength of the ground and the cover it affords on the one hand and the scattering of mines by helicopter and artillery on the other. Sure, this makes the logistic problem of resupply of a composite combat team a few degrees worse still (*cf.* Table 3); but that just has to be solved. If the combat subunits themselves carry out these simple tasks, a permanently assigned engineer subunit can surely cope within the time available with any more sophisticated work like improvement of natural obstacles or hasty demolitions.

Like most things in the land battle, it boils down to a question of terrain. If the defending commander can find and use anvil or pivot positions with enough natural strength and cover, well and good. But just as deliberate preparation of positions selected in advance limits his freedom of action, so does its opposite, over-reliance on adequate natural positions. Hasty do-it-yourself preparation within the time available between occupation and engagement broadens the commander's choice of positions and leaves him free to respond realistically to the pattern of the offensive as a whole and the way the battle in his sector develops.

Helicopter operations

The whole problem of a leg on the ground appears at its most acute within the concept of independent operations by helicopters. There seems little doubt that the Warpac armies will use assault and attack helicopters to execute or spearhead independent helicopter operations ranging in scale from *coups de main* to seizure of tactical bridgeheads and of airfields. We saw in Chapter 16 that the West, notably the US Air Cavalry, has tended to move away from earlier ideas of "vertical envelopment" towards fire support of the ground maneuver force. Also in Chapter 16 we looked at the feasibility of independent operations by helicopter forces in the mechanized defense. Now we need to probe the rationale of such operations rather more deeply, since the presence or absence of this capability has far-reaching effects on any concept of defensive operations.

Given feasibility, the notion of a helicopter force with heliborne artillery support capable of mounting a quick hammer-and-anvil operation or plugging a gap until the main mechanized force arrives is such an attractive one that we have to start by laying its drawbacks on the line. These are substantial and self-explanatory. Such a force is extremely expensive. It makes heavy demands on top grade combat manpower (of officer/warrant officer quality) and on human and material logistic resources. For the foreseeable future it will not have a true all-weather capability (the limitations now being navigation and control in poor visibility rather than flight itself). It will operate at high risk, specially in an adverse air situation. And its ground-holding capability will be extremely limited in time and space. So the arguments for such a force need to be very strong and deep rooted.

We might begin then by going back to the fundamental idea underlying Guderian's *Panzertruppen* and to the significance of an armored medium reconnaissance force. The *raison d'être* of the *Panzertruppen* was not exploitation of the tank but the value of a (relatively) small force which could move faster by an order of magnitude than the bulk of the army.[7] In those days that meant tens of kph instead of unit kph; but no matter. In the then state of the art, through to the seventies in fact, it remained possible to field light armored vehicles, first wheeled and later both wheeled and tracked, with operational and tactical mobility around 50% better than the main mechanized force. This capability gave rise to the concept of close and medium armored reconnaissance. The need for close reconnaissance has at no time been in dispute. It is on a scale two levels down (platoon to battalion), mounted in light vehicles like jeeps, scout cars or cut-down APCs and fills a string of workhorse roles like traffic control as well as reconnaissance proper.

The medium reconnaissance requirement has traditionally been met by dedicated units, normally divisional troops or corps troops, on a scale of one unit per division. This unit's primary role is gathering information, if needs be fighting for it. Its mobility and other characteristics also make it suitable for frontal and flank screens, activities of the kind now known as "economy of force operations", medium intensity (e.g. antiairborne) security operations and the like. No two armies seem to agree about the

---

7 See *Tank Warfare,* General von Senger und Etterlin's Introduction and Chapters 1 and 2.

equipment or techniques of the medium reconnaissance unit. And the mobility requirements of the tactical nuclear heyday, along with progressive cluttering by antitank weapon systems and assorted sensors, have taken equipment and techniques far away from the semiclandestine concept evolved and so successfully used by certain British cavalry regiments. Nonetheless, as long as the vehicles had an edge of 50% or so over the main mechanized force in speed, most armies accepted the need for medium reconnaissance.

Back in the sixties the US Army, especially 7 (US) Army in Germany, started to move away from the employment of dedicated units to the use of designated main force combat teams for the medium reconnaissance and screen/covering force roles. Their argument was that dedicated medium reconnaissance units were too cumbersome to be clandestine and too weak to fight and — above all — were instantly identifiable for what they were. So far other armies have resisted this line of thought. But with the prospect of main force vehicles of HIMAG-like characteristics closing the mobility gap, the value of *armored* medium reconnaissance will have to be questioned.

It seems rather unlikely that tracked armored vehicles could be made to achieve speeds even as high as 120 kph, and scarcely credible that they could average 100 kph off prepared surfaces. Quite apart from the technical problems, the HIMAG and HSTV-L trials and even the initial training program for Abrams suggest that human performance sets a limit on cross-country speed. This is a question not so much of reaction time as of the consequences at these higher speeds of the driver reading the ground wrongly.

An armored medium reconnaissance force or "ground cavalry" seems certain to have a continuing place in medium and low intensity operations, in an airborne setting and/or in extreme terrain. By contrast this element looks like being squeezed out of the main mechanized battle on grounds of performance alone. In the NATO center at least, the limited dimensions of the battlefield, the high political value of ground, the predictable density of forces on it and the consequent need for a strong covering force and a forward defense (whatever form that may take) all argue the same way. Let me reemphasize though that this in no way diminishes the need for close reconnaissance and the subsidiary roles associated with it.

With this kind of tradeoff as an ante, it may be realistic to start thinking about an extension of the role of scout and attack helicopters from reconnaissance for and fire support of the main maneuver force to the leading parts in independent rotary-wing operations. I am thinking here of "independence" at tactical level; at operational level these helicopter defensive operations would be firmly knit into the defensive plan as a whole. Just how and when this development will come is hard to say. "How" we might look at in the next chapter. "When" is probably not until the main maneuver force has vehicles of HIMAG-like mobility and until adequate heliportable antiarmor and general artillery support is available. But there seems no reasonable doubt that it will come.

In the Soviet Army it looks to be there already — as we might expect from the combination of a doctrine based on movement of masses and on offensive strategic posture. The Bundeswehr was talking about it at least 15 years back, albeit in a rather different context; here again belief in the movement of masses makes the trend inevitable. And the US Army is already so far down the road with air cavalry that it would need only to reshape and expand an existing reality.

More generally I believe independent helicopter operations have to come for three reasons. One is technical. We look to be approaching the point at which an increase in average cross-country speed can be accomplished more easily and economically — maybe even fuelwise — by getting off the ground than by staying on it. The second is that the *"Panzertruppen"*, the highly mobile core, needs mobility better by an order of magnitude than the bulk of the force. *Rotor is to track as track is to boot.*

Third, if what I wrote above about preparation of defensive positions makes sense, the evolution of the pattern of defense represents a similar logical progression. The infantry-based defense just had to be positional, entrenched in every sense of the word, both to make the most of the ground and because it could move only as fast as the attacker. With a maneuver force of M60-like mobility, the tempo of the battle was still such as to justify advance preparation to make best use of ground. With HIMAG-like mobility and the development in firepower discussed in this book, the timing and extent of preparation become very nice questions. With a helicopter force defense has to be instant. Put another way, ground-holding capability decreases as firepower extends the dimensions of the battlefield and mobility widens the scope of the maneuver force and accelerates the tempo of the battle. *But as tempo mounts, the time for which ground has to be held diminishes.* Stretching a point to make one, we might say — infantry: weeks, current armor: days, future armor: hours, helicopters: tens of minutes.

Attrition or shock effect

So we are led inexorably back to the fundamental conflict between the philosophies of attrition by pitched battle and disruption by shock effect — in mechanical terms between a static concept and a dynamic one. So much has been spoken and written by so many on this topic — without, so far as I know, ever budging anyone a millimeter from his point of departure — that it is hard to find anything new or constructive to say. Leading military men of the major armies within NATO continue to hold one or other of these two opposed and virtually irreconcilable views.

If the critical contest was purely psychological — the battle for the opposing commander's mind — then both schools of thought could be accepted as equally valid within their own reference frames. Fact is (and I say this in no light or carping spirit) the minds of commanders and managers — even, maybe, most of all successful ones — often seem to operate at several removes from observed physical reality. Yet the presence on the battlefield of corpses, wrecked vehicles, burning buildings and craters, along with the contention that war is the ultimate test of strength in a physical world, suggest that a battle has to represent, in some degree at least, an objective physical situation. To this extent the battle has a fixed reference frame; so to this extent there has to be a right answer on how to fight it.

The conflict of views is most conspicuous in terms of the offensive because an offensive is usually about linear displacement towards an objective. Again it is both intellectually easier and psychologically more attractive to develop a doctrine in active, that is offensive, terms — to assume one has the initiative. Nonetheless, the divergence is equally wide, if less evident, in defense. Whether we look at the battles of World War II or at the clashes of opinion over the defense of the NATO center, the gulf is there. It may be reasonable to draw certain parallels between Manteuffel's defense at Targul Frumos[8] and Montgomery's some 18 months earlier at Alem Halfa,[9] even to argue that both are variants on the hammer-and-anvil tactic. But the fact remains

8 3 May 1944: see *Tank Warfare,* pages 45-47, and Bibliography.
9 The defensive battle preceding El Alamein.

that the tanks in Manteuffel's hammer fired and maneuvered
while those in Montgomery's just fired.

Maybe we can cast some light on the defensive side of the coin
by looking at these views on the defense against the three
exchange rates I postulated — enemy losses v own losses, ground
ceded (*or* space) and time (page 34). In the positional (static)
concept of sea against rock or battering ram against wall, space
takes priority, own losses come a reasonable second (to the extent
that they need to be significantly lower than the attacker's) and
time is held to be firmly on the side of the defender. The more the
attacker goes on battering, the heavier his relative losses will be,
the longer the defending politicians and strategists will have to do
whatever is to be done, and the nearer will come the moment
when the defender can gain the operational or strategic initiative.

By contrast, the more strongly one believes in the operational
and tactical value to the attacker of the dynamic forces en-
gendered by the movement of masses, the more he is forced to
accept that defense is about *nullifying those dynamic forces* as
well as destroying or disrupting the enemy formations which
created them. The "dynamic" defender seeks to achieve this in
two ways. One is by *shock action,* which is another way of saying
extreme concentration of firepower in time and space. Shock
action is evidently compounded by surprise and by being applied
at a moment when the attacker is off balance — when his
momentum, and thus his commitment, is high and he cannot react
quickly and appropriately.

The second way is by *generating dynamic counterforces* which
oppose and neutralize the attacker's momentum. Doubtless I shall
be accused of "mathematical tactics", but the more I con-
template the hammer-and-anvil defense in its various forms
the more convinced I become that its evident power is rooted in a
basic physical phenomenon. By gyrating about the pivot of
maneuver (anvil) the hammer develops angular momentum
which, viewed tangentially, is just as intense as the translational
momentum of the attacker. In the mechanized battle the collision
between them is apt to take the form of threat and opposing fires
rather than physical impact of hull against hull. But the effect
remains at root one of collision, even if the final medium of
transmission is a KE penetrator.

Thus the anvil has three functions (fig. 23). One is itself to
provide the initial shock action of the defensive operation,
preferably at a time and place when the attacker is not expecting
it and is ill-poised to face it. This intense application of firepower

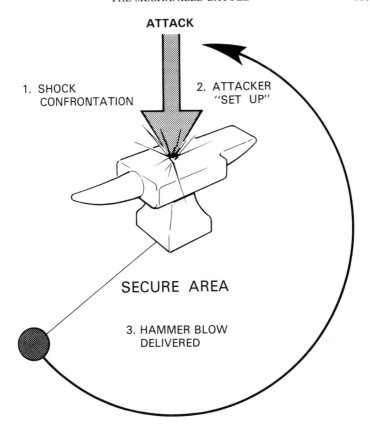

23. A diagrammatic representation of the principle of the hammer-and-anvil defensive tactic, designed to highlight the multiple functions of the "anvil"

inflicts casualties and halts or slows the attack. It also performs the anvil's second function (the one that gives it its name) of setting up the attacking force for the hammer blow. Third, by its very existence and by creating a safe area in which the hammer can form up and maneuver, the anvil allows the hammer to swing and develop its momentum.

Returning to our exchange rates, it is *time* that has to be paramount in this defense. Shock action is produced by concentration in time as well as space. The anvil can hold only for a limited time. And the hammer blow must be fast-moving to achieve dynamic effect. Second comes the ratio of enemy and own losses. This must be such as to leave the anvil credible and the attacker too battered to come again without relief or at least extensive regrouping. Space is traded off in two, maybe three ways. The attacker must be given space to develop both operational and tactical momentum so he hits the anvil hard — but not too hard. A certain depth is needed in front of the anvil to harass the enemy and canalize him onto it, hopefully to make him commit his tactical reserve prematurely. And the anvil itself may need a little depth so that it can bend rather than break.

I do not suppose many readers will go along with me, but as I wrote this last section the loose ends of this unwieldy chapter suddenly started to fall into place. At combat team or tactical formation level "like v like" holds. A defense with a substantial element of maneuver in it requires a force of much the same composition as the attack; conversely the attacker must be able to mount an instant blocking operation to fend the hammer blow. At "arm" or weapon system level "like v like" does not hold. Initially IFVs and AD vehicles will be priority targets for all weapon systems capable of engaging them; then priority will switch to attacking tanks. The defender may well dismount some men in the anvil; but only if and when the attacker also dismounts will an "infantry v infantry" contest develop. Meanwhile some tanks may well penetrate the anvil to considerable depth. But it is the halting of the attacking force *as a whole* that matters.

A hammer-and-anvil defense is a complex operation calling for contingency planning. But the defender who employs this tactic can only select the time and place in advance if (as was the case at Alem Halfa and Targul Frumos) a considerable area of real estate adds up to what one might call an "operational defile" — if terrain and physical objectives together dictate that the attacker follows a particular thrust line through a point outstandingly suited to defense. Otherwise the defending tactical commander needs to be free to acknowledge and respond to the fact that the attacker by definition has the initiative. He must choose the time and place of his stand at the last minute in response to the attacker's direction, pace and state of balance. This requirement, along with the importance of surprise, rules out physical preparation before occupation and highlights the need for blanket reconnaissance and contingency planning.

So the defense is mobile before the event. The anvil sits tight during it — the nub, I suspect, of the point Major-General Livsey is making in distinguishing "active defense" from earlier American and German concepts of "mobile defense". If the anvil breaks, the hammer blow is shortened and becomes the first phase of a retrograde action aimed at delaying the enemy and extracting the anvil. If the defense succeeds, its commander has two options. He can stay where he is and adjust his layout to produce a variant of the successful battle (as happened at Targul Frumos). But in the situation likely to arise in the NATO center, the success will become of historical interest only almost the moment it is achieved. The need will be to move extremely fast backwards and/or sideways and do it again somewhere else.

Finally the sweeping statement I made about "weeks, days, hours, minutes" may well have more weight than I allowed it. At Targul Frumos the preliminaries and the buildup on the anvil took around 5 hours. Manteuffel took just 2 hours to prepare and deliver the hammer blow, and this took something under 2 hours to sink in. These timings have to be an inverse function of speed of handling by commanders and battlefield mobility. So one might expect them to be reduced by a third or so for the forces which face each other in the NATO center today, and by half or more with the main mechanized forces of the nineties.

Turning to helicopters, we need to make one bold, even rash assumption. It is that the command skills, SOPs and communications needed for full exploitation of the helicopter's mobility exist or can be created. Given these, we can envision an independent helicopter operation being timed in tens of minutes. With antiarmor and general artillery support and direct support from assigned attack helicopters, even the "ultralight heliportable anvil" should be able to hold long enough for the hammer blow to go in and still live to fight another day. I frankly do not see it staying to reshape itself and take a second and heavier punch.

22

Concept of operations

In the history of mechanized warfare the number of those who have succeeded in setting out a coherent doctrine of the mechanized defense could be counted on the fingers of one hand — excluding I think the thumb. I lay no claim to join this distinguished few. But since there is a marked lack of postwar work based on the movement of masses and written and published in English, I felt it worth offering an outline doctrine as a basis for discussion. Now, to highlight a point, I have to make an admission. Up to here I had only minor problems with the structure I chose for this book; the reader may have perceived some of these in the shape of seemingly misplaced discussions. But at this stage I found real difficulty in framing and setting out a doctrine without simultaneously postulating a force structure. This awkwardness, which will undoubtedly show in this chapter and the next, redoubles the strength of my conviction that *concept of operations and force structure are intimately related* — far more closely I think than either is to the family of weapons.

Scenario

I will use the NATO center because it is in every sense common ground for myself and most of my readers and because General Sir John Hackett has fleshed it out so admirably in his book.[1] I will assume that the likelihood of the conflict going nuclear is extremely slight; that the Pact will go chemical as soon as things get rough; and that NATO possesses an offensive chemical capability and has clearance to use it in response. Although I myself see this as optimistic, I will take the air situation to be sufficiently balanced for either side to be able to gain temporary local control of the combat zone airspace and for both sides'

---

1   *See* Bibliography.

tactical air defense to maintain freedom of maneuver for their mechanized forces.

Within the NATO ground force I will assume that infantry formations, including reserves flown in, are deployed in a quasi-guerrilla tank-hunting role in areas of bad going, both along predicted Warpac thrust lines and in an economy of force role elsewhere; likewise that they are present in conurbations and smaller but militarily important areas of urban terrain to prevent the Warpac advance passing through these without moving up and deploying infantry in strength for street fighting;[2] and that the French Army will carry out some kind of relevant operation at least west of the Rhine. Another necessary assumption is that NATO corps and army artillery and tactical air will be cleared to attack ground targets beyond the frontier once this has been infringed. Finally I will suppose Warpac action to be based on the updated threat explained in Chapter 1.

Readiness

Almost since its foundation NATO has assumed a warning period of 10 days — or at least of several days. Reliance on this has tended to strengthen as spy planes, then satellites enhanced the likelihood of spotting troop movements in the western USSR. This is true in itself but no longer valid as a safeguard because of the relative strengths on the ground and the peacetime state of readiness of NATO forces. In Soviet eyes a surprise attack, motoring across the frontier straight off maneuvers or out of barracks, must look an excellent bet even without nuclear weapons — the more so now that Polish loyalty is open to question, there is a noisy cycle of rumblings and suppression in the GDR, and Czechoslovakia, however heavy the lid on it, remains on the simmer.

In my experience 7 (US) Army was the only NATO force to take readiness seriously, though the Bundeswehr may well do so now. While much that I write is at best theoretical and often deliberately controversial, I know what I say below to be a view widely shared among senior American and German officers at least. So I am prepared to be rather didactic about it.

As mentioned in the previous chapter, any frontier obstacle belt needs to be in position in peacetime, preferably armed but if

---

2 See *Mechanized Infantry*, Chapter 6.

politically necessary in a "safe" state. Arming and (where applicable) firing parties should be permanently on the spot under a commander authorized to arm the obstacle and fire demolitions on confirmation of a certain level of infringement. The standby forward covering force for each sector should be located in or immediately behind its deployment area and at 1 hour's notice. Shorter notice than this is intolerable for more than a few days, but 1 week in 4 at 1 hour over 3 months in the year should be acceptable. (This assumes that the covering force consists of designated units from the main maneuver force, not dedicated units.)

The rest of the standby brigade slice or task force which finds this covering force needs to be at 3 hours' notice to 75% strength and 6 hours' notice to virtual 100%. This readiness would have to be maintained for 1 month in 3, or 3 months in the year. This should pose no insuperable problem in terms of training, leave, rotation or normal wastage. But, as the British Army's experience in Northern Ireland has shown, it would pose an acute morale problem, specially for married men. This problem too is superable in the case we are considering, given a significant rethink about states of readiness.

Conventional thinking on levels of readiness like this is apt to require the men to remain on the spot and to get ready in a few minutes so that they can devote the rest of the time to the hardware. Actually hardware doesn't mind being kept at full readiness; given the few men necessary to look after it, it thrives on being battleworthy. Men do mind. Given equipment at full readiness and the distances and excellence of communications in the FRG, a high proportion of soldiers could be shuttled between their normal post and their readiness location.

The rest of the standby division for each sector should be at the same notice but in post. Thus a division would be on standby for 6 months, or two quarters in the year. I believe this pattern to be feasible, but it does imply a rather low readiness for the other 50% of the mechanized force. Here again one would like to see 50% (25% of the whole) on reasonably high readiness with the rest virtually stood down for two periods of 6 weeks each in the year. But this does start to produce genuine administrative rubs.

Finally under this head I would like to stress to civilian readers that (aside from Britain's problem over Ulster) the reason for the low readiness of the standing forces in the NATO center is financial stringency. The higher readiness machines are kept at, the fitter they are when required. Soldiers too are perfectly happy to spend periods at high readiness as long as they are satisfied that everything physically possible is being done in allowing them to lead normal lives and in caring for their dependants when they are away. My guestimate is that (again ignoring Ulster) this kind of readiness would add around one-third to the bills for 7 (US) Army and Rhine Army, maybe considerably less for the Bundeswehr. But in terms of credibility and capability alike, $130 invested in reality has to be a better bet than $100 sunk in appearances.

Proportion of reserves

The key to any concept at operational and tactical levels alike is the proportion of reserves. Convention indicates one-third at each level. Although fighting on its own territory, the Bundeswehr would I believe like to hold two-thirds back, at least at operational level. No advocate of the movement of masses school would dispute this on theoretical grounds. But within the given scenario, one has to ask whether it makes the best use of the limited depth available and/or creates an avoidable risk of the Pact armor gathering such momentum as to be unstoppable.

For my money 50% does more than represent a compromise. It offers the best flexibility and marches with the numerous other factors which look to be heading one, at tactical level anyways, away from triangular towards (literally) square thinking. In the NATO situation the question of operational reserves is rather a specious one. If one goes outside the three major armies of the center, the strength and combat worth of a formation is not a completely fixed quantity.[3] These variations may well exceed the differences between one-third or two-thirds and one-half; so realism suggests a nominal 60% or more at this level, with the hope that this adds up to 50% in combat worth.

Tank-infantry balance and size of tactical unit

Separating out the tank destroyer role somewhat complicates thinking about the tank-infantry balance. Few I believe would argue that the overall balance should be 1 to 1 in tactical terms, but with the family of weapons I have postulated each infantry

---

3 In fairness, with the combination of manning problems (now being solved) and the continuing Ulster overstretch, this is partly true of BAOR too.

maneuver squad needs to be balanced by a fire-support tank
(FST) *plus* at least a "share" of a tank destroyer (TD). This
problem, though, is an organizational rather than a tactical one;
more of it later. Like the overall balance itself, the extent of
deviations from it is not controversial. Whether units are
structured on threes or fours, the tank-heavy team needs to be 3
to 1 and the infantry-heavy team either 3 to 1 or in certain
instances to have no tanks. However, most advanced Western
armies now seem agreed that a *balanced team* is best for the most
frequent and most important types of operation; and Soviet
thinking is moving increasingly that way too. So organizationally
the need is for a balance of tank and infantry battalions or for a
balanced composite unit.

A more difficult question is the size of tactical unit. Here we
start with a problem of definition. Conventionally a "tactical
unit" is the smallest unit which can form subunits and carry out a
program of fire and maneuver, just as a "fire unit" is the smallest
unit which can produce a tactically significant weight of fire. But
if we look on a tactical unit as the smallest unit which the tactical
commander can expect to influence the battle, we find wide
diversity between armies.

My impression is that the tactical unit in this sense is assumed
to be two levels below the highest level of tactical command —
the old saw of "thinking two down". For the British this is
battalion, so that conventional definition of a tactical unit
applies — a platoon. (The British brigade, or task force, tends to
think operationally.) For the Americans and I think the Soviets,
tactical command looks to be at brigade (regiment) level, and the
tactical unit becomes the company. We know that until recently
Soviet armor maneuvered by companies; it may still do so,
although the size of the tank company has increased. One very
striking feature of Major-General Livsey's article on active
defense[4] is the importance and scope of action he sees for
company combat teams. In the Bundeswehr "operational level"
means corps; division is the highest tactical level, although it has
a bridging function too. The tactical unit is a battalion at least;
my feeling is that many German commanders in seeking shock
effect look on it as the brigade.

Having studied the American football-like complexities of the
"active defense" and tried to envision how the switch of, say, a
tank-heavy company team from "position 21" to "position 22"

---

4 *See* Bibliography.

around 500 m away could influence the battle, I am going to take the tactical unit as a *balanced battalion combat team* (or composite battalion or approximate equivalent). Working upwards from this, specific operations are brigade tasks and the tactical battle as a whole a divisional one.

Principles of the defense

Having thus cleared the ground, we can address the conduct of the battle. We may liken the positional defense to a compound armor array. It has some depth but is arranged laterally — square to the attack. It has some give, but essentially defeats the attack or is defeated; in this event a further array behind it takes over and the original one is of no more relevance unless it can be removed and repositioned. By contrast, the defense I envision here is like the response of a living organism to an insult — say a stab wound in the flesh. The organism has no hard shell to keep the blade out but rearranges itself to contain the lesion. Various specialized chemicals and cells are summoned to clot the blood, dispose of damaged tissue and destroy infection. If the defense succeeds, the original situation is finally restored. I like this analogy too because skin and muscle, like terrain, have strong and weak parts; and because if the insult penetrates to a vital organ (by analogy a political center) the defense fails and the organism must receive massive outside support if it is to survive.

The first feature then of a defense based on movement of masses (I am deliberately avoiding the term "mobile defense") is that it is aggressive. It is directed against the enemy force rather than linked to any particular piece of real estate. It strives always to contain or isolate the enemy force as a prelude to destroying it. This feature of isolation is a key one, evident in many of the Wehrmacht's successful defenses on the Eastern Front; it amounts to a particular statement of the theory of movement of masses. In the offensive the enemy is disrupted by the placing of a force as far as possible behind his center of mass — that is between this and the place or thing he is trying to defend. Conversely in the defense the attacking enemy's breakthrough force is frustrated by containing it *and* by placing a force behind it. This has the doubly "healing" effect of setting the attacking force up for destruction and of restoring the situation at or near the location of the original threat.

From this fundamental idea one can draw a number of principles in succession. First, no attempt is made to maintain lateral alignment by pulling back formations which are not under pressure. In principle they stay where they are and face inwards, "lining the lesion". Just as some organisms have the ability to shed a limb or other excrescence when it is injured or trapped and hampers them, so some forward formations may cease to be relevant to the battle. It will then be for the defending commander to extricate them; or, unlike the disused limb, they may be able to fight their own way out.

Second, while hammer blows — unlike counterattacks in the positional defense — are aimed at destroying and disrupting the enemy rather than recapturing ground, a successful blow may restore the original situation. It may even better this by going on to thrust deeper behind the enemy and/or to carry out some specific disruptive action like destroying a crossing over an obstacle. Manteuffel's 110 km northwards counterthrust west of Kiev from Berdichev through Zhitomir on to Korosten is a good historical example of such a move.

The points which follow are closely related. Anvil positions need to be organized, not necessarily for all-around defense in the conventional sense, but so that they can quickly face any direction within, say, the arc represented by a horseshoe. Since the successful hammer may become the anvil, both need to be composed of a balanced force. If the hammer has to shed some of its dismountable element to the anvil, it must pick these troops up again as it passes round or through.

More broadly, the tactical layout is conceived not laterally but in depth, with formations disposed one up. To change the analogy, one might envision the layout as a row of helical springs with their axes facing the enemy. This layout gives higher tactical commanders the largest number of options at the lowest level of unified command. At operational level, though, it would put corps headquarters out of touch with the battle and in fact limit the options. Probably the number of tiers in depth a headquarters can handle is subject to the same kind of limitation as the number of subordinate headquarters it can effectively control.

From all this, divisional and higher boundaries will be more frequent than in a conventional layout. The Soviet propensity for locating boundaries and attacking down them is well known; in fact it constitutes one of the many arguments against a linear defense. Defense in depth puts elements in the right place to counter these probes. But under normal command arrangements — like coordination of two divisions by corps — the response is too slow to parry a fast-moving thrust before it becomes uncontrollable. The need is for a rule and an SOP. For instance, each formation could be responsible for liaison and protection to its left and be authorized to cross its left boundary without specific permission once liaison had been established. I believe this would in practice reduce the risk of confusion as well as speeding up the response. It does not matter what the rule is so long as it exists and is known and respected.

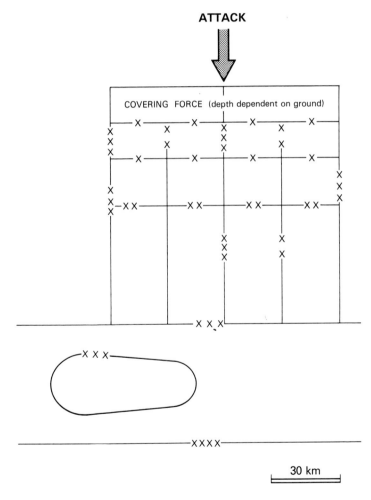

24. Schematic of defensive layout to illustrate the principle of formations deploying one up, roughly twice as deep as wide

Defensive layout

Figure 24 gives a *grossly schematic* reproduction of the layout that follows from this thinking. In scaling it (a very dangerous process!) I have thought in terms of density on the main thrust lines, assuming that some kind of economy of force operation would be employed on other sectors. In following the guideline "twice as deep as wide" I believe I have given too little depth to brigades and divisions; in the event both depth and frontage would depend on the ground within very wide limits. For the reasons explained above, a corps is deployed square. In view of some of the remarks I made in the previous chapter, it is interesting that — apart from a density difference around 1:3 — this layout is rather similar to the standard Soviet layout for *off*ense.

Covering force action

On the principles set out the covering force action becomes a tactical one and a divisional responsibility. This force is normally commanded by the headquarters of the division's air cavalry regiment and made up of —

one air cavalry squadron;

one balanced battalion combat team (with an engineer company under command);

"brigade slice" of divisional artillery in direct support (one battalion *each* general support, antiarmor and air defense);

plus forward mechanized brigade's "artillery slice" in support.

If the covering force is to be drawn from the main force, as opposed to being an add-on, the principle underlying its composition and operation has to be maximum power at minimum risk. Attack and scout helicopters can operate, and (except maybe initially) artillery can fire from secure positions within the front edge of the forward brigade area. This approach both minimizes the size of the ground force at risk and, by exceptional fire support, reduces the degree of risk to which it is exposed.

The combat team is handled as a unit, the frontier obstacle belt and the rest of the sector being kept under helicopter observation and covered by observed fire plus, as necessary, attack helicopter teams in an economy of force role. The mechanized team is held just behind its most probable position in such a way that it can either occupy this extremely rapidly or move without delay. Once the shape of the enemy is known, the combat team either moves to close a breach of the obstacle belt or occupies its principal position straightaway. Here it fights a mini-hammer-and-anvil action if the ground allows; otherwise it conducts a conventional defend and displace operation onto the forward main force position.

The main battle

I would prefer to leave the exact structure of the mechanized brigade and hence the respective compositions of hammer and anvil over to the next chapter. It is enough to say here that *in principle* both consist of a balanced force of about the same strength. However, poor ground and conventional thinking will tend to make the anvil larger and infantry-heavy. If part of the hammer's dismountable element has to be assigned to the anvil, this must rejoin the hammer as soon as pressure on the anvil is relaxed. Otherwise the hammer is unable to exploit success and loses its versatility. Depending on the ground the hammer blow may be a right or left hook or a straight punch. A straight punch saves time and is an attractive option if the anvil action has been successful, so that the anvil is in good shape and the enemy in confusion. Whatever pattern is followed, the artillery changeover from defensive to covering fires will need excellent coordination.

Following the initial encounter there are a number of options. After a successful defense, the hammer can exploit onto an objective in depth (like an obstacle crossing); or carry out a single envelopment; or become a forward anvil, with the original anvil assuming the hammer role; or pull back through the anvil, both adjusting to fight again. If the anvil is broken, the hammer assumes the anvil role and is assigned a hammer in the shape either of an air cavalry force or of the covering force (if any) or anvil of the depth brigade. If the anvil holds but the hammer is pinned down or shattered, the anvil is provided with a new hammer by the same means. *Provided each element is kept balanced,* this multi-tier defense is immensely flexible even just in terms of the battle on a given divisional sector.

A division with a penetration to its right flank simply adjusts to face the flank of the penetration. On the arbitrary rule proposed above, a division with a penetration to its left flank intervenes

actively across its boundary, having (as an SOP) established
liaison with the penetrated formation. It is when a two-way
stretch in depth and breadth leaves a gap that a mechanized force
cannot fill in time, or when local defeat looks like giving the
enemy a free run, that the independent helicopter operation
comes into its own.

Defensive fires

One of the keys to this whole concept is very intense concentration
of direct and indirect defensive fires in time and space in front of
the anvil. For this reason artillery normally has a "forward" and a
"main" position. From the forward position it can support the
formation (covering force or brigade) in front of its direct-support
formation. Once the covering force action is over, the artillery
can be leapfrogged back (and if needs be forward again) in
the normal way so as to maximize concentration and to keep as
many projectors as possible in action at a given time. Despite this
an antiarmor battalion must always be superimposed on the main
fire plan so that it is available for helicopter operations without
disrupting the main plan. Lateral massing of fire is entirely
conventional.

Despite this emphasis on concentration, I believe that in
thinking of the defense as a whole one needs to steer clear of
concepts like "killing areas" (or "killing pockets" as the Soviets
call them). These notions represent not so much a defensive
concept in themselves as a means of dealing with attacking armor
within the framework of a positional concept. Additionally they
call for ground narrowly suited to a specific purpose as opposed to
being of tactical importance or of defensive strength in the
general sense. Thus on the one hand they commit the
commander psychologically to occupying particular pieces of
ground rather than responding realistically to the actual
situation. And the ground they direct him towards is not
necessarily the ground he should be thinking of.

In *any* kind of defense the area forward of the main position is
covered by defensive fires, and the bulk of the attacker's
casualties are expected to occur there. Evidently the ground
chosen for the anvil must provide good positions and fields of fire
for direct-fire weapon systems, along with suitable locations for
artillery observers. These will be major factors in choosing the
ground and deciding the detailed layout. But they become

somewhat less important when helicopters can be used to extend
the fields of fire and view alike.

Helicopter operations

Because of their limited scale, helicopter operations must be seen,
initially at least, as tactical operations. They are ordered by
division, either on the divisional commander's initiative or in
fulfillment of a mission assigned by corps, and mounted by the
division's air cavalry regiment. The force employed is likely to
consist of an air cavalry squadron and a heliborne support troop
(but *see* next chapter), with an antiarmor artillery battalion
(including its general support mortar battery) under command.

Their goal is likely to be either the disruption of a minor enemy
force which has found its way into a substantial gap, or
containment of a major penetration until the mechanized defense
force can move or adjust to face it. We discussed procedures
in Chapter 16. Basically the action is quite likely to take the
form of a modified hammer-and-anvil operation with a dispersed
strongpoint (like a defile which can be covered from depth and
flanks) as an anvil. The distinguishing feature of these operations
is not so much their limited firepower — in fact they may pack a
very tidy punch — as their limited duration. Because the small
number of men on the ground provide very little holding power,
the whole operation needs to be very rapid and precisely timed in
relation both to its own phases and to the enemy.

The operational counterstroke

Any defense truly aimed at destroying or disrupting the
opposition has to culminate in an operational counterstroke. I
have postulated (fig. 24) a reserve corps, thus incidentally
pushing the proportion of reserves within an army from 50:50 up
to 60:40. For the employment of this reserve one might envision
either of two situations. One is a favorable outcome in which the
defense basically holds the enemy and wears him down to the
point where he is vulnerable to a counteroffensive in depth —
aimed at encircling a large force or at substantial territorial gain.
The other is a battered defense, forced progressively backwards
and inwards with severe losses to the point where one or even both
of the forward corps provide(s) the anvil for the hammer of the
army reserve.

Corps, though, is essentially an operational headquarters capable of launching a major counterstroke on its own. I have shown (fig. 24) a corps of four divisions deployed square to maximize the depth of the defense. But with a rule of responsibility for the left boundary, the corps commander might well choose to keep his right depth division in a reserve posture with an alternate defensive position rather than fully deployed in defense. He could then use it either forward or to his left flank. Equally he could pick up one of his depth divisions either in anticipation of a counterstroke or when the need for one actually arose. Again, if one or both of his forward divisions were forced back, he could concentrate it/them in a reserve posture.

Here again, the combination of the hammer-and-anvil tactic and deployment in depth with command in depth seems to offer enormous flexibility — provided of course that the forces themselves have the requisite operational mobility.

Command and control

Timing is crucial to any concept of operations based on mobility and dynamics — one reason why I suspect some armies always duck this option altogether, and the Soviets seem to give their breakthrough forces free play. Paradoxically — or maybe not — it is even more critical in the defense than in the offense. If you are using, judolike, the other guy's momentum to catch him and his energy to throw him, there is only one instant when you and he are in the relative positions needed to make your counter work. And this instant may not happen every time he rushes at you. I don't want to suggest slavish adherence to the hammer-and-anvil tactic; there are many variants of it and a number of other options. But "hammer and anvil" serves very well as the symbol, the distinguishing feature which marks a defense as based on movement of masses and aimed at disruption of the enemy. In any battle of this kind, the decision on when, indeed whether, to launch the hammer blow has to be taken and implemented almost within minutes (once again as Manteuffel's account of Targul Frumos shows).

What is more this decision has to be taken on the spot. No system of sensors, displays or whatever can give the commander the feel of the battle. He just has to be there. This means *forward command*. One secondary reason for adopting the concept I have outlined is its probable effectiveness against the Soviets, whose command and control system is stereotyped and very much "from the back".

I am not entirely convinced of the need for the tactical commander to go one stage further and actually take over command of the hammer force. This was certainly done at critical moments by both Rommel and Manteuffel — in fact it was agreed doctrine among the Wehrmacht's *Panzertruppen*. The tactical commander has to be there to *give* the order and to update the briefing; but if the subordinate commander is incapable of *carrying out* the order, maybe he should not be there at all. Partly for this reason, I myself remain unconvinced of the need in terms of command and control *per se* for a level of command between brigade and company in the mechanized battle. I concede though that other factors are at work here too; maybe we should leave that argument over to the next chapter.

By contrast there stands out from this exposition and tactical discussions earlier in the book the need for a *deputy commander* at every level from company, maybe even platoon, up to brigade. This needs to be a top-grade officer specifically appointed. The British practices of using the reserve battalion commander or a "spare" headquarters thrown up by an unsuitable force structure and of making the second-in-command's appointment a consolation prize are not enough. This is another reason why I question the need for a battalion-level headquarters. But even if these remain, so does the requirement for a task force commander — in the true sense of the word — superior to battalion.[5]

By the same token there is a need at each level for a *battle headquarters* which the commander can use as a tactical headquarters or the deputy can command a task force from. Some examples may serve to force these points home — the dismounted element of a platoon clearing through a coppice or of a company in a blocking position, the hammer force (or the anvil), a helicopter task force, a mechanized economy of force team securing a flank. Likewise the existence of a deputy commander and a second command and communications setup for him confers a genuine capability of fighting round the clock.

In entering the lists in this philosophical disputation on how the defensive battle should be fought one is not so much offering a hostage to fortune as laying his neck on the block. So I was keen

---

5 Again not in the British sense of a synonym for brigade commander.

to find some appropriately pithy last words that just might etch themselves into the minds of those whom I cannot resist calling the "apostles of position". The word I came upon is so drab that it could even be memorable — *"reuse"*. Designers and users alike share the fantasy of a superchopper, supertank or super-whatever which finds an ideal position and sits there spouting fire and sweeping the battlefield clean. Even if such a "super system" existed, it would seldom find ideal positions; even when it did, the battle would soon roll on past or away from it. So we are back to *numbers*. One way to have numerical equality or superiority is actually to possess it. Another, open to the defender but not to the attacker, is to *use the same soldiers and weapon systems, even the same pieces of real estate over and again*. This, along with the focus on the aim of destroying or disrupting the enemy as opposed to holding ground, is what I take a defense based on maneuver to be about.

23

Force structure

After years of trying to fit novel types of hardware into an existing force structure, I was fascinated to discover how, without this constraint, the members of the family of weapons slipped into place beside one another and how a natural recycling of weapon system and mode of employment harmonized hardware and tactics. At the same time this combined concept seemed to point naturally towards a particular force structure in terms of both arms and levels — so much so that by the time I came to grapple with an operational concept I had a clear mental image of the structure needed. This picture had a few gray zones, though, notably the organization of the maneuver force below brigade level. Additionally a number of professional readers have asked me how the kind of organizational proposals I made in *Tank Warfare* and *Mechanized Infantry* could be fitted in to existing armies.

Combat arms

I was careful to reply that the organizational kites I flew were both theoretical and international, so they evidently would not fit any particular army as it and they stood. Nonetheless the Canadian land service has long had a single "combat arm" (armor *plus* infantry). And the French and Swedish Armies took the plunge some years back by forming composite battalions, balanced with two companies each of tanks and mechanized infantry. The US Army evidently continues to have doubts about the existing structure of its mechanized force, and the extremely healthy three-cornered debate that is going on between air cavalry, armor and infantry could well produce a change. Under the continuing pressure of Northern Ireland, which after 11 years has become more a way of life than a campaign, the British Army has had to use so many units out of role (armor and artillery as infantry) that the constraint of "arms" superimposed on that of regiments has come to look a shade ridiculous.

The Soviets are definitely moving towards a balanced force; but in their case, maybe because of scale, they are working downwards from the "combined arms army". I suspect the motor rifle division is being brought into balance and the number of these increased at the cost of tank divisions. Certainly the term "shock army", once highly significant, has become an honorific. With much of their own terrain very open, political aims which call for a strategic offensive and a continuing belief in the dominance of the tank, it would be surprising if the Soviets did not retain a proportion of tank divisions with a 3 to 1 tank/infantry mix. There is not much evidence as yet of composite units; by contrast one has the impression that arms rivalry is even more active in the Soviet Army than among its more traditional counterparts.

Looked at from outside the Bundeswehr presents some contradictions. One is that an operational concept based on movement of masses and shock effect is wedded, partly for political reasons, to a tactical doctrine which seems to owe more to American influence (probably in fact to the characteristics of the American equipment they formed with) than to the lessons learned by the Wehrmacht on the Eastern Front. As the protagonists of the *Panzergrenadier* the Bundeswehr founded two equal but separate arms, armor and mechanized infantry. I for one always imagined these were to work "arm-in-arm" and form balanced combat teams, but things did not work out that way. Possibly owing to the personal characteristics of the middle-piece officers available at the time of formation of the Bundeswehr, the armor took on a rather dashing, cavalry tinge, symbolized by Leopard 1, while the mechanized infantry became very much that in tribal outlook, tempo and tactics. This struck me with equal force in both working with and umpiring the Bundeswehr.

With the introduction of Marder some tank battalions acquired a small amount of organic in-house infantry only, it seems, to lose this again in the reorganization of the mid/late seventies. This produced a bifurcation of the panzergrenadiers. Ten "heavy" *Panzergrenadierbataillone* were brigaded 1 to 3 with tank battalions in the ten armored brigades. Thirty-four "light" *Panzergrenadier-/Jägerbataillone* were grouped in brigades of the same name with a tank battalion (or equivalent) either organic or available for attachment — shades of the original light divisions of the Wehrmacht favored by von Brauchitsch. While some balance is redressed at divisional level, it looks as though the "like *v* like" school has won.

It is extremely interesting that the two major armies with doctrines based on movement of masses each recently seem to have had the idea of a light mechanized force. With the Soviets the BMP fever[1] was relatively short-lived. We now see BMPs frisking around alongside T54/55s in Afghanistan and T62s in the Iraqi Army, while the Soviet forces facing NATO have been at least partially reequipped with the ponderous and technically obsolescent MTLB. It will be even more interesting to see whether the Germans follow the Soviets back into the balance their predecessors learned the hard way in World War II.

In my previous books I postulated three combat arms —

cavalry, which provided the eyes and ears of the main mechanized force as well as its helicopter support, and was the eyes, ears and fist of the airborne or light force (based on the standard infantry battalion);

armor, comprising both the mounted and dismountable elements of the main mechanized force;

infantry, the standard infantry battalion (probably equipped with a light workhorse APC) plus parachute battalions, special forces and the like.

With an 18 months' lag between the writing of a book and its wide dissemination, what one writes is inevitably overtaken by trends if not by events. Study of recent American (and to some extent German) published material on combat helicopters, along with contemplation of the continuing Rhine Army/Ulster dichotomy of the British Army, the mounting importance of noneuropean scenarios for the major NATO powers and the increasing scale and sophistication of the terrorist threat all look to point to a need for *two armies.* I use that phrase deliberately because it makes a good cry and a useful point of departure; but in fact the requirement is for two types of combat force, backed by common supporting arms and logistic services.

The best pointer is maybe the evolution of the US Air Cavalry. It is deeply striking how, the more this force extends its existing capabilities and takes on new ones, the more firmly it remains integrated in thinking and tactics with US Armor. Second, as we saw in Chapter 20, armored cavalry's role in the mechanized

---

1 See *Mechanized Infantry,* pages 34-37, and Bibliography (McCaslin).

battle looks like being squeezed out between improved main force mobility and increasing integration of mechanized rotary-wing elements. Medium ground reconnaissance might thus provide the resources needed for air cavalry to take another step forward.

In parallel with this trend, we saw in Part 4 how the advent of compound armor makes the nonmechanized or light force increasingly dependent on the helicopter as its primary direct fire antiarmor weapon system. The value of helicopters in nontactical roles — communications, casevac, troop carrying and logistics — to light forces operating in extreme terrain goes without saying and has in any event been demonstrated in Vietnam and Afghanistan. Yet again, numerous examples, most notably perhaps Ulster, have proved the value of helicopters in low-intensity operations varying from urban guerrilla warfare through isolated terrorist strikes and crowd control to the policing of large land and sea areas. But most of these tasks, to some extent even the antiarmor one, call for different training, different surveillance and armament packs, maybe even different machines from the helicopter roles in the mechanized battle. Even a heli-borne operation under these conditions would be quite a different ballgame from the independent helicopter operation envisioned in earlier chapters.

So looking one stage further ahead I believe the combat arm structure could be rationalized to two —

armor, providing the entire teeth of the mechanized force;

infantry, finding the whole combat element of the light force.

Each of these basic arms would consist of two types of unit — a helicopter unit, and a composite ground unit covering all other requirements. Evidently basic flying training could be given in a common school which would also cater for the rotary-wing pilot requirements of the artillery and the technical and logistic services. But this training would need to be followed by "operational conversion" at the armor or infantry school, just as it is in dedicated units of most air forces. This system would have the added advantage that pilots would be found from their respective arms, including the artillery, and would be assured of serving in their chosen environment.[2] Additionally it would give a

---

2 In the view of myself and many other British officers, the decision to abandon regimental helicopter flights/squadrons in favor of a centralized Army Air Corps added up not only to a gross breach of faith with many talented young officers but a serious loss of operational capability.

deeper and new meaning to the cavalry tradition on the one hand and to the "light infantry" or "rifle corps" tradition shared by many armies on the other. I believe the need for integration of thought now looks to favor this solution over an air cavalry arm serving both types of main force.

The only other controversial element in my suggestion is the composite tank-infantry battalion, integrated down to platoon level. Two advanced armies have shown the composite principle to work. Once the psychological barrier is broken at the key battalion or "unit" level, there is no reason why integration cannot be continued down to platoon. I have had this argument in both my previous books and in outline in an article in *Armor Magazine*;[3] I do not propose to repeat it here. Quite apart from the tactical advantages of the FST/IFV pair, the composite platoon solves a number of long-standing command, manning and administrative problems.

A question at once more real and more interesting is the provision within this structure of an attractive and varied career for the regular officer and the long-service enlisted man. The argument, in both the United States and British Armies though for slightly different reasons, always was that the armored man would not see the world (other than Germany) or gain experience of medium- and low-intensity operations; while the infantryman would remain ignorant of the decisive NATO theater. It now looks as though this problem may soon arise in the Bundeswehr and may rear its head again in other armies of ex-colonial powers like Belgium and France.

For starters we need to single out the top-grade officer. Although his needs are already largely catered for, his case is always used to oppose a dichotomy of the kind I have suggested. By the time he has attended an advanced course in his own arm and commanded a company, he will be thoroughly versed in all aspects of his arm's operations. At Command and Staff College he is mixed in roughly equal proportions with colleagues from the other combat arm and from the supporting arms and services as a whole, plus a sprinkling of foreign officers.[4] If the course is run on a basis of supervised mutual instruction (like Staff College Camberley) he gets all the broadening he needs. The best of this select bunch could follow the course with a staff tour on the other

---

3 November/December 1980.

4 Could not this be more than a sprinkling? The *Führungsakademie* seems to do much better in this respect than Fort Leavenworth or Camberley.

side of the house. Others would be further broadened by the Joint Services Staff Course (or the like) which most armies offer.

I took the top-grade regular officers out first, because it is *necessary for the service* that they should be trained across the board. For officers who do not enter staff training and for enlisted men, there is normally no *direct* benefit to the service in their being trained outside their own arm and its environment, specially if the existing combat arms are "broadened" in the way suggested. The requirement here is one of incentive to join and to extend service, and of morale during service.

I have always seriously wondered whether switching men or units about for this purpose (which has cost the British Army a deal in hard cash and much more in loss of efficiency) is based on what the men themselves want or simply on what G1 thinks they ought to want. With an army stretched widely enough across the world to make this kind of switching significant, there would be no problem whatever in offering armored men and their dependants, who tend to shuttle between home (the UK or USA) and the FRG, virtually free long furloughs in "faraway places with strange sounding names", mainly existing R and R centers. This is the kind of simple solution which looks extravagant but in fact produces a massive saving in direct costs along with an imponderable boost to morale and efficiency. There would be exceptions, but every army needs and has a system for individual transfers.

If nonetheless the interests of the service and/or the real or imagined wishes of individuals call for a long-service career to be divided between various roles and stations, the British Army hit some years back on an excellent system which it has never exploited widely and which could I believe be applied *mutatis mutandis* to other armies. In one of the many contractions and reshufflings which have been the hallmark of the British Army since the mid-fifties, this precise problem arose over the Household Cavalry, consisting of two regiments which were to be merged with a third.[5] Out of this came one tank battalion (to be rotated in due course between the tank and reconnaissance roles) along with a Household Cavalry regiment stationed at Windsor, made up of a combined horsed squadron for ceremonial and two squadrons equipped with vintage light armored reconnaissance vehicles, mainly suitable for internal security duties. Individuals are rotated between Windsor and the tank battalion.

---

5 British cavalry regiments consist of a single battalion, equivalent to an American squadron.

This seems to offer a very tidy solution for an army organized
on a regimental basis or recruited with strong territorial links.
The regiment consists of two units plus a static element serving as
depot, maybe basic training center and cadre for reserve unit(s).
Whichever combat arm the regiment originates from, one
standing unit is mechanized and the other light (this pattern
being duplicated at battalion or company level in the reserve).
Officers and men can either remain with one of these or rotate
between them as the needs of the service and/or their personal
wishes require. To simplify reallocation of manpower between
combat arms and technical and logistic corps, artillery, engineers
and the rest could be formed (again as they now are to some
extent) on the same local basis.

This system, to which the British Army at least could very easily
be switched, removes constraints on role and field force structure
while giving full rein to the aspects of tribalism, a shared home
base and the links with society which are so important to
recruiting and morale — and indeed to an army's political
health.

Size of basic self-accounting unit

A more intractable problem is matching the structure of a
composite mechanized unit and a conventional light unit in size
and level of self-accounting unit. One must assume that the
conventional structure and strength of a battalion is right for the
labor-intensive nonmechanized unit. For the kind of mechanized
warfare I have envisioned in this book, a battalion at first sight
looks a bad fit. We might then examine the composition of each
subunit and the function of each level of command.

In *Mechanized Infantry*,[6] with a "gun tank" (tank destroyer)
and a "support tank" (combined fire support tank/infantry
fighting vehicle, like Merkava) I postulated a platoon of 8 major
vehicles (plus a runabout) and 49 men. With the vehicle family
we are looking at in this book, the platoon might contain 4 types
of vehicle — TD, FST, IFV and CSV (*see* Appendix). If we
envision 3 sections[7] each of 1 FST and 1 IFV (the basic pair), we
need a headquarters of a CSV (plus a runabout) and a support
section of a pair of TDs. This gives 10 major vehicles (11 in all)
and a strength of 50. Evidently this would be a captain's

---

6 Chapter 11.

7 I am deliberately introducing the term "section", which I shall indicate by two dots
over the symbol, so as to stay with the standard term "maneuver squad".

command with a (first) lieutenant as deputy and a first sergeant. The function of the platoon commander is to group and maneuver his balanced force in whatever way required. The deputy provides a relief for round-the-clock working and takes charge of specific tasks such as using the grouped maneuver squads to clear through cover, block a defile or cover a demolition party; or coordinating the tank destroyers in an overwatching position. The platoon sergeant is responsible for specialist training and discipline in post and for reconnaissance, resupply and the like in the field.

This platoon, which roughly adds up to a conventional tank platoon and mechanized infantry platoon stuck together, is the tactical unit in the conventional sense — the smallest balanced subunit capable of fire and maneuver. If we take 4 of these and tack on the normal company-level bits and pieces, we come to something like the large composite company of around 250 postulated in *Mechanized Infantry* (fig. 25). The most striking and to my mind questionable difference is that, by replacing the KE gun of the Merkava-like FST/IFV proposed in *Mechanized Infantry* with a combined general support armament we have reduced the number of KE guns by 14 or over 40%. This gives a ratio of 12.8 men per KE gun — very high at company level. Nonetheless this company adds up to a powerful flexible unit — a "tactical unit" in the sense of being capable of influencing the battle.

At this point, though, we head into a nest of problems of great interest on three counts. They demonstrate why attempts to marry up a tank and a mechanized infantry battalion to form a balanced combat team is wasteful in men and relatively ineffective. They show that grassroots integration, important as it may be, presents real structural problems. And they indicate that it may be necessary to insert a level of command for organizational and administrative reasons although this is superfluous or even undesirable in terms of the tactical command structure *per se*.

Let us look first at the composite platoon of fig. 25 with its 10 vehicles and 50 men. Even then there is no really suitable vehicle which the deputy commander can take to perform a separate mission; and giving the commander a man of first sergeant caliber with a scout car to ride around in does not exactly solve the gamut of the administrative problems. Trouble is to have a viable dismounted subunit you need 3 squad IFVs. Pair these with 3 FSTs and you have 6 vehicles. Add to these 3 sections a

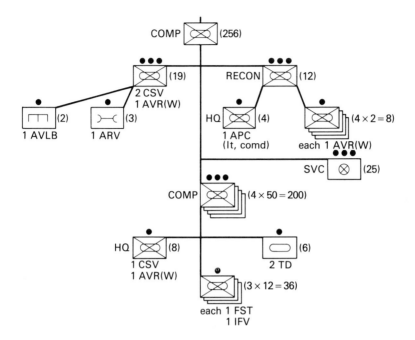

25. The large composite company
Strength   256 all ranks
Armored vehicles   8 TD
(*see* Appendix)   12 FST   20 KE guns
                         12 IFV
Totals major 40   6 CSV   18 cannon + LP 76-mm guns
         light <u>10</u>   1 APC (light, command)
               50   9 AVR(W)
                           1 ARV
                           1 AVLB

pair of TDs to give a balanced capability, and you have an unwieldy subunit none too strong on antiarmor firepower. Try to boost this into a small company (around the same size, after all, as the former Soviet tank company) and you hit two more snags. You are attaching a substantial if minimal tail to a rather small set of teeth which is bad on cost-manpower effectiveness. Worse, it is hard to see what a platoon then consists of and what tactical capability it has. So evidently all this needs another look.

Suppose for a moment, though, that we accept a large composite company like that of *Mechanized Infantry,* Chapter 11, or fig. 25 as the tactical unit — after all, it is not far short of tank battalion strength in major armored vehicles and puts 12 maneuver squads plus headquarters elements (around a company) on the ground. Certainly a brigade headquarters with modern command aids could control 5 or 6 of these units, and they would split off very neatly to form a task force under the deputy brigade commander. But then we come up against the question of who is to provide and hold the specialist, logistic and administrative elements normally found at battalion level.

Each company of around 225 combat officers and soldiers and a service platoon of only 25 is going to need at least the same again, probably more, to back it. So every 5 or 6 composite companies will need a service company of 250-300 men. This service unit has to have its own command and administrative elements, communications, vehicle complement and the rest. Somewhere has to be found to deploy it; and complications are going to arise when composite companies are regrouped. By contrast the extravagance of providing each composite company with complete organic specialist and administrative backup is self-evident.

So we are led back to look at a composite battalion — not for the reasons of rank structure, assessment and promotion prospects so beloved of peacetime armies, nor for effectiveness of tactical command — but to arrive at an organization which is truly viable in the field. Before we start talking of extravagance and unwieldiness, we should do well to recall that this single unit is to pack the same punch as a tank battalion/infantry battalion combat team probably numbering around 1500 men. Figure 26 outlines a possible organization for such a battalion with an overall strength of 1000 including 176 wholly specialist/ administrative personnel and a further 56 who ride in CSVs but have some kind of support role. The unit fields 80 KE guns (at 12.5 men/gun) along with 64 multipurpose cannon/76-mm weapon packs (*see* Appendix). It can dismount 36 squads (252 men) and a skeleton battalion structure of command elements. It has a conventional rotary-wing and armored close reconnaissance/liaison capability. So even if I have underestimated the administrative backing it looks an interesting starter.

Given assured backup from the reconnaissance platoon and the service company, the composite company can afford to have its backend streamlined a bit. Additionally the antitank platoon commander could play a "battle captain" role either with his own platoon grouped or with the TD sections farmed out and the maneuver squads grouped under him. The composite platoon has a balanced headquarters element capable of "squaring the box"

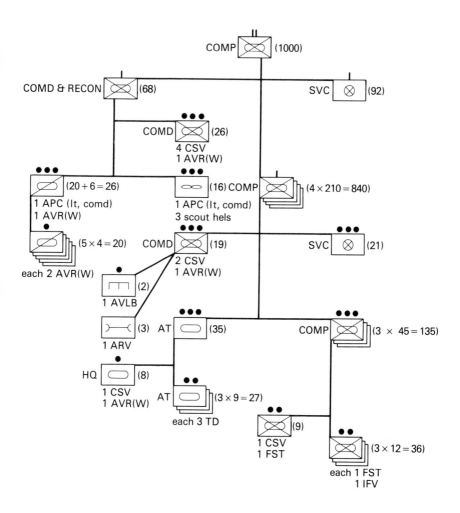

26. A composite battalion

Strength   1000 all ranks including 232 administrative[1]

Armored vehicles	32 TD	
(*see* Appendix)	48 FST	80 KE guns
Totals major 152	36 IFV	64 cannon + LP 76-mm guns
light $\underline{\quad 22}$	28 CSV	36 maneuver squads + HQs
$\overline{174}$	2 APC (light, command)	
	20 AVR(W)	
	4 ARV	
	4 AVLB	
Helicopters	3 scout/liaison	

Note

[1]Including two per CSV complement in a wholly or partly administrative/reserve capacity.

in fire and maneuver, of splitting into subplatoons of FSTs and
IFVs, or of taking a TD section under its wing for specific tasks.
To keep the company and thus the battalion down to manageable
size, the number of composite platoons has to be reduced from
the ideal of 4 to 3. But for my money this is fair because either the
TD platoon, or the dismountable elements under the battle
captain proper or TD platoon commander, can provide a pivot of
maneuver. I guess it is better to take the slight loss of balance and
flexibility at this level rather than restricting the battalion to 3
fairly massive companies.

If we accept this solution, we need to examine with some care
the role of brigades. In this composite setup even the large
platoon, as it stands or modified, is, as remarked earlier, the
tactical unit; but only in the most limited sense of the term. Full
balance and flexibility comes only at company level; so the
company commander has the clear-cut task of fighting the battle
on the ground. Battalion with its affiliated artillery and helicopter support is evidently capable of conducting a phase of a
battle, like the anvil. This is the point though at which we run
into the problem of too many chiefs. Even if as many as 8
companies are involved, this is a single battle requiring a single
commander and just one gunner and aviator as advisers; and with
modern aids there is no reason why a single headquarters should
not control it. Hiving off a task force under the deputy brigade
commander and then interposing two battalion headquarters
between him and the companies is almost the worst possible
solution.

The need is *to design the command elements* of battalion and
brigade to share the required tasks economically and effectively
in battle, while each headquarters as a whole retains its conventional status and functions out of contact. To knock one
objection on the head before it is raised, I believe that, with
a large company, the company commander will play the figure-
head role in the soldier's loyalty (as he often does anyways). So
the battalion command setup needs to be able to command a
working reliefs with the other battalion headquarters. By the
same token the stand-down battalion headquarters of whichever
phase of the battle is (relatively) inactive can take on an
emergency task force role such as blocking to a flank. In effect,
battalion headquarters act as task force or tactical headquarters
for brigade. So the brigade command element can be geared to
round-the-clock operation of a single headquarters working at a
clear-cut level. This way of working bears some resemblance to

the British procedures I knocked earlier. But here we have only one kind of battalion headquarters, and it and brigade are purpose-designed to interlock. This avoids overlap, cuts out an unnecessary command level and saves key officers and specialists.

The brigade tactical command task is to fight the complete hammer-and-anvil battle or whatever similar tactic is called for. Brigade is thus the level for major coordination of artillery and helicopter support. Logistically it probably need have no more than a monitoring and supportive function provided that division is a logistic headquarters. (I appreciate this is a switch from current US Army practice, but in this solution the division is the level at which full tactical balance of the maneuver force is achieved and the formation whose composition is most likely to remain constant.)

Air cavalry

I shall use (I hope correctly) current American terminology to discuss the missions and organizations of helicopter units, because it is far better developed and documented than that of other Western armies. Most of the groundwork for this discussion is excellently laid in a recent article in *Armor Magazine*.[8] This paper proposes an air cavalry attack troop (ACAT). Briefly the (then) existing air cavalry troop (ACT) is a reconnaissance unit with limited fighting power, comparable to a medium armored reconnaissance troop.[9] The attack helicopter company (AHC) is a fighting unit, primarily antiarmor, with a reconnaissance capability limited to target acquisition, command and control. The ACAT proposed by the author is a balanced organization combining these two functions but designed to operate mainly in support of the ground maneuver force, with only a screening or economy of force role away from it. I now want to consider the extension of this unit's role to independent helicopter operations (Chapters 16 and 21) and the integration of air cavalry into the main mechanized force on the assumption that armored medium reconnaissance is phased out. (Like everybody else, though, the air cavalry will continue to have a need for *close* ground reconnaissance and the associated secondary roles.)

---

8 *See* Bibliography (Sayre).

9 British "squadron".

One glaring omission from discussions I have read is the use of helicopters to *observe and control artillery fire*. Certainly with one of the primary antiarmor systems (Appendix) in the artillery's hands, this becomes a key role for command, control and scout choppers. For speedy application of fire, artillery forward observers also need to fly with platoon or even section headquarters. In a word the tie-up that now exists between armor and artillery needs to be replicated between helicopters and artillery. With a strength of 296 all ranks, the proposed ACAT fields 20 scout, 20 attack and 7 utility helicopters. Each of its 4 platoons can field a team of 5 attack and 2 command/scout helicopters and has an organic close ground reconnaissance capability. One of the roles of the utility helicopters is scattering mines, but with only 7 in the troop most will be needed for command and logistic purposes.

As the reader will have gathered I am all for grassroots integration, but at an experimental stage of extending the air cavalry squadron's capability it makes sense to leave the ACAT alone and graft on a separate squadron which one might call a *support squadron*. When not required for independent helicopter operations, the support squadron, suballotted as needed, can do much to flesh out the ground element of the ACATs, thus relieving other units of responsibility for the helicopter force's security and giving it increased flexibility of operation.

In its primary role the support squadron tacks on to a scout/ attack helicopter squadron just as a battalion of infantry does onto a tank battalion. Its roles are to establish a pivot of maneuver and to lift in, supply and protect the direct support antiarmor artillery (which we have said will have a mortar subunit attached for general support). One must not, however, rule out the possibility of *offensive* helicopter operations like the Soviets envision. We might then list the missions of the support squadron like this —

landing and recovering organic infantry and engineer detachments;

scattering mines;

lifting and protecting artillery battery;

self-protection;

own forward resupply.

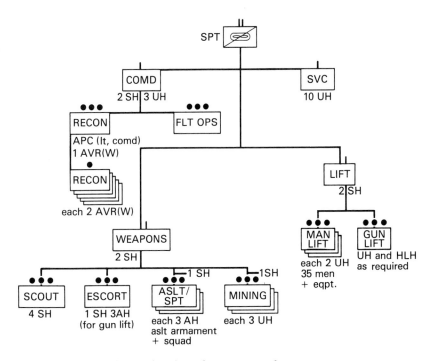

27. Possible organization of an air cavalry support squadron
Strength approx. 550
Helicopters Scout/command 12
Attack/support 12
Utility, say 55 (some may be heavy lift types)
Armored vehicles APC (light, command) 1
AVR(W) 11

By analogy with existing air cavalry organizations, this requirement might produce a structure something like fig. 27.

With this new dimension of independent operation, the air cavalry element evidently justifies a much larger proportion of the combat manpower in the mechanized division. This goes along with United States trends and much of the more forward-looking German thinking.

The future airmechanized division

All the arguments deployed so far in this book point towards a single type of mechanized division in which the replacement of armor and infantry units by composite battalions represents a

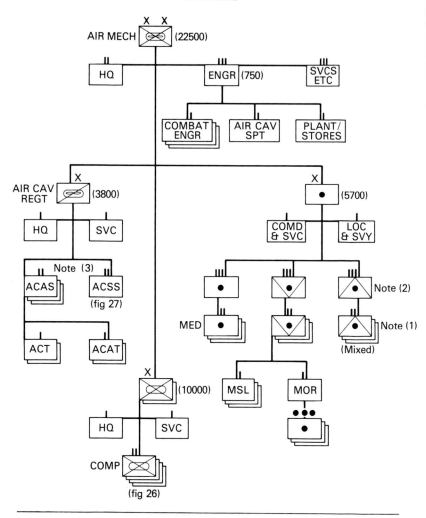

relatively minor change of emphasis. The nature of the threat, future equipment capabilities and limitations, and the resulting concept of operations I outlined in Chapter 22 call for a shift of the weight of combat manpower away from the mechanized maneuver force as such towards the helicopter element and the artillery.

The resulting division will be extremely powerful and extremely expensive, so once again the reader needs to recall that a single mechanized battalion packs at least the punch of an existing tank and infantry battalion combined. The extension of

28. Main combat elements of a future airmechanized division
Strength approx. 22,500

Armored vehicles (approx.)		*Helicopters* (approx.)	
256 TD	640 KE guns	Scout — liaison/command	40
384 FST		Scout — armed	140
288 IFVs 512 cannon + LP 76-mm guns		Attack/support	160
224 CSVs 288 maneuver squads + HQs		Utility	130
32 ARV		(maybe some replaced by heavy lift)	
32 AVLB		(Total helicopters	470)
(Total 1216)			

190 AVR(W)
   APC (light, command) — not
     calculated

Surface-to-surface artillery[1]		*Primary antiarmor weapon systems*		
Medium guns	54	TD	256	640 KE
ATGMS	72	FST	384	
Mortars	36	Armed scout hels.	140	
		Attack hels.	148	360 CE
		Arty. ATGMS	72	
		Total (approx.)	1000	

Notes

[1] AD artillery not detailed.

[2] Each artillery regiment headquarters has a functional command out of contact but is affiliated to air cavalry regiment/brigades as an across-the-board headquarters in the field. Composite battalion and company commanders have an across-the-board gunner in the same way.

[3] When an ACAS is in direct support of a brigade, affiliations to brigade and composite battalion headquarters are as for gunners.

the helicopter element in size and role, the trebling of mobility of the mechanized force and the expansion of the artillery increase the dimensions of this division's battlefield, the tempo of its operations and above all its ability to concentrate fighting power in time and space. While designed as the principal tactical formation in a larger force, this division, with long-range artillery, specialist engineer and logistic increments, would be entirely capable of acting at operational level with its brigades as the main tactical formations.

The division depicted in outline at fig. 28 should prove a very hard nut to crack. As I just remarked, it is extremely expensive in hardware but, despite rather generous allowances for support personnel at all levels, fields a major antiarmor weapon system for 22.5 men. By conventional standards it looks unwieldy; but if one is going to combine flexibility and balance of rotary-wing aviation, armor and infantry with adequate artillery support into groupings large enough to perform specific tactical tasks on a scale comparable with that of the threat, this becomes the smallest self-contained formation. It is roughly double the size of a Soviet division and maybe 20% larger than a typical Western division — but with over 3 times the antiarmor firepower.

I am always horrified at the spendthrift wastage of manpower in American and British headquarters and logistic elements which results in a tail of around 40% of the teeth manpower compared with the Soviets' 15-17.5%. It is quite wrong to suppose that this difference stems from the Soviet Army treating its soldiers rough. Their casualty evacuation and treatment facilities are streamlined but effective. As apostles of mobility the Soviets are scarcely likely to run their armor short of fuel or ammunition; and food is a tiny proportion of the lift in any mechanized formation. The major difference looks to lie in the size of headquarters. The Soviets somehow seem able to run a corps with a staff roughly the same size as a Western (or at least Anglo-American) brigade headquarters.

This is another story — and one that surely needs an airing. But since there seems to be no way of trimming the size of the headquarters and the still grosser logistic top-hamper of Western armies, manpower-effectiveness has to lie in packing as much fighting power as possible under each headquarters. The alternative to this massive, powerful and balanced division would be a corps of 2 mechanized divisions, 1 artillery division and 1 air cavalry division. But apart from the evident loss of cohesion, this would create so many headquarters and logistic units that there would be nobody left to do the fighting.

The crunch from applying this principle of organically combining the elements of a balanced force really comes at platoon level. Even the 5-vehicle platoon (CSV, 2 TD, 2 FST) I suggested in *Tank Warfare,* still more the 8-vehicle platoon of *Mechanized Infantry* (readopted in modified form in this book) aroused sharp criticism among British readers. First, there are two ways of tackling this problem. One is to have a properly constituted, balanced, coherent organization commanded by an experienced officer — a captain or in the Bundeswehr an

Oberleutnant — with a junior officer or warrant officer (US version) as deputy and a platoon sergeant of first sergeant (British WO2) quality to support them. The other is to take two greenhorn platoon commanders, one with 3 or 4 tanks and the other with 4 IFVs, have them sit in each other's pockets and hope they will produce a neat, coordinated piece of fire and maneuver. After all the standard American tank platoon has 5 tanks; and the American or German attack helicopter team, under a captain, consists of 7 or 8 machines.

I have long believed that the British method of training young career officers has been a major factor in preventing the modernization of organizations and the evolution of cost-effective combat units. And the same may be true to some extent of the US Army. The taxpayer, specially the British taxpayer, might just be prepared to invest in the production of quaint survivals, punch-drunk from having the corners knocked off them, who know how to begin and end letters correctly and never to ask for "another" drink. He will scarcely be willing, though, to provide these P.G. Wodehouse character with millions of dollars' worth of toys they do not know how to play with even if they wanted to. Many experienced officers in the three armies I know best feel that officers entering via short-service commissions (or the equivalent) and through the ranks are more useful from the start, more trainable and better motivated — and frequently stay on to reach the top. I fail to see why armies should be afflicted with cries of "Keep it simple!" when national interest is calling out "Make it effective!" Maybe the august academies could one day bring themselves to place more stress on electronic and mechanical engineering than on the social variety and more emphasis on soldiering than on socializing.

24

Training, logistics and manning

An airmechanized force of high cost and immense complexity, such as is needed to counter the Warsaw Pact armored threat, cannot just be tacked on or dovetailed in to an existing conventional army. To realize its potential the forces must be introduced in one across-the-board package covering R & D, procurement, training, supply and repair — and most of all manning.

Western armies seem to suffer from an unhappily low and declining *state of training*. This is evidently linked to the attitudes and talent of junior and middle-piece officers, to organizational problems and to resources. Another factor in training standards is the quality of noncom instructor, but (except maybe in the very early days of the Bundeswehr) I have never seen or heard of reason to criticize these splendid men's performance.

As things are at present, junior officers fight shy of training their men. They mostly lack the knowledge even to supervise noncom instructors; training is undisguisably "work" and thus out of image; what is more, a young officer's ability to do his own basic job and see that his men can do theirs ranks very low as a factor in annual assessment. By contrast at company and battalion levels the standard of training rates very high in assessment of the commander — so much so that gamesmanship steps in and training for war is replaced by training for training. This art is encouraged in some armies, indeed in NATO as a whole, by various competitions distinguished mainly by squabbles over the rules and the refereeing. Because it requires significant resources and acquires little merit, crew training — the stand-or-fall level for a mechanized force (*cf.* page 45) — often gets squeezed out.

Unless very special efforts are made, little effective training in basic crew and dismounted skills is achieved within the small conventional platoon. This is simply because a platoon is likely to possess only one or at most two qualified instructors, and they may not be experienced enough to *organize* instruction. The composite platoon of around fifty men with its first sergeant should have the resources to *organize and carry out* the basic level of skill training internally — thus putting the ball squarely in the platoon commander's court. The same goes for refresher and broadening training (adding a second skill) at this level. With the command, antitank and three combat platoons of the composite company envisioned (fig. 25), each platoon can be made responsible for upgrading training and specialist advice in one subject — signaling, gunnery, driving, weapon training, fieldcraft. So the individual training buck stops with the company commander. This way individual training would, I think, quickly become fashionable. Likewise, once it was firmly under the wing of the mature platoon commander and his first sergeant, crew training might suddenly be found to need far fewer resources than tradition suggests — say the unit's driver training area with a spot of help from a dozer blade, rather than precious time booked on a tactical training area.

Staying at the lower level a moment longer, we should maybe take a glance at physical fitness and the type of exercise variously known as arduous, adventure, expedition or survival training, or escape and evasion. I always was convinced that these exercises, originally introduced into armies as a whole to train for survival and operations by remnants in nuclear war, are of extreme value in any context, the more so since they also offer a chance to learn the ground intimately (page 232). Over the years the bulk of the time, imaginative effort and material resources have come to be diverted from the original very down-to-earth concept to projects which are in every sense of the phrase far out and to arduous sports like skiing and offshore sailing — all excellent things in themselves but yet another instance of training for training or, more precisely, training for prestige.

It is at the higher levels of collective training, though, that this art of training for training achieves its apotheosis. If the vast cost in money, fuel and adverse public relations of unit and lower formation training is not to be wasted, objective goals have to be set and assessment has to be if not objective at least realistic and unbiased. A model for this exists in the sphere of tank gunnery. When units fire at the Bergen-Hohne NATO Ranges (for instance) they are backed up by a team of instructors and assessors from their national armored gunnery school plus an

allied team of range staff.[1] Programs are worked out by COs and
unit gunnery officers in conjunction with these teams, and expert
technical backup is available if needed. As a result, most units
achieve really high standards, much sound knowledge is imparted,
unit instructors are brought up to the mark — and the assessment is accepted without question by all concerned.

Sure, gunnery is a "hard" subject and tactics is not. But the
clue seems to me to lie in the fact that planning, resource
provision and assessment is taken out of the chain of command
and placed in the hands of experts who know the subject, the
doctrine, the problem areas, the ground and the rest of the
resources and who are there to help the CO or company
commander as well as to assess his unit. I believe this point is
strongly borne out by the results of, and reactions to, visits by
BAOR combat teams to the Suffield Training Area in Canada. A
tactical training setup like this on a NATO basis, with an allied
team of advisers and assessors, would not just remove all
possibility of bias but lead to exchanges of ideas and gradual but
inevitable coalescence of doctrine. Maybe that's just why it
doesn't exist!

Moving up a level or two further, I believe the same principle
could be applied to CPXs. Experience suggests that, even if two
or three levels of headquarters are being exercised (as opposed to
acting as higher or lower controls), only one level gets much
value. Once again the waste of time, money and fuel in turning
out these controls is considerable; once again accidents or
damage are likely to cause bad public relations. With a
permanent CPX setup run by an expert team, just one
headquarters could be exercised at a time. The higher and lower
control inputs could be largely prerecorded and operated by
ADPS. There is also a certain need for the semicontrolled type of
CPX in which a formation can get used to working with its
subordinate headquarters, but this type of exercise loses much of
its value by not being umpired. The permanent CPX setup could
produce scenarios for these semicontrolled exercises, umpire
them expertly and produce an objective report on performance
and changes needed.

Finally one has to face up to the awful reality of major exercises
with troops. Tolerant as the Germans are of having their land
chewed up and generous as their allies are in paying compen-

---

1 The Israeli Army, which has a considerable reputation for hitting the target, has
developed this type of procedure even further.

sation, the question is not so much whether these large maneuvers have any training value as how serious the false lessons they teach are. For instance, to keep damage within tolerable limits, the vehicles of mechanized platoons and even companies all "track" each other when moving across country. For various reasons, usually associated with civilian traffic and fear of getting lost, they all bunch. One spends hours at the lower levels of training trying to eradicate these vices only to find that, the moment the outfit hits virgin ground, they all come back again. Nobody would question the worth of mobilization-type exercises like the Reforger series or Crusader 80. And evidently troops who have flown across the Atlantic expect to do something when they get to the other side. But once again it should be possible to combine specific goals (such as marrying up with heavy equipment and testing its battleworthiness) with CPXs for the chiefs and escape and evasion for the Indians — not least with the object of familiarizing everybody with the ground.

To be effective then every type and level of training must and can have a kind of governing body which sets goals and standards, monitors achievement and assesses results as far as possible objectively and, where value judgments are involved, expertly and fairly. Sophisticated hardware makes for objectivity in training; nobody is in much doubt if someone is flying an aircraft or navigating a ship correctly. Within this framework, each buck has to stop at the right place. Above all, training has to be *training for war,* not an exercise in assiduously, shall we say, tickling the palate of the next commander up the chain. Any weakness at the levels of individual skills or crew training must be eradicated because it will affect real performance at higher levels, even if gamesmanship and circumstance combine to mask the defect.

Likewise, as I remarked at the start of this chapter, the effective operation of an airmechanized force means treating everything about that force as part of a single package. So another thing that has to change is the conservatism of the *logistic services.* In fairness there is a deal of opposition to changes in replenishment techniques among the combat arms too; but this could be because they have learned the hard way that the burden of such changes and the problems that go with them come to rest with their own service subunits while the supply organization goes its own sweet way.

At this point I would like to make a very sharp distinction

between on the one hand supply and on the other maintenance and repair. (I use the general terms since each army has its own.) Again one can write only of the armies he knows, but few would dispute, I think, the excellence of the *technical* services in Western armies. They are technologically and managerially competent at every level from graduate engineer to junior technician or operator; they are dedicated to the task of getting hardware working and keeping it that way; they work cheerfully under appalling, sometimes ridiculous, conditions and are always ready to improvise or cannibalize when needs be. As they have gotten increasingly integrated into combat units, these men have become "more Catholic than the Pope", often setting an example in soldierly qualities too. I found putting these men in as tank or platoon commanders to be more than a morale-boosting gesture or an exercise gimmick; they often show up some of the proper crews.[2]

We can use the excellence of these technical services to examine the qualities which go to make a good logistic organization. They attract good people because they require *and make use of* high professional or craft qualifications; they have a real job with tangible and measurable results in peace as well as war; and they are eminently employable outside the armed forces. These men feel secure because it is evident to all, from the most bandy-legged of generals to the meanest of financiers, that the army will grind to a halt without them. So they set about the management of the maintenance and repair problem in a rational and realistic manner. They look first at the two ends of the chain, which they may influence but cannot control. In the British Army at least the "EME" is the CO's technical adviser in name and in fact. Likewise, in R & D establishments and production facilities you find "maintenance advisory teams" of graduate engineers and experienced top-grade technicians carrying at least as much weight as user representatives.

Once having gotten itself a clear picture of these ends, solved some of the problems there and pinpointed the rest, the repair organization can analyze what lies between them and organize itself and its work to match. It is highly impressive how repair unit functions and organizations, along with inspection and maintenance schedules, keep pace not just with the introduction of

---

2 Though combat units see less of them in high- and medium-intensity operations, the same goes for ammunition and explosives experts. In the pattern of urban guerrilla warfare and counterterrorism that has become so much a task of Western armies today, these men have earned a name for courage which exceeds even their technical repute.

new hardware but with the underlying technological changes which accompany this.

If the airmechanized force of the nineties is to get the replenishment it needs, the supply services have to follow their technical colleagues' example. We already examined (Chapter 15) the nitty gritty at the sharp end of the logistic chain and postulated two distinct types of resupply. TDs and FSTs with external magazines, and probably attack helicopters, need complete armament packs brought forward in dedicated vehicles and exchanged by mechanical handling for used or part-used magazines/packs, which then go back for maintenance and refilling. Other vehicles and helicopters with a wider spread of roles need a flexible resupply system which for one reason or another will involve manhandling; but luckily most such vehicles have enough men around (like IFV or heliborne maneuver squads) to do this. Artillery will need analogous specialized and versatile systems, probably rather more complex and more flexible in grouping and breakdown.

Crossloading is costly in time and repair, vulnerable to enemy action and likely to cause damage or initiate corrosion. So standard packs need to be run right through from a depot where they and their contents can be expertly handled under good conditions to the vehicle from which they will be fired. This can easily be done by the mixture of pallet, container and semitrailer techniques that some call "body-swopping" — in the hope, I guess, that this term if nothing else may spark the logisticians' imagination. Trouble is logistic units like to stay wedded to their own hardware in case some horny-handed tanker or such chips the paint.

Given dedicated equipment and proper filtration at the time of refueling helicopters and armored vehicles, *fuel* can be safely and economically crossloaded from pipelines or large tanks to smaller tanker vehicles or pillow tanks much further forward than ammunition can be crossloaded. Again some form of body-swopping technique will reduce turnround times and save prime movers and drivers. When *water* is a problem, it can be handled in the same way as fuel (though on a much smaller scale).

Food is such a minute proportion of the total lift as to be scarcely worth discussing. But I can see no reason why it should not be handled along with the two types of ammunition replenishment described above.

Most armies now have stores subunits for spares integrated into or organic to their various levels of maintenance and repair unit.

This system should surely be normal in peace and war, and should be extended to the (hardware) "survival packs" carried on CSVs (Chapter 15) and to on-board spares for primary vehicles.

By contrast the principle of forward supply does not seem to have gone nearly far enough. Organic service platoons and companies should not be saddled with vast lifts of major commodities. They can do a much better job for their air and armored vehicle crews by concentrating on specialized services and carrying only enough replenishment for emergencies — like when fuel has to be got forward to a vehicle which has run out or when a tank has had to jettison its magazines.

The prospect of a battle fought at really high tempo makes it hard (for me at least) even to ballpark the amount of replenishment which needs to be held forward. Let us stay with the yardsticks that the combined fuel and ammunition lift is constant for armor and that fuel is always dominant for aircraft. Given a reserve in its organic service subunit for genuine emergencies, I suppose then a troop or company might need 6 hours of major commodities at 30 minutes' notice and a squadron or battalion 24 hours' worth at 2 hours' notice *plus* a further 24 hours (with a rather different commodity balance) at 6 hours' notice. These packets should be manned and operated technically by logistic personnel but controlled and guided by combat units' organic service and/or reconnaissance subunits. The composite company's service platoon needs an officer whose primary task is to reconnoiter, set up and control running replenishment points.

Just as the high standards of training and the harmonized man/machine interface of the Soviet Army constitute two hidden strengths, the conservatism of the logistic services and the lack of professionalism, even enthusiasm among young *officers* in most Western armies add up to two blatant weaknesses.[3] Let me say by contrast that the warrant officers (however defined) and noncommissioned officers of the five armies I have had the privilege of getting to know are as fine a body of men in character, dedication and professional skill as one could hope to find anywhere. If NATO's members, or the Alliance as a whole, want to set about fielding a mechanized force capable not just of deterring but if needs be of defeating the Warsaw Pact in Europe and elsewhere, the manning problem just has to be tackled.

---

3 *Cf.* Stanhope: *see* Bibliography.

Draft or no, I doubt the Western countries need face an overall recruitment problem of quantity or quality any more. Those who can see rather further than politicians care to mostly reckon that unemployment will continue to mount in the advanced countries even when there is an upturn in trade. This is simply because the more forward developing countries are now living by their hands; so the advanced countries have to learn to live by their heads instead. Again, the introduction of women into all but the direct combat elements of the forces (and maybe even there) opens up a whole new pool of skill and brain. With a sound, broad base and a reasonable selection system, the standard of senior enlisted personnel and warrant officers (or the equivalent) can be expected to rise even higher than it is now. This step-by-step promotion is already leading to commissioning in the early forties after a full first career. Additionally, outstanding individuals can be and are being singled out for commissioning at around 30. I have never heard anybody in any service dispute the inestimable value of this "cream of the cream" — as superbly skilled, versatile professionals, as father-figures for the young soldier, or just as folks.

Again we have only to look at the young officers of navies and air forces to see models of zeal and attainment. Their quality is patchier because they have not as yet gone through the finer meshes of the selection net. But they are there because they want to go to sea or want to fly. They tell their friends and on occasion the media as much with great articulateness, verve and charm. In most countries now they have a mid-career option of leaving the service and doing their thing in civilian life, or of moving upwards towards administrative tasks and high command responsibility. It is not easy to find men of the requisite quality, but this is simply and objectively because the combination of mental and physical qualities required is so high.

Among all these people in the three services, successful enlisted men and young sailors and airmen all of them dedicated to doing an extremely demanding professional job they love, the young army officer stands up like a sore thumb. It is easy to castigate him; but the problem is a real one which merits constructive analysis.

Flying a strike aircraft or an attack chopper, commanding a fast patrol boat or watchkeeping in a ship at sea are major professional tasks. They constitute a worthwhile challenge in the eyes of any young man who inclines to combining intellectual and mechanical skills with physical activity in these kinds of way.

Commanding an armored vehicle, or even a group of them, rather heavily populated by a mixed bunch of soldiers, no more appeals to this type of man than would the prospect of taking his crusty old folks and his least favorite sister and brother-in-law, complete with yelling brood, on an outing to the nearest State Park.

Then there is the boy who "just loves folks" or "wants to do something with people". Here there are two snags. First, he often means he's too lazy or stupid to do anything that is difficult or demand rigorous discipline. Second, if he is sincere, what he wants to do with these "people" is more likely to be praying than soldiering. Fact is the "wonders of science" appeal of armored vehicles just does not exist any more for the educated middle-class kid who spends his whole childhood surrounded by the kind of gadgets that modern armored vehicles contain. This appeal has shifted down market to the enlisted man, whose childhood may have been marked by lack of all these things resulting in envy and a longing to acquire them — or at least have them to play with.

So the only ways a kid of officer potential is going to gravitate towards the army in peacetime are family tradition and/or parental pressure, subuniversity intellectual ability, a brutal streak,[4] snobbery or sheer inability to think of anything else to do. And there is no reason why those who do so gravitate should have much aptitude in intellectual or control tasks or readiness to master technical mysteries. Sure, this is an exaggerated picture, a caricature; but I guess it is not too far from the truth right now and is moving nearer still.

So we need to weigh rather carefully what an army officer is about. I certainly do not believe he is about the complex but relatively low-grade multiskill tasks entailed in commanding an armored vehicle. Hard as I tried, I was never able to match the level of skill as a tank commander of even the above-average noncoms in my company or battalion, let alone the real professionals. I have seen few enough officers try to do so — and none succeed. Certainly if the picture I drew just now about recruitment of enlisted men is anywhere near the mark, there should be no problem about producing good vehicle, squad and section commanders.

This brings out the point that most Western armies, except the Wehrmacht and now maybe the Bundeswehr, always had *far too*

---

4 I know most armies go to great lengths to steer clear of boys of this kind, but the significant number of army officers who later turn mercenary suggests that this factor is present.

many officers. Whatever system of grafting on or in warrant officers a given army employs, definitely a company and probably a battalion should be able to run efficiently for a sustained period *without any officers present.* Let me stick my neck out one stage further and say that this should go for maneuvers as well as routine life in post. Because armies function in man's natural element, land, their peacetime operation does not call for the levels of judgmental decision which arise all the time in operating ships or aircraft.

Here, then, is the first thing army officers are about — *taking complex judgmental decisions.* Fact is an army officer is unlikely to take more than one really important and difficult decision in his whole career; many are never called on to do this at all. But the *leitmotiv* of an officer's training is (or in my view should be) that he takes this decision quickly and soundly if he has to. The second thing an officer is about is surely *leadership.* Earlier on I took this word as an example of how gobbledygook can gild words which convey uncomfortable ideas; so now I need to unscramble it.

I am inclined to think that the only type of leadership an officer as such as is now required to perform is that contained in the hard old meaning of the word — getting people to cooperate in doing things, specially dangerous things, which they would not otherwise do. Every other vehicle or squad commander in an officer's setup will be just as capable as the officer is of handling his own vehicle or squad, maybe even the whole setup. The officer's job is to unmask first, to lead a dash down a forward slope or across a gap, to close range and intensify the fight, to go forward and recover a casualty, to cover his setup out when they break. At a higher level this type of leadership — like the exercise of forward command — simply requires the commander to be where he can and can be seen to exercise direct control over the battle. Here again, the deputy or exec will be just as capable as the commander of running the battle from the headquarters.

By contrast I believe the all-caring, super-welfare figure which several modern armies have forced officers to become is going out of date again. Valuable as paternalism may be as an aid to discipline and morale, it is no longer acceptable in Western societies and is known to be a major disincentive to recruitment. It just has to go. The modern educated warrant officer or noncom is entirely capable of dealing with routine administrative and personal problems. For more serious matters soldiers now very properly expect the backup of the *professional* services they find in civilian life.

Rather to my own astonishment, it looks like I worked my way through to a conclusion, albeit a surprising one. Those parts of an army which fly, go to sea or in some other way regularly encounter conditions outside normal human experience need specially trained and selected officers in low-level executive jobs (like flying an airplane) under the eye of similar but more experienced officers who take operational (that is flying or sailing) decisions. A high proportion of these officers leave in their early/mid 30s to go on doing very much the same thing in civilian life. A few — 25% or so maybe — go on to staff training and high command or senior staff appointments. This may have been true of armor in the past, in my generation for instance; but is no longer so.

For the rest, an army's routine command structure should be built upwards through the ranks by progressive and more rarely jump promotion. This will produce the full requirements of specialist middle-piece officers, amounting maybe to *two-thirds* of an army's entire officer requirement and offering the successful a whole-life career with a ceiling of major or lieutenant-colonel. Additionally a few outstanding individuals will make the grade into the higher command and staff structure.

Superimposed on this lower hierarchy should be the career officer — around *one-third* of the whole at the stage of recruitment. With a complete backswing from modern trends to the officer mystique of old, they should become beings apart. Since there is no real job for them with troops until they are capable of commanding a composite platoon, they should follow up a bachelor degree with the 3-4 years of full-time applied and/or higher academic training now common to most professions. They would make their first permanent appearance with a unit as captains around the age of 26. From recruitment onwards they would have had a link with a regiment or unit and would be expected to build a reputation in advance of arrival by gladiatorial and/or academic achievements. They would then spend, say, 2 years commanding a platoon, 1 year as battle captain or as battalion S2 or S3,[5] 1 year on an arm advanced course and 2 years as company commanders.[6] Then it would be Command and Staff College *or out*. To ensure quality the

---

[5] Respectively intelligence officer, adjutant.

[6] This is not so radical as it sounds. I recall studies which showed that the pick of British officers were apt to spend less than 6 years with troops before commanding a battalion. The argument is about whether this is good or bad.

planned wastage rate at this stage should be around 25%, unplanned wastage being made up for by the few making the jump from the lower hierarchy.

In a word, these officers are treated from the start as top management trainees. This approach may be anathema to the military mind. But it works very well in many spheres where there are no real jobs for very young men in their formative period. It would put paid to the image of young army officers as the *lichnyi chelovieki* of twentieth-century capitalism. And it offers a worthwhile challenge, specially since even the 25% wastage would be extremely eligible for management appointments in slightly less demanding and rewarding fields.

Fact is this is not too different from what now goes on in the British armed forces — to a far greater extent, I believe, than it does in those of reputedly less class-ridden societies. To my mind there is just one more leap to be taken, partly to give a really good opening to men coming up from the ranks, partly to get rid of the appalling reality and worse image of the young officer I tried to depict above. My experience is that in the FRG, France, the UK and the USA alike resistance to this shift in the center of gravity comes from very similar combinations of influences which would merit a book to themselves if they could ever be brought into the open.

Some of what I have written above may fall harshly on traditionalist ears, but all it really amounts to is that armies — or substantial parts of them — just have to get around to manning equipment rather than equipping men. In the all too frequent pictures we have seen in the past 30 years or so of armed, partially mechanized conflict, one of the continuing themes is the way the action slips back into the kind of norm familiar from the latter part of World War II. In the Iraq-Iran conflict, in progress as I write this, both sides have tanks and IFVs with a round-the-clock capability. But fighting stops at dusk and starts again around dawn just like it always did. Countries which lay claim to a serious military capability have to break out of patterns like this.

Suppose in industry two firms have similar organizations and machines turning out competing products. The one that works 6 days and two to three shifts just has to win out over the one that single shifts on a 5-day week. Because of the direct interaction of opposing military forces, this is doubly true of warfare. However little experienced officers might care to admit it, a lot more than tactics has always been the opinion of the senior officer present. His arbitrary view has held sway over training goals and (largely) standards and of course over personnel selection and promotion. As air forces and navies know so well, the proper use of sophisticated equipment means *objectivization across the board* — which is of course why so many army officers hate hardware so much.

I reckon the aspects I have touched on in this chapter go to make a fundamental point on which airmechanized forces of the future may stand or fall. In the fifties an army's hardware could still be reasonably well handled within a fixed, traditional force structure and by employment of command, control and logistic techniques derived from tradition, venerable if no longer admirable and largely unrelated to the task in hand. In the sixties and seventies most folks reckoned this was still good enough; in so far as attention in those decades focused on medium- and low-intensity operations they were proved right. In another decade or so an army will have come to look much more like an air force, the fact that most of its sophisticated hardware is still on the ground being conspicuous rather than significant. So armies will need to adopt many of the broad principles evolved and proven by air forces, principles which underlie the comments of these last two chapters.

Appendix

FAMILY OF ANTIARMOR WEAPONS

Category	Preferred solution	Backup/Alternative solutions	Development targets	Related systems/remarks
SURFACE-TO-SURFACE				
Hand-held/crew served				
ATGMS	Improved Sagger (manual wire command link, 120 mm HEAT, 3000 m)	MILAN, TOW	Warhead only — improved HEAT or downward-looking SFF (in which case semiautomatic guidance)	Easy 2-man lift; must be EW-proof. NOT lethal v frontal arc
Rocket launcher	RPG7V equivalent (85 mm HEAT, 500 m) + *fougasse* kit	RPG7D equivalent (paratroops, etc)	Warhead (*see above*) Hit chance/effective range	1-man operation essential. NOT lethal v frontal arc
Antiarmor hand grenade	RKG3M equivalent (HEAT, *c.* 20 m)	—	Weight reduction	—
Antiarmor limpet mine	Adapted from rigid limpet assault mine (UK)	—	Dedicated design	—
Armored vehicles				
Tank destroyer (TD)	S Tank configuration, MLC40, HIMAG mobility, crew 3. 105-mm/72 L rifled (APDSFS, HEATFS, AP/HE, HEDP, SMK) + hull MGs, slaved/external MG Swims with on-vehicle	120-mm smoothbore (FRG), (APDSFS, HEATFS, ?HEDPFS, SMK) (*Mounting to be compatible with this gun*)	Evolutionary development	Only 3 natures to be stowed at one time **Related vehicles** (*see* Chapter 15) IFV (LP 76-mm cannon/MG) 1 + 2 + 6

Fire-support tank (FST)	External gun configuration (cf. pl. 2) MLC 40, HIMAG mobility, crew 3. 105-mm/51 L rifled (= M68) (as TD) + coax. MG, slaved/external MG Swims with on-vehicle screen	120-mm/46 L smoothbore (FRG) (as TD) (*Mounting to be compatible with this gun*)		CSV (as IFV) 3 + 3 (subvariants as required) ADV AVLB AEV/ARV SP mountings for tubed and heavy rocket artillery

Artillery (*Note.* For submunition details *see below*)

ATGMS (airportable/heliportable)	Ballistic trajectory, terminal active homing guidance, 30-kg warhead (HEAT or HEP); 9-10 km essential, (say) 20 km desirable (*see* Chapter 12) Twin launcher + 4-rd transporter on 10-t tracked mounting	Line-of-sight ATGMS as for helicopters (*q.v.*)	Warhead, range, accuracy	Alternate warheads (free flight): minelet bomblet Must have EW-proof command/fire control system Vehicle family: CV (and subvariants) ARV 120-mm mortar (*see* below)
Munitions for medium tubed artillery	Copperhead (HEAT, semi-active homing); minelet carrier shell	—	Guided shell with terminal active homing. Evolution of submunitions	—

FAMILY OF ANTIARMOR WEAPONS (*cont.*)

Category	Preferred solution	Backup/Alternative solutions	Development targets	Related systems/ remarks
Munitions for heavy tubed artillery	Bomblet (M42) carrier shell	—	Improved submunitions	—
120-mm SP mortar (airportable/heli-portable)	HE, SMK, rocket-assisted minelet carrier, 8-9 km. Mounting as ATGMS (*see above*)	Light gun/howitzer	Antiarmor sub-munitions, range	—
AIR-TO-SURFACE				
Rotary wing				
Armed scout heli-copter	Gazelle SA342M equivalent, 2 × ATGMS (*see below*)	(Many types available)	(*See below*)	—
Attack helicopter	Cobra AH1S equivalent, 6 × ATGMS (Hellfire) + 30-mm chain gun + 2 × FFAR pods	(Many types available)	Successor ATGMS: 20-kg warhead, 1.25 Mach, TV head + manual wire com-mand link, 6000 m, facility for heli-copter to maneuver during guidance phase KE ammunition for chain gun (*cf.* British Rarden gun) "Smart" rockets with improved lethality	Chin turret options Grenade launcher/ Minigun 20-mm cannon (APDS, HEDP)

Fixed-wing armaments (*Note.* For submunition details *see below*)

ATGMS	To be based on a combination of artillery ATGMS warhead (maybe with multiple sensors) + guidance and an existing air-to-air or air-to-surface missile, 6000 m desirable	?"Smart" rockets	Reduced time of flight Evolution	—
Delayed effect munitions	Dispenser for shaped charge minelets (*see* below)	Carrier rocket with "smart" bomblets	Optimize weight-bulk-effectiveness	—
Cannon	(Preferably multitube, high cyclic rate)	(Many types available)	KE ammunition (*see* above) Evolution	Requirement doubtful
NONBALLISTIC				
Mines	Existing types, track-cutting and HEAT	(Many types available)	Fuze improvements	Development priority to go to minelets
Maroon	Static canister discharging bomblets, multiple pneumatic pressure fuzes *and/or* remote command detonation	Artillery support	Submunition improvement	For helicopter operations. Requirement doubtful – parameters need exploring
SUBMUNITIONS				
Minimissile	Based on artillery ATGMS	Passive homing (heat seeking)	(Too early to specify)	For aircraft bombs and heavy SSGW

FAMILY OF ANTIARMOR WEAPONS *(cont.)*

Category	Preferred solution	Backup/Alternative solutions	Development targets	Related systems/ remarks
"Smart" bomblet	HEAT, heat seeking	Unguided bomblet (*see* below)	Improved size-effectiveness SFF warhead	For aircraft bombs and heavy SSGW NOT lethal *v* frontal arc
HEAT/FRAG bomblet	M42 equivalent	—	Improved size-effectiveness	NOT lethal *v* frontal arc
Track-cutting minelet	Existing types	—	Reduction of size and cost for assured minimal track-cutting effect	For tubed and rocket artillery and scattering from helicopters
HEAT minelet	Existing types	—	Size reduction. Fuzing and anti-lift improvements. Suitability for dispensing from fixed-wing strike aircraft	Mostly as lethal element in a mix with track-cutting minelets
Scatterable anti-personnel mine	Existing types	—	—	As supplementary antilift device for antitank minelets

294

Bibliography

Notes

1. Only key works are included, as comprehensive subject lists of books and articles, including the annual Staff College Classified List of Published Articles (SCCLIPA), are obtainable from/available for consultation at the Library of the Ministry of Defence/Royal United Services Institution for Defence, Whitehall, London SW1A 2EU.

2. I have listed articles by periodicals and by authors within these, since my own experience suggests this is the easiest arrangement for both readers and librarians.

3. See separate note at head of Soviet section.

Books

CARVER, FIELD-MARSHAL LORD, *The Apostles of Mobility: the theory and practice of armoured warfare*, London, Weidenfeld & Nicolson, 1979.

CLAUSEWITZ, CARL VON, *On War*, trans. Graham, London, Routledge, Kegan Paul, 1962.

DE GAULLE GÉNÉRAL CHARLES,
    La Discorde chez l'ennemi, 1924[1]
    Vers l'armée de métier, 1934[1].

GUDERIAN, HEINZ, *Panzer Leader*, trans. Fitzgibbon, London, Michael Joseph, 1952, and New York, E.P. Dutton.

HACKETT, GENERAL SIR JOHN W., and others, *The Third World War — a future history*, London, Sidgwick & Jackson, 1978, and New York, Macmillan Publishing Co.

HART, CAPTAIN SIR BASIL LIDDELL (ed.), *The Rommel Papers*, trans. Findlay, London, Collins, 1953, and New York, Harcourt Bruce Jovanovich Inc.

HUARD, PAUL, *Le Colonel de Gaulle et ses blindés*, Paris, Librairie Plon, 1980.

LUCAS, J. and COOPER, M., *Panzergrenadiers*, London, Macdonald & Janes, 1977.

MAHAN, A.T., *Naval Strategy — compared and contrasted with the principle and practice of military operations on land* (latest edn.), New York, Greenwood, 1975.[2]

OGORKIEWICZ, R.M., *Armour — the development of mechanized forces and their equipment*, London, Stevens, 1962.

OWEN, MAJ.-GEN. J.I.H. (ed.), *Brassey's Infantry Weapons of the World*, 2nd edn., London, 1979.

SENGER UND ETTERLIN, GENERAL DR F.M. VON, *Panzergrenadiere*, Munich, J.F. Lehmanns Verlag, 1961.
    Taschenbuch der Panzer 1976, Munich, J.F. Lehmanns Verlag, 1976.
    Die roten Panzer (new edn.)[1].

SIMPKIN, RICHARD E.,
    Tank Warfare — an analysis of Soviet and NATO tank philosophy, London, Brassey's, 1979, and New York, Crane Russak and Co. Inc.
    Mechanized Infantry, Oxford and New York, Brassey's/Pergamon Press, 1980.

STANHOPE, HENRY, *The Soldiers: an anatomy of the British Army*, London, Hamish Hamilton, 1979.

TSE-TUNG, MAO, and GUEVARA, CHE, *Guerrilla Warfare*, foreword by Liddell Hart, London, Cassell, 1962.

Articles

Armada

CARVER, FIELD-MARSHAL LORD, "Tank and anti-tank", 1977.

---

1 Latest publishing details not available.

2 This particular book is based on a series of lectures. The full work of the same name is out of print, though widely available in libraries.

298 BIBLIOGRAPHY

Armies and Weapons

(editorial) "The Merkava unveiled", No. 40, Dec. 77/Feb. 78.

Armor Magazine

ABBEY, LT.-COL. CHARLES W., "Tank versus helicopter", Nov./Dec. 78.

AKIMOV, COL. A., "A Soviet motorized infantry battalion in the attack", Mar./Apr. 80 (reprinted from *Soviet Military Review*, No. 4, Apr. 79).

BACKOFEN, JOSEPH E., Jr.,
"Kinetic energy penetrators versus armor", Mar./Apr. 80.
"Shaped charges versus armor", July/Aug. and Sept./Oct. 80.

DOUGHTY, MAJ. ROBERT A., "Copperhead", Mar./Apr. 78.

FITZMORRIS, COL. LAWRENCE B., "Developing tomorrow's vehicles", May/June 80.

HALL, CPT. WAYNE M., "The active defense", May/June 80.

MCMASTER, A.W. III, "Soviet armor — a study in efficiency", Jan./Feb. 78.

OGORKIEWICZ, RICHARD M.,
"Latest trends in tank technology", May/June 76.
"Trends in tank technology", July/Aug. 80.

O'NEILL, CPT. TIMOTHY R., "Needed now: an antiarmor doctrine", Jan./Feb. 76.

SAYRE, CPT. GORDON E., "Air cavalry attack troop", Nov./Dec. 78.

SENGER UND ETTERLIN, GENERAL DR F.M. VON, "The new German armored carrier [i.e. Marder]", Jan./Feb. 70.

SIMPKIN, RICHARD E., "A new proposal for fighting vehicles", Nov./Dec. 80.

WOODS, LT.-COL. THOMAS G., "A true mobile defense",[3] Sept./Oct. 68.

(editorial) "Is this Russia's tank killer?",[4] Mar./Apr. 77.

(various) Report of US Army Armor Conference 1979, July/Aug. 79.
Report of US Army Armor Conference 1980, July/Aug. 80.

Defence

DODD, NORMAN L., "Armoured operations for the 1980s", Oct. 79.

Defense & Foreign Affairs Digest

OGORKIEWICZ, RICHARD M., "A thunder of guns — a comparison of rifled and smooth-bore tankguns", Nov. 77.

Flight International

RICHARDSON, D., WARWICK, G. and LAMBERT, M., "The changing face of modern warfare — battlefield helicopters; the types available", Feb. 79.

WHEELER, B.C., "The world's military helicopters", July 75.

---

[3] General-Major Balck's 11 PzDiv, Chir River Battle (Stalingrad area), 7-20 Dec. 1942.
[4] Hind A and D helicopters.

Infantry

LIVSEY, MAJ.-GEN. WILLIAM J., "The active defense", July/Aug. 79.

McCASLIN, CPT. JAMES M., "Soviet doctrine: the BMP in the offense",[5] Jan./Feb. 77.

TIMMON, CPT. RICHARD F., "AT missiles in the Yom Kippur War", Jan./Feb. 74.

International Defense Review

DONNELLY, C.N., "Soviet tactics for overcoming NATO anti-tank defenses", July 79.

FURLONG, R.D.M.,
   "Main armament for the XM1 tank — storm over the selection", June 76.
   "The US Army's armoured combat vehicle technology program — blueprint for a
   lightweight main battle tank", Jan. 79.

GEDDES, J. PHILIP, "AH-64; the US Army's advanced attack helicopter", Aug. 78.

OGORKIEWICZ, R.M., "The US Army's armoured combat vehicle technology program — a
   closer look", May 79.

SCHREIER, F.,
   "A tank designed to cost — the US Army's XM1", June 76.
   "The combat-improved Chieftain — first impressions", Feb. 76.

(*various*)

   "Marder; West Germany's new APC enters service", Aug. 71.
   "The Soviet BMP vehicle family", Dec. 75.
   "The Leopard 2AV; German hope for a standard NATO tank", Jan. 76.
   "Improved Chieftain for Iran", Apl. 76.
   "Details of the Soviet T-72 battle tank", June 77.
   "AUSA '79 — crash programs to counter deployed Soviet armour", Jan. 80.

Military Review

OGORKIEWICZ, RICHARD M., "In tomorrow's armies", Feb. 74.

NATO's Fifteen Nations

DUPONT, R., "Le véhicule de combat d'infanterie AMX10P et la famille AMX10",
   Oct./Nov. 73.

Revue militaire générale

   "Le véhicule de combat d'infanterie AMX10", May 73.

Soldat und Technik

   "BMP, der sowjetische Schützenpanzer", May 76.

Truppenpraxis

BELDE, H.J., "Sowjetischer Schützenpanzer BMP", Sept. 77.

Wehrtechnik

GERMERSHAUSEN, R. and ROMER, R., "Flügelstabilisierte Geschosse", Feb. 76.

---

[5] See this article for details of relevant Soviet source material.

Unpublished

BACKOFEN, JOSEPH E., JR., "Armor/armor penetration: land, sea, air and space", Battelle Columbus Laboratory Report (undated).

BACKOFEN, JOSEPH E. JR. and WILLIAMS, LARRY W., "Soviet kinetic energy penetrators — technology/deployment", Battelle Columbus Laboratory Report, 5 Feb. 1979.

MANTEUFFEL, GENERAL H. VON, "Some thoughts on the employment of the Panzer-grenadier Division Grossdeutschland in the defensive and tank battle of Targul Frumos (Rumania), 2-5 May 1944" (courtesy of the Library, Staff College, Camberley).

Mechanized Infantry: Past, Present, Future
(Issued by United States Infantry School, Fort Benning Ga 31905, USA, Reference ATSH-CDT dated April 23, 1979.)

"Concept studies on S Tank successor", *Bulletin No. 5*, 24 July 1979, Försvarets Materielverk, Informationsenheten, Fack-104 50, Stockholm.

Soviet Publications

Author's note. I decided to include this section on Soviet material to reinforce the point I made in the Introduction about nonavailability of Soviet material to those concerned with policy decisions on doctrine, force structure and hardware. I must stress that I have barely started a research program on this material and, with a very few exceptions, have not so far seen many of the works listed in full. However, even a brief glance at the lists of contents contained in the Library of Congress and other abstracts and at the standard Soviet military bibliographies provided a number of insights which I incorporated in this book. Other useful references are given in some items of the main Bibliography, notably the Backofen and Backofen/Williams papers and Donnelly's and McCaslin's articles (q.v.).

I hope this list may encourage other Western authors and editors on both sides of the Atlantic and the Channel to make use of all this material and to point out to their national authorities the folly of ignoring it.

I should like once more to express my deep indebtedness to Professor John Erickson of Edinburgh University and to Joseph R. Backofen, Jr. of the Battelle Columbus Laboratories.

Since I believe transliterated Russian to be equally confusing to those who speak the language and those who do not, I have listed the authors' surnames (in Russian alphabetical order), a translation of the title and the date of post-World War II publications on one side, with the available publication details in full in Cyrillic script opposite. I have grouped books under the most appropriate subject headings, but some cover all aspects of the field and appear twice.

Strategic and operational levels — general

VATSIETIS, *Doctrines of future war.*

GALAKTIONOV, *The operational mobility of armies.*

YEGOROV, *Red Army tactics and operational doctrine from 1930 onwards.*

TRIANDAFILLOV, *The character of the operations of modern armies.*

TUKHACHIEVSKII,
  Questions of modern strategy.
  New military questions.
  Tactics and strategy.

Strategic and operational levels — armored and mechanized

AMMOSOV,
  Organizational aspects of mechanization and motorization.
  Tanks in breakthrough operations.

BABADZHANYANA (ed.), *Tanks and armored warfare* (1970).

KALINOVSKII, *What mechanization can offer future war.*

KRYZHANOVSKII, *The basic mechanized formation in land force operations.*

KUZNIETSOV, *The mechanized formation.*

LOSIK (ed.), *The buildup and operational employment of Soviet tank forces in World War II* (1979).

RADZIEVSKII, *Offensive tank operations* (1970).

SUKHOV, *Tanks in future wars.*

FAVITSKII, *The role of mechanized forces in future operations.*

Armored and mechanized tactics

AMMOSOV, *The combined-arms mechanized battle.*

GLADKOV, *Combat of armored units.*

GROMYCHENKO, *The armored meeting engagement.*

IGNATIEV, *Operational procedures of tank units and subunits.*

KALINOVSKII. *Tanks in deep penetration groups.*

ROTMISTROV, *The employment of tanks in the break-in battle against defended localities.*

FRUNZE (ed.), *Offensive and defensive tank operations.*

BIRYUKOV, G., and MEINIKOV, G., *Antitank warfare,* Moscow, Progress Publishers, 1972 (in English only, reviewed in *Armor,* Jan./Feb. 80).

Стратегические и оперативные труды, общие

Вацетис, И. И., *О ъоенной доктрине будущего.* *
Галактионов, М. Р., *Оперативная подвижность армий.* *
Егоров, А. И., *Тактика и оперативное искусство РККА начала тридцатых годов.* *
Триандафиллов, В. К., *Характер операций современных армий.* *
Тухачевский, М. Н.,
  Вопросы современной стратегии. *
  Новые вопросы войны. *
  Тактика и стратегия. *

*Сравни Е1(стр. 305).

Стратегические и оперативные труды, танковые и мотомеханизированные

Аммосов, С. Н.,
  Организационные формы механизации и моторизации. *
  Танки в операции прорыва. *
Бабаджаняна, А. Х. (Маршала бронетанковых войск) (ред.), *Танки и танковые войска,* Москва, Военное Издательство Министерства Обороны СССР, 1970.
Калиновский, К. Б., *Что может дать механизация в будущей войне.* *
Крыжановский, В. П., *Легкие мотомеханизированные соединения в армейской операции.* *
Кузнецов, Ф. И., *Мотомеханизированные соединения.* *
Лосик (Маршала ронетанковых войск) (ред.), *Строительство и боевое применение советских танковых войск в годы Великой Отечественной войны,* Москва, Воениздат, 1979.
Радзиевский, А. И., *Танковый удар,* Москва, Военное Издательство Министерства Обороны СССР, 1970.
Сухов, И. П., *Танки в современной войне.* *
Ефавицкий, В. В., *Роль механизированных войск в современной операции.* *

*Сравни Е1(стр. 305).

Бронетанковые мотомеханизированные тактики

Аммосов, С. Н., *Бой мотомехсоединений.* *
Гладков, П. Д., *Бой броневых частей.* *
Громыченко, А. Е., *Встречный бой танков.* *
Игнатьев, А. А., *Боевые порядки танковых частей и подразделений.* *
Калиновский, К. Б., *Танки в группах ДД.* *
Ротмистров, П. А., *Применение танков в прорыве сильно укрепленных полос.* *
Коллективный Труд Военной Академии
  Фрунзе, М. В. (ред.), *Наступательный и оборонительный бой танков.* *

*Сравни Е2 (стр. 305).

Combat vehicle technology

ANTONOV (ed.), *Tank* (1954).

BABADZHANYANA (ed.), *Tanks and armored warfare* (1970).

BIRYUKOV,
    Armor (1954).
    Military applications of armor (1961).

GRUZDIEV, *Tanks* (1944).

MOSTOVIENKO, *Tanks* (1956).

PLATONOV (ed.), *Tracked transporters and tractors* (1978).

RED'KII, *Armored personnel carriers* (1961).

SELIVOKHIN, *Tank* (1958).

(*various*) *Tanks and tracked vehicles* (1940).

Soviet Bibliographies

Soviet military works on strategic and operational matters (1917-1940), published 1965.
Soviet military works on tactical procedures (1917-1940), published 1970.

(*Note.* Works listed above and undated are taken from one of these bibliographies.)

Техника бронированных машин

Антонов, А. С. (ред.), *Танк,* Москва, Военное Издательство
  Министерства Обороны СССР, 1954.
Бабаджаняна, А. Х. (Маршала бронетанковых войск) (ред.),
Танки и танковые войска, Москва, Военное Издательство
Министерства Обороны СССР, 1970.
Бирюков, В. С., *Броня,* Москва, Военное Издательство Министерства
  Обороны СССР, 1954.
Бирюков, В. С., *Применение брони в военном деле,* Москва,
  Военное Издательство Министерства Обороны СССР, 1961.
Груздев, Н. И., *Танки,* Москва, НКТМ СССР, Государственное
  Издательство Машиностроительной Литературы, 1944.
Мостовенко, В. Д., *Танки,* Москва, Военное Издательство
  Министерства Обороны СССР, 1956.
Платонов, В. Ф. (ред.), *Гусеничные транспортеры-тягачи,* Москва,
  «Машиностроение», 1978.
Редькин, М. Г., *Бронетранспортеры,* Москва, Военное
  Издательство Министерства Обороны СССР, 1961.
Селивохин, В. М., *Танк,* Москва, Военное Издательство
  Министерства Обороны СССР, 1958.
(Коллективный труд) *Танки и тракторы,* Москва, Государственное
  Издательстбо Оборонной Промышленности, 1940.

Советские иблиографии

E1
*Вопросы стратегии и оперативного искусства в советских
  военных трудах* (1917-1940 гг.), М. Воениздат, 1965 г.

E2
Вопросы тактики искусства в советских военных трудах
  (1917-1940 гг.), Воениздат, 1970 г.

A - U

Index